OBSESSION
&
POSSESSION

WENDY MORGAN

OBSESSION
&
POSSESSION

An Exclusive 2-in-1 Edition

PINNACLE BOOKS
Kensington Publishing Corp.

PINNACLE BOOKS are published by

Kensington Publishing Corp.
850 Third Avenue
New York, NY 10022

First Pinnacle Books Printing of *Obsession*: November 2003
First Pinnacle Books Printing of *Possession*: December 2003

ISBN 0-7394-3927-8

Printed in the United States of America

OBSESSION

For my sister-in-law,
Stacey Staub
With much love from The Wenster
And, as always, for Mark and Morgan

PART ONE

One

Megan McKenna glanced at her chunky gold bracelet watch as she followed her boyfriend up the walk toward Zoe's house. "We're pretty late," she told Shea, reaching up to smooth her long, dark brown hair. "Zoe will probably be annoyed."

"Zoe's *always* annoyed. She'll get over it." He reached back and caught her hand, giving her fingers a squeeze.

And even though they'd been going out for over six months, since February break, she still felt all fluttery at the warm skin-to-skin contact.

Maybe eventually, she'd stop feeling this way whenever Shea touched her. Maybe holding hands with him would become no big deal.

Maybe.

But for now, it was still a semi-big deal.

And so was what had just happened in his car.

He had picked her up on time for the party. But instead of heading directly over toward Zoe's, he'd turned onto Soundview Drive. The winding, tree-lined road led to the quiet park where Meg and Shea had spent a lot of time this summer—after dark, when the picnicking families and church groups, kite fliers and frisbee players had all gone home.

There, parked in their usual isolated spot in a grove of pine trees, they had spent some feverish stolen moments. It was Shea who put on the brakes, as always, pulling back, straightening his clothes, and saying, "We better stop while we still can."

And as always, Meg had thought, *While* you *still can.*

He'd started the car and driven toward Zoe's while Meg checked her flushed face in the visor mirror and reapplied her lipstick with a trembling hand . . . and wondered how Shea could always stop them from going too far when she felt powerless to.

When she *wanted* to go further.

But . . . wasn't it supposed to be the other way around?

Wasn't the girl supposed to protect her virtue?

If it was up to Meg, her virtue would have been history by now. She'd known, from the first time she'd been alone with Shea last winter, that she was ready to stop the flirting, teasing games she'd been playing with all the guys she'd gone out with until now. She'd known Shea was *the one*—that this thing with him could be serious; that she'd wanted it to be—*expected* it to be.

None of her friends at the Adamson-Swift School—the friends who had long ago dubbed her Sister Meg—would suspect that Shea Alcott was a virgin, too.

Not that Meg was a hundred percent positive about that. He'd never *told* her he was a virgin, and he'd never asked about her status. They didn't talk about that stuff. They just parked and went at it until Shea stopped just before the point of no return, and Meg invariably felt frustrated—and guilty for not being the one to pull back first. Not that she ever protested or tried to push things further. That wasn't her style.

Now, they climbed the wide steps in front of the sprawling brick colonial where Zoe Cunningham's end-of-the-summer bash was in full swing. Shea let go of Meg's hand before reaching out to knock on the massive wooden door.

And Meg sighed inwardly and wished he didn't have a *thing* about being affectionate in front of other people. She wouldn't have minded making an entrance holding hands—especially since Shea's old girlfriend, Maura Nealey, was supposed to be here.

"Don't bother knocking," Meg said, reaching out and turning the doorknob. "They'll all be outside in the back. No one will hear."

The door was unlocked, as she'd known it would be. She pushed it open and walked into the familiar center hall, with its sweeping, broad staircase and hand-painted tile floor.

"Come on," Meg said to Shea, leading the way through the living room, dining room, and sunny glassed-in porch that Tara Cunningham called "the conservatory."

From there, they could see the crowd on the three levels of wooden decks that descended gradually to the lush, landscaped yard—Mrs. Cunningham called it "the garden"—with its spotlights, statues, benches, and winding flagstone paths.

Meg and Shea slipped out through the double french doors and were immediately engulfed by the crowd.

"It's about time," Zoe said, grabbing Meg's arm and tossing her smooth, pale hair. "Where *were* you guys?"

"Sorry," Meg said, glancing at Shea, who was being pulled away by a chattering Allison Maine, an irritating little blonde with a penchant for flirting with other people's boyfriends.

He gave Meg a helpless, *sorry, what can I do?* shrug.

"Meggie!" a high-pitched voice squealed in her ear, and she found herself wrapped in a viselike embrace and the strong scent of expensive perfume that was her friend Chasey Norman's trademark.

"You're back!" Chasey had spent the summer in the south of France with her mother and her mother's new boyfriend. "I thought you weren't coming home until Labor Day."

Chasey shrugged and shook her head, her riot of silky red curls bobbing furiously. "I didn't want to hang out there for another whole week. I mean, I was really getting homesick."

"For Crawford Corners?"

"Yeah, right, Meg. The town beach really compares to the French Riviera." Chasey shook her head. "I was actually homesick for you guys." She draped her sun-bronzed arms around Meg's and Zoe's shoulders. "I can't wait to, like, fill you in about everything."

"I can't wait to hear about it, Chase," Zoe said distractedly, "but right now I have to go rescue my cousin from Andy Dorner."

"Andy Dorner? *Eeuuh*." Chasey made a face.

"Your cousin's here?" Meg asked Zoe. "I thought she wasn't coming until your parents get back from California."

"Yeah, well, that's what I thought, too. But she drove up from Louisiana with some kid who needed to get here by this weekend. I didn't find out she'd be here early till she called me two days ago. What could I say? That she had to stay in a hotel until my parents got back? But she's actually pretty cool, and she swore not to tell my mother about this party."

" 'Mirabelle the Southern Belle' turned out to be *cool?* You're kidding." Meg had been listening to Zoe complain all summer about how her cousin from Louisiana was going to be coming in the fall to attend the private college in nearby Spring City, and how Zoe was going to be stuck entertaining her.

"She's cool enough not to deserve being slimed by Andy Dorner," Zoe said, and hurried away.

Meg turned to Chasey. "So, Chase, tell me about France. Did you hook up with that guy—what was his name? Jean?"

"Jacques. I hooked up with him for about two seconds before I realized he was a real jerk. He really changed since last year."

"Maybe he was just on his best behavior because he was an exchange student over here."

Chasey shrugged. "Whatever. I blew him off pretty fast."

"So what else is new," Meg said, shaking her head. Chasey blew *everyone* off.

"No, listen, Meg, I met this guy from New York when I was flying back yesterday—his name's Billy, and he's, like, gorgeous."

"Oh, yeah?" Meg felt something furry brush her bare legs and looked down to see Mrs. Cunningham's Persian cat, Jewel. Meg sensed that she wanted to be picked up. Not wanting to get fur all over the black brocade top she was wearing, Meg crouched down and petted the purring animal. "Good kitty. Good girl."

"He's gonna be a sophomore at NYU, and he's driving up to see me next weekend," Chasey was saying.

"Who?" Meg asked, glancing up.

"Billy! Who was I just talking about? Meg, what's up with you and that stupid cat? She always gravitates right to you. Whenever I go near her, she hisses at me."

"Well, no one likes to be called stupid, Chase. And you know Jewel—Zoe said she hisses at everyone."

"Except you."

As if to punctuate Chasey's remark, Jewel rested her front paws lovingly on the tops of Meg's thighs and gave a pleased, *"meow."*

Chasey shook her head. "It's so weird how animals are always trying to climb all over you. What are you, like, Dr. Doolittle?"

Meg rolled her eyes and was about to reply when Zoe reappeared with a willowy stranger in tow.

"Guys, this is Mirabelle Moreau," she said. "Mir, these are my two best friends, Meg McKenna and Chasey Norman."

Meg gently moved Jewel's paws from her legs and stood up.

The girl wasn't the Miss America contestant clone Meg had expected of someone Zoe had dubbed "Mirabelle the Southern Belle." Instead of a blond bouffant, she had long, silky brown hair that hung loose to the middle of her back, parted in the middle and tucked casually behind her ears. Rather than fair, delicate skin, she had a healthy glow, and she wasn't wearing any makeup. Her clothes were simple, too—cut-off Levi's and a plain off-white tee shirt.

"Nice to meet y'all," Mirabelle drawled. She said nice, *"nahs."*

Chasey said, "Wow, where are you from? You have this amazing accent."

"Ahm from *Nu-awlins*," was the reply.

Chasey blinked.

"She's from New Orleans," Zoe translated briefly, then said, "Mirabelle, you can hang with these guys while I go inside and make sure no one's in my parents' bedroom. I saw Kate and Joel heading in a few minutes ago, and ol' Tara will freak if she finds anything out of place when she gets home Tuesday."

Zoe dashed toward the house without a backward glance.

Meg turned to Mirabelle and was startled to find that the girl's strange, light green eyes were narrowed intently on her, as though she were pondering something. She cleared her throat and shifted uncomfortably. "So, Mirabelle, have you ever been in Crawford Corners before?"

"I was here last spring with my mother to visit the college. We stayed here with Aunt Tara and Uncle Greg, but Zoe wasn't around. I haven't seen her since her family came down for Mardi Gras about four years ago."

Chasey shot Meg a blank look that meant, *What* the heck did she say?

It took a second for Meg to decipher Mirabelle's drawled reply. "Oh, that's right, you were here around Easter time, right? That was when Zoe came with me and my family to Florida for a week."

"Yes." Mirabelle was still watching her.

Meg wished she would stop. The rapt expression in her pale eyes was disconcerting. Meg caught her bottom lip in her top teeth. *Why's she looking at me this way?*

At her feet, Jewel purred and rubbed against her bare leg. Meg reached down and stroked her fur again, then looked up to see that Mirabelle was still fixated on her.

"Have you ever been to France, Mirabelle?" Chasey asked brightly, swaying slightly back and forth in time to the music that was blasting from the stereo speakers.

"France?" The girl shifted her gaze briefly from Meg. "No, I never have been."

"Really? You should go sometime. I just spent the summer on the Riviera, and it was great."

"How nice," Mirabelle said politely, and shrugged. "I've never been abroad."

Meg noticed that Jewel was now rubbing affectionately against Mirabelle's ankles.

"You *haven't?*" Chasey sounded surprised. *"Never?"*

Oh, come off it, Chase, Meg thought. She hated when her friend slipped into this act. There were few among their crowd at Adamson-Swift who hadn't been to Europe, and Chasey liked to think she was more worldly and well-travelled than most.

Meg knew her friend was basically big-hearted, and she could usually forgive her for her snobbish tendencies. Chasey had grown up in a lower middle class neighborhood in Stamford, moving to Crawford Corners only about eight years ago when her mother—a buxom, predatory gold-digger—divorced her father and married a rich older businessman with a severe heart condition. He had died a few summers back, and though Chasey and her mother still lived among the elite, they were less tolerated now that their blue-blood benefactor was out of the picture. Meg knew Chasey was forever trying to convince herself—and others—that she belonged here.

Now she gave Mirabelle a wide-eyed stare and said, "Why haven't you ever been to Europe?"

Mirabelle shrugged. "I don't like to fly," she said, and stooped down to give the cat a brief pat on the head.

"You're *kidding!*" Chasey said. "Why not?"

"Because I was warned not to," Mirabelle said simply, rising. She flicked her steady gaze back to Meg.

"Huh?" Chasey said.

An odd feeling stole over Meg. She couldn't seem to tear her eyes away from Mirabelle's. "What do you mean, you were warned not to?"

Mirabelle glanced briefly at Chasey, then turned back to Meg and shrugged. "It's a long story."

Meg frowned and was about to pursue it when Shea suddenly appeared beside her.

"Hey, I'm back."

"It's about time," Meg said. She stepped closer to him and fought the urge to slip her hand casually into his, knowing he wouldn't like it. "Shea, this is Zoe's cousin, Mirabelle . . ."

"Moreau," the girl supplied.

"That's right, Moreau. She just moved up here from New Orleans to go to college. Mirabelle, this is my boyfriend, Shea Alcott."

"Nice to meet you," Shea said smoothly, and shook her hand. "Where are you going to school?"

"Wainwright College."

Shea nodded. "Are you living on campus?"

"Yes, but I can't get into the dorms until Wednesday, so I'm staying here at the Cunninghams' for a few days."

"Geez, Shea," Chasey cut in. "You haven't seen *me* since June— aren't you going to say welcome back or anything?"

He grinned. "Welcome back, Chasey—how's it going? When'd you get home?"

"It's going great," she said, looking relieved to have the focus move away from Mirabelle, "and I just flew into JFK last night." Chasey shot a pointed look in Zoe's cousin's direction.

Again, Meg wondered what Mirabelle had meant by being warned not to fly.

And again, she felt uncomfortable when she noticed that those light green eyes were still fixed on her, probing, as though Mirabelle could see straight inside to Meg's very soul.

As the plane rattled and thumped its way to a lower altitude, Candra Bowen decided she hated flying.

Not that she'd ever done it before.

And not that she was afraid of crashing, or anything like that.

She *knew*, with a familiar certainty that should have calmed her, that they weren't going to crash.

So she wasn't *afraid*.

Just . . . uneasy. Because up here, hurtling through the air thousands of feet above the ground, she had no control over anything that happened.

And Candra liked to be in control.

She glanced out the window, hoping to see something, but there was only the same milky mist that had been there ever since they'd reached the mainland.

It had been several hours now since Candra had stared through the window and bid a silent farewell as Jamaica's mountainous countryside gave way to the sparkling aqua waters of the Caribbean Sea. For the first time in all her seventeen years, she had left the island that had always been home.

She'd been ready—hell, she'd been *longing* for this day ever since Grandmother had told her their employers, the Drayers, were moving back to the States and wanted to take them along. But as eager as she'd been to leave Jamaica behind, Candra had been shocked to feel a tear trickling down her smooth brown cheek as the plane ascended and the tiny land mass had vanished for good.

Candra had quickly wiped the tear away and glanced at Grandmother to see if she, too, was emotional. But the old woman's eyes had been squeezed tightly shut, and she was wincing and gripping the armrests as though bracing for an inevitable collision. She had pretty much stayed that way for the past few hours.

Grandmother had never flown before, either.

Now, as the Fasten Seat Belts sign suddenly *dinged* and lit up again, Candra heard her grandmother give a little gasp.

"Don't worry," Candra said, turning toward her. "We'll be fine."

Rosamund Bowen looked terrified. Her dark chocolate-colored skin seemed tinged with a chalky hue. "How do you know?" she asked her granddaughter.

How do you think *I know?* Candra wanted to ask her. *How do I know anything? You're the one who taught me to listen to the voices in my mind. And right now, they're telling me we're going to be fine.*

But she didn't say that. The woman sitting in the aisle seat on the other side of her grandmother had her nose buried in a paperback, but she looked like the nosy type who might be eavesdropping.

She'd glanced up sharply earlier when she'd heard Candra call Rosamund "Grandmother." Candra had known what she was thinking. *That black woman is her grandmother?*

Candra's skin was so pale that people always assumed she was white. Actually, her mother had been, but her father, Rosamund's son, had been Jamaican.

"Didn't you hear the pilot a few minutes ago?" Candra asked her worried grandmother. "He said it's almost time to land in New York City. We're coming down—that's why it's so bumpy."

The plane lurched again. Her grandmother gave a little shriek and clutched Candra's wrist.

Candra rolled her eyes and said again, "Don't worry."

Then she turned back toward the window to see what she could see. Nothing—just a thick cloud bank.

When would she be able to catch a glimpse of New York City? Mrs. Drayer had told her that she might be able to see the Statue of Liberty before they landed.

Imagine that—the Statue of Liberty.

Did the Drayers have a better view from where they were sitting now, up in first class?

No, Candra told herself. *Of course they don't. They can't see any more than you can.*

Still, she wondered what it was like up there, beyond the curtain that was kept carefully drawn to keep the rest of the passengers from peering into that privileged cabin.

Candra knew she should be grateful to her grandmother's employer for buying her and Rosamund their plane tickets, and she hadn't really expected to be in first class. But that didn't stop her from resenting the Drayers, who, of course, were.

What were they doing up there, right now? Candra closed her eyes and conjured a mental picture of the four of them.

Craig, who at seventeen was exactly Candra's age, would be playing with one of his hand-held computer games and saying, "Yes!" every time he scored a point. His mother would shush him, and he would naturally ignore her. He was good-looking in a lazy, cocky way, and acted as though he had the run of the world. He never lost an opportunity to remind Candra that she was "the help."

His sister, Jane, was no less self-centered and snobby, but at least she was quieter about it. At fifteen, she was just starting to lose the baby fat that had plagued her, and showed every hint of becoming a lean, Waspy matron like her mother. Right now, Jane would be wearing her CD Walkman and bobbing her head in time to the music.

Monica, Candra knew, was probably flipping idly through her copy of *Vogue* and checking her Rolex every few seconds. She was the perfect, punctual type and would know exactly what time they were supposed to land. In a few minutes, she would take out her jewel-encrusted compact and powder her straight, small nose before carefully gliding a silver tube of burgundy lipstick over her thin lips.

Jonas, her husband, would be beside her, sipping a cocktail—not his first. His perpetually ruddy complexion attested to the fact that he was a drinker. He would undoubtedly be leafing through an ubiquitous sheaf of business papers on his lap.

Jonas Drayer was a powerful, important real estate developer, and Candra knew that he was largely responsible for the exclusive new Coral Sands resort that had opened last month in Ocho Rios. Before that, he had been involved with the sparkling new Sea Breeze resort, which was now invariably filled to capacity.

The Drayers were unlike other American corporate families who relocated to Jamaica, then high-tailed it back to "civilization" as soon as their business was finished. They had been on the island since the tourist industry had revived in the late seventies. Jonas worked for a large real estate development company based in southwestern Connecticut, and he and his colleagues had played a major role in turning Ocho Rios into a resort town.

The Drayers had lived in the hills above the port, where several celebrities owned estates. Their home was lavish, with two swimming pools, a tennis court, landscaped gardens, and sweeping views of the sea. Candra and her grandmother, who was their housekeeper, had lived in the servants' quarters that were built into the sloping land at the back of the big house, underneath the main floor.

When Candra was little, Craig and Jane had been her playmates, and she had liked them, though they were spoiled and liked to brag about the new toys they were always getting. But as the Drayer children grew older and were sent to boarding schools in the States, the bond between them and Candra had been replaced by an invisible line that she knew better than to try to cross. These days, neither Craig nor

Jane tried to hide the fact that they looked down on her from their lofty perches, and it had been a decade since Candra had had a real conversation with either of them.

In the years while her children were growing up, Monica had spent a lot of time back home in Connecticut. Lately when she had been in Jamaica, she had talked incessantly about "home," and so had Craig and Jane. Candra knew that the three of them had finally pressured Jonas into this move back to the States.

She knew, too, that it had been Jonas's idea to take Rosamund and Candra with them. Unlike his wife and children, he had considered them part of the family—at least, to the extent that he was concerned about what might happen to them after the Drayers left Jamaica.

Rosamund had been working for the family since before Candra was born. Good jobs were hard to come by, and Jonas had told Candra's grandmother that he hated to think of the two of them living in some shantytown like many of the locals did. So he had offered to move them to Connecticut, and Rosamund had accepted. Candra knew her grandmother probably would never have agreed to leave Jamaica if her sister Letitia hadn't happened to be a maid on an estate in Greenwich, Connecticut. According to Jonas, that was only about twenty minutes away from his house in Crawford Corners. And Spring City, where Aunt Tish lived, was even closer.

Candra, too, had been excited about the prospect of moving to America. There, she knew, she would finally have the opportunity to make something of herself. And someday, she kept telling herself fiercely, *she* would be flying in first class.

There was another *ding*, and the pilot's voice came over the intercom. "Ladies and gentlemen, please fasten your seat belts, put your tray tables up, and bring your seats to an upright position as we begin our final approach into John F. Kennedy airport. We should have you on the ground in six minutes."

This is it, Candra thought, catching her bottom lip in her top teeth in anticipation. After all that waiting, she was finally about to land in this new country and begin her new life.

The clouds were beginning to thin, and she focused intently on the window, wondering if she'd get to see the Statue of Liberty in the harbor after all.

But as the clouds became mere wisps and the view opened up, she saw that they were over land, and flying low. Fascinated, Candra studied the tops of houses and buildings and trees, and noted the miniature cars moving about the gridlike streets.

Then she heard it.

The voice.

As always, it was a mere whisper, slipping subtly into her mind so that she was barely aware of it at first. She narrowed her black eyes and strained to hear what it was telling her.

She's down there . . . You have to find her . . .

Candra frowned, puzzled.

Who? she asked herself. *Who's down there?*

But there was no answer.

Only an echo that said simply, and urgently, *Find her.*

"Hi, Meg," said a voice behind her.

Startled, Meg jumped and spun around to see Mirabelle sitting on the window seat. Jewel was in her lap, looking contented as Zoe's cousin stroked her.

"I'm sorry," the girl drawled. "I didn't mean to scare you."

"It's okay." Meg pressed a fist against her wildly pounding heart and shook her head.

She had just come out of Zoe's bathroom, where she had been try-ing to remove as much cat fur as possible from her black shirt. Jewel had insisted on jumping into her lap while she'd been sitting on a bench out on the deck, and she had found herself covered in fine white hair. Finally, Zoe had come along, chased the cat away, and told Meg where to find a lint brush.

Mirabelle hadn't been here in Zoe's bedroom when Meg had passed through it a few minutes ago.

Did she follow me up here? Meg wondered, then discarded the idea. *Don't be ridiculous. Why would she do that?*

Maybe because she's been staring at you all night.

Meg shifted her weight and said, "Well, I guess I'll get back to the party." She started to move away, knowing somehow that Mirabelle was going to stop her.

She was right.

"Wait, Meg, don't go," the girl said, standing up and setting the cat lightly on the floor. Jewel promptly stretched and trotted over to rub against Meg's ankles again.

"I came up here because I wanted to talk to you about something," Mirabelle said.

So she was following me.

"You did?" Meg asked, trying not to appear as thrown as she felt. "What is it?"

"Before, when I said that thing about not flying?"

She nodded.

"Well," Mirabelle continued, "I thought I should explain what I meant. I didn't want to say anything in front of your friend, but I knew you would understand."

"What do you mean?"

Mirabelle moved closer to where she was standing, and idly picked up a crystal figurine from Zoe's dresser. "I mean," she said, running her fingertips over the piece, "that there are certain things you just don't tell certain people. But the second I saw you, I sensed that you were someone who . . ." She trailed off and looked up at Meg. "I knew that you were like me."

"Like you?"

"Meg, I've been getting vibes from you since the second I got here."

Meg fought the urge to take a step backward. Suddenly it crossed her mind that Zoe's cousin might be a lesbian.

Is she putting the moves on me? she wondered. In a way, that would almost be a relief. At least, it would make sense.

"The reason I don't *fly*," Mirabelle said abruptly, "is that I was warned not to."

Meg blinked. "Excuse me?"

"I was warned by a witch."

"A . . . *witch?*"

"Uh huh. Cecile's my neighbors' housekeeper back home. She practices voodoo, and she taught me."

Meg just stared.

"Anyway, she's psychic—most witches are—and she told me that I should stay away from airplanes because she saw a lot of negative energy in me about that. That was years ago. I haven't flown since." Mirabelle carefully set down the crystal figurine, folded her arms, and looked directly at Meg. "Now I don't need Cecile to tell me things. I'm in tune with my own sixth sense."

She's crazy—she must be. Just act like you understand what she's talking about.

"Cecile taught me how some people are born with . . . certain powers," Mirabelle went on. "*She* was. And I was, too. My father comes from an old Creole family. He doesn't know it, but his grandmother was a voodoo priestess. Cecile told me that. She said I must have gotten my abilities from her. Cecile taught me how to cultivate them, and how to recognize the same sensitivity in other people. I hardly ever meet anyone who has it, but I sensed it in you right away."

"In me?" Meg echoed.

Mirabelle peered closely at her for a long moment. "Maybe you weren't even aware of it. Meg, I'm sorry. I thought you might be . . ."

"Be what?"

"Practicing."

"Practicing *what?*"

"Witchcraft."

Now Meg did take a step backward. She couldn't seem to find her voice.

"I'm really sorry," Mirabelle said again. "You look really freaked out. I didn't mean to scare you or anything. It's no big deal."

No big deal?

"It's okay." Meg's voice came out slightly hoarse.

"I guess I could be wrong, but—" Mirabelle shook her head. "Look, Meg, forget about it, okay?"

"Okay." She hesitated. "I'd better get back downstairs."

"Right. Do me a favor?"

"Yes?" Oh, God. What was Mirabelle going to ask of her?

"Can you just tell Zoe I went to bed? I don't mean to be antisocial, but I'm still zonked after that long drive."

"Sure," Meg said, almost sighing with relief.

"Great." The girl yawned and stretched, then kicked off her sandals and bent to pick them up.

In that moment, Mirabelle seemed just like anyone else.

Not like a witch.

Don't be ridiculous, Meg. She's not a witch!

But she said she was.

"G'night," Meg said swiftly to Mirabelle, and left Zoe's room without a backward glance.

As she hurried down the stairs, she let the rest of the thought enter her mind.

And she said you were a witch, too.

Candra had never been in a stretch limousine before.

This one was shiny black, and it had been waiting for the Drayers right outside the chaotic airport terminal.

At first, Candra hadn't expected to ride in the limo, and she didn't think Rosamund did, either. But after Craig, Jane, and Monica had clambered in, the chauffeur stood holding the door expectantly, and Jonas had given Candra's arm a little nudge.

"Go ahead," he'd said. "Get in."

She'd looked at him in surprise, then ducked into the plush, dim interior, thinking, *This is going to be the first time of many.*

Now that she was here in America, she would waste no time figuring out how to become as wealthy—no, wealthier—than the Drayers. And someday, she would treat Craig and Jane with as much contempt as they directed toward her.

I'll show them.

It was a familiar refrain, one that had been running through her head since childhood.

She settled on the seat facing the three Drayers, with Jonas on one side of her and Rosamund—still looking numb from the flight—on the other.

The car seemed to glide along the highways, and Candra spent the whole trip sneaking furtive glances out the tinted windows. It felt strange to be driving on the right-hand side of the road, with oncoming traffic way off to the left. She marveled at how every road was wide and paved. Here, there was no livestock wandering in the streets, and the houses she saw beyond the highway were all set close to each other, in neat rows.

She didn't want Craig and Jane to catch her looking excited or intrigued. They were both doing their best to act blasé about the whole trip, but Candra could tell that even they were excited about being back in New York.

"Over there, Candra," Monica said at one point, "is Manhattan."

She glanced out the window and saw the glittering skyline to their left. Only a narrow band of river separated them from it.

"Oh, geez, we're not going through the city, are we?" Craig asked. "That'll take forever."

We're not? Candra thought, disappointed.

"No, we're taking the Triborough," Jonas told him.

Candra was riding backward, so she could watch the skyline fall away behind them without anyone noticing that she was staring at it.

Someday, she thought, *I'm going to be a part of that. I'm going to buy things in the most expensive stores and eat in the finest restaurants . . .*

Candra lost herself in her familiar fantasies.

Soon they were zooming over an enormous bridge, and shortly afterward, the road opened up and there wasn't as much to look at. They seemed to be out of the city, and though the road was still lined with buildings and houses and neon signs, everything was more spread out now.

"Look, Daddy," Jane said, reaching across and tapping her father's knee. "See that sign?"

"Welcome to Connecticut," Jonas read. "We're almost home, honey."

Almost home. Candra's first limousine ride was almost over.

As the big car sped through the dark night, that same feeling she'd had on the plane started to come over her again.

The feeling that she was getting closer than ever to something—or someone—significant.

She listened intently for the voices in her mind again, but they weren't speaking to her now. This was more of a vague sensation that she was connected to this place somehow. She needed to find that connection, whatever it was.

The feeling grew stronger as the limousine finally slowed and left the highway.

"The town of Crawford Corners is about a mile down the road that way," Jonas told Candra and Rosamund, pointing in the opposite direction from the one in which they were turning. "We live over here, by the water."

Rosamund gave a polite nod.

Candra stared absently out the window, focused intently on her intuition.

Her instincts were telling her that whatever she was supposed to find here in America was nearby, waiting for her.

Two

"Hey, look!" Zoe said, pointing. "A fortune-teller!"

"Where?" Meg bit the last wisp of pale green cotton candy off the sticky paper cone she was holding.

"There." Zoe indicated the tent that was set off from the rest of the midway, in a shady grove of trees. A brightly painted yellow and blue sign read, *Fortunes: $25.*

"That's pretty expensive," Meg said, dropping the cone into a wire trash basket and licking her fingers.

"So? She's probably really good at it," Zoe said. "Come on, let's go do it. Maybe she can tell us who we're going to marry."

Meg thought of Shea. "Okay, why not?"

They started for the tent, carefully stepping over the coils of electric cables that stretched across the ground. The carnival always came to Spring City during the last week of summer. Meg and Zoe had been coming to it for years. In the early days, they had both been into rides and junk food. Meg still reveled in those things, but Zoe's purpose had evolved. She was hoping to meet a college guy. The carnival grounds were, as she put it, "crawling with men" from nearby Wainwright University.

She'd invited her cousin Mirabelle to come with them today, but luckily, she'd been busy registering for classes. Meg hadn't seen her since the party last weekend, and she wasn't looking forward to another encounter. Every time she thought about what Zoe's cousin had said to her, she still got a chill.

Like right now.

It came over her as they were approaching the fortune-teller's tent, and made Meg stop short. Mirabelle, and her talk about witches and warnings, had suddenly popped into her head.

Meg reached out, grabbed Zoe's arm and blurted, "Wait."

"What?" Her friend turned around and looked at her in surprise.

"Just . . . I don't know. I suddenly have this weird feeling . . ." Meg shrugged, still clutching Zoe's bare, tanned arm. She felt rooted, as though she couldn't make her feet continue toward the tent.

"Are you sick or something?" Zoe pulled out of her grasp and ran a careful hand over her smooth, blond pageboy. "Maybe it's all that cotton candy you ate. Or that stupid upside down parachute ride. I told you not to go on it."

"It's not that. I'm not sick." Meg looked over her shoulder at the carnival grounds. She felt momentarily reassured by the sun-splashed summer day beyond this shady spot. She could hear the familiar sounds of calliope music, laughing children, and barkers yelling, "Step right up . . ."

Zoe tossed her head. "Then what's wrong with you?"

Meg caught her lower lip with her front teeth. She glanced at the fortune-teller's tent in front of them.

She couldn't escape a sudden inexplicable feeling of foreboding.

This is crazy. What the heck is wrong with you?

She forced back her vague uneasiness and told Zoe, "All right, I'll come with you. But I'm not going to do it. I'll just wait while you do."

"Whatever," Zoe said with a shrug, and continued toward the tent.

Meg followed reluctantly.

Moments later, they were standing in front of the tent. Somehow, it seemed eerily quiet here, as though the carnival were off in the distance, instead of just beyond the trees behind them.

Meg looked toward her friend for reassurance. Even Zoe looked a little nervous now. She met Meg's glance, her hand poised, about to lift the flap.

"Come on," Meg whispered, clutching Zoe's arm and pulling her back, "Let's get out of—"

"Hello!" a woman said loudly as she threw the tent flap open, startling them. "Come in, *mon.*"

Meg glanced from the woman, who looked harmless enough, clad in a flowered housedress and scuffed sandals, to Zoe, who shrugged as if to say, *It's too late now—we have to go through with this.*

They stepped into the tent.

Behind them, the woman dropped the flap, shutting out what little light had filtered in. She said in her lilting voice that bore a trace of accent Meg couldn't place, "I'm Dalila Parker."

Meg found herself feeling slightly reassured by the woman's appearance. She had been expecting someone darker, more mysterious. Dalila, with her smooth black skin and white, toothy smile, could have been a pleasant, middle-aged housewife.

Harmless, Meg told herself. *She's harmless. Maybe this will be fun.*

But then the woman walked briskly around in front of Meg and

Zoe, looked more closely at them—no, at *Meg*—and appeared startled.

"It's *you*," she said, peering into Meg's face, recognition seeping into her almond-shaped eyes.

Taken aback, Meg shot an apprehensive glance at Zoe, who shrugged.

What on earth was the woman talking about? Meg cleared her throat nervously and said, "Excuse me?"

"I know who you are. I saw you just the other day over on Elmont."

"Elmont Avenue?" Meg shook her head. That was the main drag in the worst section of Spring City. The kids at Adamson-Swift were always joking about hanging out on Elmont, though of course, no one Meg knew had ever actually ventured there. It was seedy and dangerous, infested with hookers and drug dealers.

"I saw you," Dalila Parker repeated. "On Elmont. You were walking outside of my apartment building."

"Sorry, but I've never set foot on Elmont Avenue!" Quickly, then, so she wouldn't offend the woman, Meg hastily clarified, "I mean, it's not that there's anything wrong with it . . . I've just never been there before, because it's pretty far from where I live. In Crawford Corners."

"No, *mon*," the woman said firmly, still staring at her.

Meg frowned, not just at the denial, but at the woman's use of the word *mon*. The first time she'd said it, it had sounded like *ma'am*. Now Meg recognized that it was some sort of island dialect.

This crazy woman was calling her *man*. And who did she think she was, telling Meg she was wrong?

Meg looked her in the eye and said, "*Yes*. I live in Crawford Corners."

"But you've been on Elmont. I saw you."

"You couldn't have. I've never been there before in my life. I don't even know exactly where it is." She looked at Zoe. "Right?"

Her friend, looking a little anxious, only nodded.

Dalila shook her head. "No. I saw you there, *mon*."

"You couldn't have. Maybe it was just someone who, you know, kind of looks like me," Meg suggested, trying to keep her voice level.

After all, lots of teenaged girls had long, straight black hair and wore it parted in the middle. Lots of them were of medium height and had an average build, just like she did. And though Meg's dark complexion, almond-shaped ebony eyes, and angular features were what Shea admiringly referred to as "exotic," there was no reason for Meg to think that she was all that unique—that this strange woman hadn't simply mistaken her for someone else.

But Dalila Parker was still shaking her head. "Looks are one thing, but—there's something else about you. An aura."

An aura.

Meg swallowed hard and stared at the woman. Mirabelle's words were echoing through her mind again.

Dalila Parker went on, "I feel it now—the same sensation I had the other day when I passed you on the street. Very few strangers are capable of creating such a reaction in me. I'm always in tune, but the intensity . . ." She shook her head resolutely. "It's you, *mon*. I don't make mistakes."

Meg was barely aware of taking a step backward. The woman's fierce gaze was boring into her. Meg tore her eyes away, looked at Zoe. *She's some kind of nut,* she wanted to say. *Let's get out of here.*

But Zoe was fixated on Dalila Parker. "Are you really a fortune-teller?" she asked breathlessly.

For the first time, the woman focused on Zoe. "Yes—among other things."

Those last three words sent a chill through Meg.

Zoe was oblivious. "I want to know about my future. You can tell me, right?"

"I can tell you." Again Dalila's gaze slid back to Meg. It lingered there, probing.

Then, abruptly, she snapped into a businesslike persona, saying briskly, "I charge twenty-five dollars for a session. Up front."

"No problem," Zoe said, promptly taking two tens and a five from her purse. She handed the bills over to Dalila, then nudged Meg. "Go on, Meg, pay her."

"I'm not going to do it, remember? You go ahead. I'll wait for you."

"Oh, come on," Zoe urged. "It's no big deal."

Dalila addressed Meg. "You don't want to have a reading . . ."

Meg couldn't tell if it was a question or a statement. She shifted her weight to her other foot and said, "No."

"Why not?"

She just shrugged. How could she tell this strange woman about the uneasy feeling that had overtaken her?

"You're afraid," Dalila said softly. "You feel something you've never felt before, or perhaps not this strongly—something dark. Dangerous."

How could she know that?

Meg took another step back. "I do not," she said, trying to force lightness into her voice along with the denial, trying to let this woman know she thought she was off her rocker. That had to be it. The woman was just playing some stupid game, trying to seem like some kind of mystic. Which was ridiculous.

Except that Mirabelle . . .

"Yeah, *mon*," Dalila said in that irrefutable way of hers. "For you, this is no longer crazy and fun. It's frightening."

"*I'm* not scared," Zoe said confidently, tossing her blond head.

Dalila paid no attention, still focused on Meg. "For you, it's frightening," she repeated, "and do you know why?"

Meg shook her head, her eyes locked on the woman's.

"Because you have it."

"I have what?"

"The power," Dalila said simply.

"I don't know what you're talking about," Meg told her, hearing a high-pitched edge of hysteria in her own voice. But somewhere deep inside of her, Dalila's words had been acknowledged, accepted.

The power. You have the power.

"You don't understand now," Dalila was saying. "But you will. In time."

Meg blinked. "Listen," she said tersely. "This is ridiculous. First, you tell me you've seen me in your neighborhood, where I've never been before in my life. And now you're telling me I have some kind of power? And you want me to pay you twenty-five bucks so you can look into your crystal ball or tea leaves or whatever and tell me about my future?"

"I don't have a crystal ball and I don't read tea leaves," Dalila said evenly in her strange, sing-song voice. "That's not what I'm about. This isn't a carnival hoax, *mon*."

"Well, whatever it *is*, I'm really not into it."

Dalila just looked at her silently for a long moment. Then she shrugged. "You're not ready to accept it yet. Who can blame you? You're young. In time, you'll be ready. And when you are, you'll come back to me. You'll find me on Elmont—the apartment over Rivera's Newsstand on the corner of Twelfth."

"Yeah, right." Meg took a step toward the tent flap.

"What is that?" Dalila Parker asked, pointing toward Meg's neck.

Puzzled, Meg looked down. What was she talking about?

Long black fingers snaked forward. Before Meg could react, Dalila had swiftly unbuttoned the top button of her sleeveless white blouse and lifted the delicate gold chain that hung inside at the base of her throat.

Meg froze. How had the woman even known it was there? Her

blouse had totally concealed it. "What's what?" she asked, trying to keep her voice level.

"This tiny ring you're wearing on the chain."

It was her baby ring, the one her mother had placed on her minia-ture thumb when she was an infant. According to Giselle, the ring had worked its way down the line of fingers to Meg's pinky as she grew. It was visible in all of her baby pictures, a thin gold band and gleaming green stone snugly resting in the folds of Meg's chubby little hand. When, as a toddler, she had finally outgrown it, her mother had put it on a chain. Meg had worn it around her neck for as long as she could remember.

She couldn't take it off. Her mother had the chain soldered years ago.

And Meg rarely gave it much thought.

But now . . .

How had Dalila known the ring was there?

Meg shivered slightly as the woman's cool knuckles brushed her collarbone where she still grasped the chain. Beside her, Zoe was gap-ing.

"Do you know what this stone is?" Dalila asked.

"It's . . . jade."

"Yes. Are you a Virgo?"

For a moment, Meg, taken aback, thought she'd been asked if she was a *virgin*. Then she realized she'd heard wrong. Dalila was asking about her zodiac sign. "A Virgo? Why?"

"Libra? Aquarius?"

"Why do you want to know?"

"Because you are wearing jade. I'm very curious about the signifi-cance."

Shrugging, Meg said, "My mother gave it to me when I was born. Maybe she just thought it was pretty."

"It's more than pretty, *mon*. Jade is a powerful stone."

"Would you mind letting go of it, please?" Meg asked, pulling back.

Dalila's fingers loosened from the chain, and the ring thumped lightly against Meg's skin again.

The woman looked as though she wanted to say something more. But she remained silent, looking thoughtfully at Meg, who buttoned her blouse again and shifted uncomfortably under the glittering black gaze.

It was time to get out of here.

"Zoe," she said abruptly, "I'm leaving. Are you coming?"

"Meg! I want my fortune told," Zoe protested.

"Forget it," Dalila said.

"But you told me—"

"No, *mon*." Dalila pressed the twenty-five dollars back into Zoe's hand. "Here, take this. Go."

Meg grabbed Zoe's arm and pulled her out of the tent. She could feel Dalila's eyes behind her, peering out from the flap in the canvas.

The woman's words echoed in her mind even after she and Zoe were back on the crowded midway, making their way toward the parking lot.

You'll come back to me.

Candra walked briskly down Broad Avenue, the main street in downtown Crawford Corners. She skirted to the right, around two mothers with baby carriages who lingered on the sidewalk outside the drug store, then to the left to avoid a kid on a skateboard.

Candra walked with purpose, as though she were on some important mission, when in fact she was basically roaming aimlessly through the streets and had been ever since she'd gotten off the bus here a few hours earlier.

It wasn't dark yet, though it was past seven o'clock. The sky still held the smoky blue-gray remnants of early September dusk, and the air was as sticky and warm as it had been since this morning.

It had been a scorching Saturday. Candra was accustomed to hot, humid weather, but in Jamaica it was often tempered by breezes off the Caribbean and by frequent afternoon rainstorms. Here, the concrete roads and sidewalks absorbed the heat and held it long after the sun had gone down.

At least the bus had been air-conditioned. Candra had managed to cool off during the long ride over from Spring City this afternoon. She'd spent a long, sweltering morning in Aunt Tish's tiny apartment there. Finally, Grandmother had told her that she and Aunt Tish were going out, and that Candra should take the bus back to the Drayers' house.

She had assured her grandmother that yes, she knew exactly how to get to the Drayers' place from the town common. But after she'd stepped off the bus there, something had made her pause.

And instead of starting her long walk toward the exclusive mansion out on Soundview Avenue, Candra had listened to her instincts.

In the hours since, she had wandered up and down the quiet streets of Crawford Corners, her eyes darting ahead, scanning the people who were strolling the sidewalks and watering their lawns and driving by in their cars, searching . . .

For what?

For whom?

Candra had no idea.

All she knew was that something—or someone—was beckoning her. And maybe whatever or whoever it was had something to do with the feeling Candra had had, all her life, that something was missing.

Candra reached Long Neck Road, the broad expanse that marked the edge of town. As always, she paused and debated continuing straight ahead to Soundview, and heading back to the Drayers'. And as always, she decided against it after listening carefully for the faint whispers in her mind that told her to stay in town for just a little while longer.

She turned around and walked back along Broad Street until she reached the intersection of Highland Boulevard. She stood on the busy corner and frowned. The spot was the heart of town, a crossroads where cafes and pubs were teeming with Saturday night action. Candra surveyed the scene wearing a detached expression.

Which way do I go next? she asked her inner self, reaching up to push her long, straight black hair away from her face.

And that was when it happened.

A pretty redhead about her own age ran up to Candra, grabbed her arm and said, "Hey, what are you doing here?"

Puzzled, Candra eyed the girl and said nothing. She couldn't have if she wanted to, because the girl just kept chattering on without stopping for a breath.

"I mean, Zoe told me you were spending Labor Day weekend at your house on Natucket. I'd be out at our place in Newport if it wasn't for the party tonight. Is that why you stayed in town? Hey, you know, you look *really* tan—you must have spent *some* time on the beach over the past few days, right? I mean, you weren't this dark when I saw you at Zoe's party last weekend, were you?"

Again, the stranger didn't wait for a reply. The whole time she was talking, she'd been looking Candra up and down. Now she wrinkled her perfectly bobbed nose, smoothed the expensive-looking black sleeveless dress she was wearing, and added, "What's with that raggy tee shirt? The grunge look went out a long time ago, you know?" She laughed, a rippling, easy laugh of someone who had few cares in the world.

Candra glanced down at herself. Then she looked back at the girl, who went on in an amused voice, "I mean, I didn't realize you were such a Yankee fan."

Candra debated telling this rude girl the truth—that she had obviously mistaken her for someone else. And that her grandmother had bought her the navy tee shirt, with its superimposed *N-Y* symbol of the New York Yankees, for a dime at the second-hand clothing store on Elmont Avenue the other day.

Candra had been so pleased when she saw the shirt. What could be more American than baseball? She had thought it would help her fit in here.

Obviously, she'd been wrong. The girls in Crawford Corners didn't wear tee shirts.

Anger and resentment swirled dangerously inside Candra, and she narrowed her eyes at the impeccably dressed redhead standing in front of her.

Then she heard a horn tooting nearby, and a voice called urgently from the curb, "Chasey, come on!"

The redhead immediately looked over her shoulder. Candra followed her gaze and saw a square-jawed blond boy in khakis and a blue blazer beckoning from the driver's seat of a shiny red convertible.

"Oops, gotta go. That's Billy, the one I told you about. Isn't that an excellent car? We're on our way to that party—you know, up at Kathleen's father's cabin. Aren't you going?"

Candra shook her head.

The girl shrugged and hurried toward the waiting car, calling over her shoulder, "See you in school on Tuesday, right?"

Candra said nothing, just stood on the sidewalk and watched as the redhead got into the convertible. It pulled away from the curb with a smooth purr, and Candra saw the girl slide across the seat to snuggle right next to the boy.

She caught her bottom lip with her front teeth and watched as the car disappeared around a corner. Then she thoughtfully turned away from Highland and headed back toward Soundview.

She needed to go back to the Drayers' now.

She needed to be alone in the quiet basement apartment she shared with Rosamund to think about what had just happened—and figure out why it was significant.

Three

Meg stood on the top step of the gray stone Adamson-Swift School, waiting for Shea. He'd promised to meet her here at seven forty-five, and it was already ten to eight. If he didn't show up within the next few minutes, she was going to have to head inside without him.

After all, it wasn't a good idea to be late on the first day of senior year, especially when you'd been assigned to Mr. Pfeiffer's homeroom. The man had a formidable reputation among students at Adamson-Swift, but Meg had managed to avoid any contact with him before now.

Where the heck was Shea?

She was anxious to see him, if only fleetingly, before they headed for their separate homerooms. Four whole days had passed since Thursday night, when they'd had their last date. On Friday morning, Meg and her family had sailed on her stepfather's yacht to Nantucket for Labor Day Weekend, and Shea had gone to his mother and stepfather's country house in the Berkshires. Meg had tried calling him when she got back home late last night, but the housekeeper had answered and told her he wasn't home yet.

A little twinge of panic was building in the back of Meg's mind now. Shea was *always* on time.

What if something had happened to him over the weekend? What if he'd fallen off his horse, or had been injured diving into the pool? What if his stepfather, Duncan, who liked to drink and liked to drive his Jaguar at top speed—often simultaneously—had gotten them into an accident on the way back to Crawford Corners last night?

Oh, for God's sake, Meg told herself in disgust. *Stop being ridiculous. You sound like Grandma McKenna.*

Her mother's mother was always wringing her hands and worrying about something. Whenever anything was a little *off*, Gram feared the worst, imagining some disaster or misfortune.

Despite—or perhaps *because* of—her worrywart mother, Giselle had adopted a carefree, easy-going attitude. She rarely worried, even when it might be warranted, and she had done her best to instill the same optimistic outlook in Meg and her half sister, Carrie.

But Meg couldn't seem to help this pessimistic fretting about her boyfriend's well-being. For the past week or so, ever since those strange encounters with Mirabelle and Dalila Parker, she had had this *feeling* that something was going to happen.

Something bad.

Maybe, she thought for the zillionth time, she should have had the fortune-teller look into her future after all. That way, at least, she'd know what was going to happen, even if it was horrible, instead of being tormented by uncertainty.

On the other hand, Dalila Parker wasn't exactly the most credible, balanced person in the world. Meg told herself once again that leaving had been the right thing to do, no matter what Zoe said.

"Meg!"

A shout from the sweeping lawn below caught her attention, and relief coursed through her when she looked down to see Shea hurrying from the parking lot off to the side. She had been so distracted she hadn't even seen his familiar blue car coming up the drive.

"*There* you are," she said, as he hurried up the steps toward her.

As always, she noticed how good-looking he was, with his wavy dark hair, aqua-colored eyes, and broad-shouldered build. He looked crisp and polished in his school uniform: navy blue pants, starched white shirt, and maroon and blue striped tie.

He seemed about to hug Meg, but then seemed to remember where they were. He just smiled and said, "Sorry I'm late. I overslept. We didn't get back until after midnight last night. Mom insisted on Duncan sobering up before we drove home."

"Why didn't she just drive?"

"Are you kidding? No one drives the Jag but Duncan," Shea said sarcastically. "He doesn't trust anyone else with it."

Meg rolled her eyes. "Someday, Shea, he's going to total that car."

"Yeah, well, I hope Mom and I aren't in it when he does."

"Don't even say that." Again, Meg felt a little shiver of apprehension.

Shea caught her fingers and squeezed them, then quickly let go. "How was Nantucket?"

"Fine. It rained all day Sunday, though. And by the time the sun came out on Monday, it was time to head back here. And naturally Mom, being Mom, waited until the last minute to start packing. Then she had to decide what she wanted to bring with her, since we were closing up the house for the season."

"I can't believe summer's over."

"I can't believe this is the last 'first day of school' we'll ever have here," Meg replied. She reluctantly glanced at her watch. "Actually, we'd better get going. It's two minutes to eight."

"Uh-oh." He reached out, tugged at the mammoth wooden door, and held it open for Meg. "See you in Government, right?"

Meg nodded. It was the one class they would have together. Buoyed by Shea's earlier touch, she fleetingly expected him to give her a peck on the cheek before they parted ways. Of course, he didn't—just smiled, waved, and headed off to the right, while Meg went down the corridor to the left. *Don't be disappointed*, she told herself.

After all, she *knew* Shea would never venture to be so daring inside the school, where a teacher or the headmaster could cast a disapproving frown, or worse yet, reprimand them. As class president for the fourth year in a row, Shea prided himself on walking the straight and narrow, and on pleasing everyone.

He'll make a good politician, Meg told herself as she hurried toward her homeroom. And that was exactly what Shea had planned for himself—after Harvard Law, that was.

They had only been dating for six months, but lately, Meg had found herself daydreaming about Shea's future—*their* future. *Being First Lady wouldn't be so bad*, she told herself, smiling slightly.

She opened the classroom door and slipped inside, past a glowering-as-usual Mr. Pfeiffer, just as the eight o'clock bell sounded.

Homeroom was extended to a half hour today, so that forms could be filled out, seat assignments could be made, and Mr. Pfeiffer could give a stern speech about what he expected from his students.

From across the aisle, Chasey kept trying to catch her eye as the teacher droned on. When Meg finally dared to glance at her, Chasey quickly pulled her red curls straight back from her face, mimicking Pfeiffer's slicked-back style, scrunched her eyes, and thrust her lips forward in a striking parody of the man.

Meg quickly glanced away and covered her mouth with her fist, holding back a laugh. Pfeiffer clearly wouldn't put up with any nonsense. And the way he was going on and on about his "classroom rules" up there, you'd think he was a drill sergeant, instead of a homeroom monitor.

Mercifully, the dismissal bell finally rang, and everyone immediately jumped up.

"Sit down," Pfeiffer barked.

Startled, they obliged.

"I don't want a stampede for the door every day," he said, glaring around the room. "We'll have an orderly dismissal, row by row."

With that, he jerked a hand toward the first row, signalling that those students could leave.

Meg watched them filing silently toward the door and hoped this wasn't any indication of how her senior year was going to be.

She wanted to have *fun* in school for a change. Freshman year had been too full of adjustments to be anything but stressful. Then, Meg had spent her sophomore year dealing with the emotional turmoil of her grandfather's illness and eventual death, that following summer, from lung cancer. Junior year, Meg had been preoccupied with SATs and state Regents exams and keeping her grades up so that she'd be able to get into an Ivy League college. Her mother, who had never gone to college, had her heart set on Meg's getting a top-notch education.

Well, she'd aced the SATs and the ACTs and the Regents exams. Now all she had to do was maintain her A average and cruise through this last year of high school. And now she had Shea, the most excellent boyfriend in Connecticut.

No matter what, this was going to be a good year, Meg told herself fiercely, as her turn came to rise and walk out of Pfeiffer's classroom.

Still, she couldn't shake that tiny niggling doubt—that vague sensation of foreboding that Mirabelle and Delila Parker, damn them, had somehow triggered.

"Hey, Meg, wait up," she heard someone calling behind her as she headed down the hall toward first period.

She turned and saw Chasey breathlessly approaching. "Can you believe that Nazi?" was the first thing she said when she reached Meg. "I mean, it's *homeroom*, you know?"

As usual, her friend didn't pause for a response. She just plunged on with, "Listen, Meg, what was the deal on Saturday night? I mean, when I stopped to think about it, while Billy and I were on the way to the cabin, I thought, *Geez, Meggie seemed a little strange*. Kind of like you were, you know, *on* something. But I was like, *she doesn't do that stuff*—right?"

For the first time, she stopped talking and looked at Meg, waiting for her to say something.

Meg sidestepped a skinny, acne-faced kid—obviously a freshman—who had halted in the middle of the hall to consult a school floor plan. Then she frowned at Chasey and said, "*What?*"

"What do you mean, 'what'? I was asking you what was up on Saturday ni—"

"Chasey, what are you talking about?"

Her friend stopped walking and looked exasperated. "I'm *talking* about Saturday night, Meg, when I saw you on Broad and Highland and you were—"

"I wasn't in Crawford Corners on Saturday night, Chasey. I was at the movies on Nantucket with my sister."

"But I *saw* you. Not only that, I talked to you."

"Geez, Chasey, I guess Kathleen's party was really wild. You must have been out of it," Meg said on a laugh, and resumed walking.

But somewhere in the back of her mind, a faint warning was nudging its way in. She tried to ignore it, but she couldn't.

And as she glanced at Chasey, she saw a fleeting image of Dalila Parker's stubborn, knowing expression, heard the woman insisting that she had seen Meg around her neighborhood.

"What are you talking about? I saw you *before* the party!" Chasey looked puzzled. "Remember? I asked you if you were going. I mean, I was totally sober, Meg. *You* were the one who seemed spacy. That's why I thought maybe—I mean . . . what's wrong? Why are you looking at me like that?"

"Like what?" Meg shook her head, trying to get hold of herself. But she felt panic building inside.

"Like you're really scared or something. God, Meg, what's *with* you?"

"Nothing," she murmured. "I'm fine."

But she wasn't fine. Not at all.

Suddenly, she was petrified.

Crawford Corners had a population of nearly twenty-five thousand people, but the public school system didn't reflect that. Most of the local kids went to Adamson-Swift, the huge stone private school outside of town, or else were shipped off to exclusive New England boarding schools.

Candra, of course, would be attending Crawford Corners High.

Craig was in his last year at the all-male Lawson School near New London. He had left yesterday afternoon, and Candra hadn't been sorry to see him go. He was even more cocky here on his home turf than he had been in Jamaica.

Jane, too, lived away from home. She went to Miss Trevor's, an all-girls boarding school someplace in Massachusetts. Their semester didn't begin until next week, so she was home the morning of Candra's first day at Crawford Corners.

When Candra walked up the stairs into the kitchen to say goodbye to her grandmother, she wasn't thrilled to see Jane there, with her nose poking into the refrigerator. She knew, before the girl even turned around and spotted her, that she was in for some kind of snide remark.

Sure enough, "Oh, Candra, you're not wearing *that* to school?" Jane had the breeding not to actually make a face, but her tone conveyed her distaste.

Trying not to show the dismay that instantly came over her, Candra ignored Jane and crossed over to the counter, where her grandmother was arranging slices of melon on a crystal platter.

"I'm leaving now, Grandmother," she said.

Rosamund nodded. "Did you eat something?" she asked in her thick island dialect.

"I'm not hungry." Candra's accent echoed Rosamund's.

But not for long, she thought. She had long ago learned to mimic the Drayers' smooth Yankee accents so perfectly that there had been times, in Jamaica, when she'd been mistaken for an American. Now that she was here in the States, she would use it to fit in.

But her grandmother frowned whenever she overheard Candra making an effort to sound American, and besides, she wasn't about to let Craig or Jane hear her imitating their speech patterns.

So she maintained her lilting Jamaican patois when she said to Rosamund, "I'll be back right after school is over."

Again, her grandmother nodded. She wasn't the affectionate type, and Candra knew better than to expect a kiss goodbye or a hug.

"Have fun, Candra," Jane called as she walked out of the kitchen, toward the back door.

Reading the sarcasm that tinted the girl's words, she didn't bother to reply.

The September morning was cloudy and chilly. Candra rubbed her bare arms as she made her way around the sprawling house and through the large iron gates that separated it from the road. In Jamaica, where the temperature rarely fell below seventy, she hadn't needed coats or sweaters.

Now, all she had were a few of Jane's cast-offs that Mrs. Drayer had given her a few days ago. And though the clothes were far more expensive than anything Candra had ever owned, she wouldn't be caught dead in them. At least, not in front of the Drayers.

Today, she was wearing her favorite outfit—a peach-colored, pleated cotton skirt and a deeper coral top. The warm shades made her skin glow. On her feet were her white leather sandals, and she had painted her toenails a bright orangey color that accentuated her outfit. She wore her favorite jewelry, too—a matching necklace, bracelet, and earrings made of tiny shells she had collected. Her straight, black hair hung in a single braid down her back.

The walk into town took almost a half hour. By the time she spotted the boxy yellow brick school down the block, she was no longer cold. In fact, she felt slightly breathless, and her hairline was damp from the exertion.

Restless with anticipation, she picked up her pace and hurried toward the building.

But as soon as she caught sight of the students milling on the broad steps in front of Crawford Corners High, she stopped short.

Jane had been right. She was dressed all wrong.

Nobody was wearing anything colorful, let alone a skirt. They were all, even the girls, dressed in monochromatic-looking jeans and tops, and nearly everyone was wearing sneakers.

Candra had never felt so conspicuous in her life. She couldn't leave the sidewalk and make her way through that crowd. They would all look at her, maybe even laugh at her.

And if she didn't fit in from her very first day, she never would.

So she kept walking.

Past the groups of busily chattering kids, who didn't seem to notice her out here beyond the fringes of the school grounds.

As soon as she was out of their sight, she slowed down and wondered what to do.

She couldn't go back to the Drayers'. Her grandmother would never, ever understand why she wasn't in school. She would have to wait until this afternoon to go home, and pretend she had spent the day in classes.

She felt in her skirt pocket for the crisp bill her grandmother had given her last night. She was supposed to use it to buy her lunch. It was only five dollars, but she remembered that here, that was quite a bit of money. Five dollars in America was the equivalent of several hundred in Jamaica.

For five dollars, she could go to one of the cafes on Broad Street and buy a cup of coffee and something to eat.

So she did just that. In a cheerful, lace-curtained place called Betsy's Kitchen, she ignored the curious stares of the few people at nearby tables.

And when the waitress said, as she filled Candra's cup, "Cutting school already, hon? It's only the first day," she didn't reply.

The steaming black liquid wasn't as aromatic or smooth as the Blue Mountain coffee Candra was used to, but she drank it anyway. And she ate every crumb of the buttery croissant.

Feeling better, she strolled back out onto the street again and thought about where she wanted to go next.

After taking a moment to tune into her instincts, she turned right and crossed Highland Boulevard, headed toward the other side of town, where she'd never been.

Broad Street soon opened up and the sidewalk ended. Candra walked briskly in the grass along the side of the road, barely noticing the wooded landscape or the few houses she passed. She was on her way . . . somewhere.

Soon, she was standing at the bottom of a steep slope, realizing this was it.

At the very top of the hill, like a fortress, was an imposing stone building. To reach it, you had to follow the road that led from where Candra was standing, passed through the gap in the stone wall, and wound its way upward.

Candra stood there for a long time, staring at the building, wondering why she had been drawn to it.

Then she looked around until she found the sign and read the ornate lettering that told her where she was.

Adamson-Swift School, Est. 1810.

"Hello, is Meg there?"

"Speaking," she said into the receiver, which she had snatched up the instant it had rung.

"Hi, Meg, it's Mirabelle." In her southern accent, the greeting sounded like, *Hah, May-ig.* "I got your message. My roommate said it was urgent that I call you immediately, no matter what time I got home. Is something wrong? Is Zoe okay?"

"Zoe's fine," Meg said. Although, her friend was probably bursting with curiosity by now. When Meg had asked her for her cousin's phone number, Zoe had immediately wanted to know why she needed to talk to her. Naturally, Meg had made something up, though she knew Zoe hadn't bought her flimsy excuse. She didn't really care. The last thing she needed was for Zoe to get involved in this.

Whatever *this* was.

"Meg, are you all right?" Mirabelle asked.

"Actually, I . . ." Meg hesitated. She had been so anxious to talk to Zoe's cousin that she'd rushed straight home after school and spent the last few hours in her room, waiting by the phone.

She'd rushed through dinner, even though Sophie had made her favorite meal, a spicy seafood stew with yellow rice. Luckily, Carrie had chattered nonstop about her first day as a freshman at Adamson-Swift, so no one had paid much attention to Meg or noticed her silence. When she'd asked to be excused, her parents had been so wrapped up in Carrie that they hadn't realized Meg had barely touched her stew.

"Meg?" Mirabelle's voice nudged on the other end of the line.

"Sorry." She tried to focus, and again realized she no longer wanted to discuss what had happened. Right now, it would be so much easier to forget the whole thing. Except—she'd already tried that, and found that she couldn't.

"Are you okay?" Mirabelle asked again.

"Yeah, but . . . guess maybe I shouldn't have—I don't know, Mirabelle. I wanted to ask you about something that happened to me. For some reason, it seemed like you would be able to help. But I shouldn't have bothered you. I know you're really busy and everything."

But Mirabelle said in that drawl of hers, "I'm not too busy to talk to you. You sound upset."

"I am—a little." Sitting at her desk, Meg picked up a pen and idly doodled a rectangle on a pad of paper near the phone. "Can I ask you something?"

"Sure."

"It's about this fortune-teller I saw at a carnival last week."

"Oh, right. Zoe told me you two went to one, but chickened out of having a reading."

"Actually, *I* chickened out."

"That's what Zoe said."

"Oh." Meg clutched her pen. She drew a larger rectangle, enclosing the original one. "The reason I backed out was that the woman made me nervous, Mirabelle."

"Why?"

"It was something she said. Did Zoe tell you?"

"She told me that you got nervous and wanted to leave, but she didn't say why."

"She said she had seen me before, recently, on Elmont Avenue in Spring City. But I've never been there in my life."

"Maybe she mistook you for someone else."

"That's what *I* said. But she told me she never makes mistakes about things like that. And she also said—well, never mind about that. It's something else that happened today at school that's really bothering me."

"What happened?"

"My friend Chasey accused me of being on Broad Street on Saturday night, and I wasn't even in town. She told me that we had a conversation and everything, and that I seemed all spacy. Then she got angry and walked away in a huff when I kept insisting that I hadn't been around. I didn't know what to think. I mean, Chasey's a little scatter-brained sometimes, but she was really stubborn about this. She was absolutely convinced she had talked to me."

"I see," was all Mirabelle said.

There was a pause.

Meg plunged on awkwardly. "I don't know why I decided to bug *you* about this."

But she knew why. Because of what Mirabelle had said to her. And because something told her that the girl would have an answer for her.

"It's okay," Mirabelle said. "I'm glad you—"

"No. I mean, it's really ridiculous and I know it's no big deal and everything. I guess I just thought . . . It was just what that fortune-teller said about seeing me . . . And then Chasey—I mean, I obviously couldn't have been in two places at the same time, so—"

"That's not necessarily true," Mirabelle interrupted.

Meg froze, her hand that was clutching the pen stopping in mid-doodle.

Had she just heard what she *thought* she'd heard?

"Excuse me?" she said after a moment, when Mirabelle didn't elaborate.

"Maybe we should meet in person and talk about this, Meg."

"But what did you just say?"

"I said that it's not necessarily impossible for a person to be in two places at the same time."

Part of Meg wanted to blurt out that Mirabelle was obviously off her rocker, but another part—the same part of Meg that had been experiencing vague anxiety for the past week—kept her mouth shut.

"Unless you have a double walking around, Meg, and unless you're mistaken about never having been on Elmont and about being out of town Saturday night—"

"Of course I'm not mistaken!"

"Then you have obviously *been* in two places at once. Two people can't have made a mistake about seeing you."

Meg swallowed. Then she said, in a small voice, "Maybe I do have a double."

"Maybe."

But even as Mirabelle acknowledged the possibility, Meg remembered Dalila Parker's insistence that it had been her. *It's you, mon. I don't make mistakes.*

And then there was Chasey. *I saw you . . . I talked to you.*

How could Chasey, who had known Meg for almost ten years, have mistaken some stranger for her? Even if there was another seventeen-year-old girl in Crawford Corners who had similar looks, how could she be a spitting image of Meg? And surely a stranger would have immediately told Chasey that she'd mistaken her for someone else.

"Meg?" Mirabelle asked. "Are you still there?"

"I'm here."

"Let's meet and talk about this in person. Why don't you come on over to my place? It's still a mess—we haven't finished unpacking yet—but—"

"I can't," Meg said, glancing at the clock on the nightstand near her bed. It was nearly eleven o'clock. Her cat, C-A-T—pronounced as one word, Cee-ay-tee—was curled in a ball on Meg's pillow. The animal yawned and gave Meg a reproachful look, as if to say, *Come on, it's bed-time.*

"How about tomorrow morning?" Mirabelle suggested. "I don't have class until noon."

"Unfortunately, I do."

"Oh, that's right. Y'all are back in school again."

"I get out at two-thirty. Can I meet you then?"

"No, I have classes, and then a lab. Why don't we get together after dinner? Are you allowed to go out on a school night?"

"Yes, until ten o'clock," Meg said. If it were up to her mother, she probably wouldn't even have a curfew. But her stepfather insisted on setting *some* limits for Meg. Not necessarily because Lester Hudson cared. Just because he thought she should set a good example for Carrie.

"I'll tell you what, Meg," Mirabelle said. "Come on over to my place at seven. Do you have a pen handy?"

"Yes." She scribbled the address Mirabelle gave her next to her doodled rectangles. Then, because Zoe's cousin seemed ready to hang up, she said hurriedly, "Mirabelle?"

"Yes?"

"When you said a person could be in two places at once, what did you mean?"

"I'll explain tomorrow, Meg. G'night, now."

With that, there was a click, and then a dial tone.

Meg sat there, clutching the receiver. She felt as though there were, indeed, two Megs—but they were both *inside* of her.

One Meg wanted desperately to call Mirabelle right back and insist on an explanation.

But the other Meg was more apprehensive than curious, and

wanted, even more desperately, to avoid the entire issue. And it was this other, fearful Meg, who was becoming more pronounced by the second, who eventually won.

Carefully, she replaced the phone in its cradle.

Then she sat for a long time, staring off into space.

Four

This time, as Candra approached Crawford Corners High School, she was wearing a pair of jeans and the navy blue tee shirt with the Yankee emblem. She thought fleetingly of the redhead she'd encountered on Saturday night. What had she said?

Grunge is out.

Well, obviously, she didn't know what she was talking about, because Candra was dressed just like everyone else who stood on the lawn outside of this school. And as she made her way through the little knots of kids laughing and joking with each other, she was thankful that she hadn't tried to infiltrate their turf yesterday. They were throwing curious glances her way as it was, recognizing that she was a newcomer. At least now she *looked* like the rest of them.

She ignored the questioning looks and held her head high, finally reaching the double glass doors. The main lobby was fairly empty since it was still early. Candra paused inside and glanced down at the pink schedule card in her hand. It said that she was supposed to report to homeroom at the beginning of the day, in room 1G.

She walked closer to the first door down the corridor to her right and checked the number on the little plaque above the door. 1A. She was heading in the right direction.

She noticed, as she made her way down the hallway past the few kids who were at their narrow metal lockers, that this place bore little resemblance to her old school back in Jamaica. That had been smaller and darker and far shabbier, with cracked windows and scuffed, chipped floors. Here, everything looked new and shiny, and the place smelled as though someone had just gone through it with Pine Sol.

Candra stopped in front of the classroom marked 1G and hesitated only a moment before pushing the door open.

A woman—the teacher?—was sitting at the desk, writing in a large black notebook. She glanced up, saw Candra, and smiled pleasantly. "Yes?"

Remembering to use her American accent, she said, "I'm Candra Bowen."

The woman frowned briefly, then looked as though she had just remembered something. "Candra!" she said, standing up and walking toward where she hovered in the doorway. "You're our new student from Jamaica. I'm Mrs. Birch. Welcome to Crawford Corners."

She nodded and studied the teacher. She was middle-aged and had a dimpled, round face with soft brown eyes and a double chin. Her gray pleated dress hugged her generously padded hips and bust and had a large, floppy bow that tied primly under her chin.

Mrs. Birch reached out, and for a moment Candra didn't know what she intended to do. Then her own right hand was being caught into the woman's grasp. It was more of a warm squeeze than a handshake.

Candra felt a surprised little flutter of emotion from somewhere deep inside of herself. When was the last time *anyone* had reached out and touched her? Not even Mabel, her best friend back on the island, had embraced her when they'd said goodbye last week.

"We were expecting you to be here yesterday," the teacher commented, releasing Candra's hand. "I wondered if you had been delayed in coming over from Jamaica."

"No, I wasn't. I just . . . couldn't be here yet. My grandmother needed me to help her at home."

"You live with your grandmother? Then your parents are . . ."

"Dead," Candra said succinctly, looking directly into the woman's eyes.

Mrs. Birch shifted and cleared her throat. "I'm so sorry. . . . Let me get you your paperwork to fill out so you can be caught up when the other students start coming in. You can take that desk at the end of the first row. We have a seating chart, and I reserved that one for you. If you have any questions about anything, you can just ask the girl who will be sitting across the aisle from you. Kim volunteered to help you get acclimated."

Candra wasn't going to ask anyone for anything if she could help it. She would find her way around on her own. But she nodded anyway and said, "Thank you."

She took her seat and spent the next ten minutes filling out forms with the pen Mrs. Birch loaned her. She hadn't thought to bring one with her, and she realized belatedly, when she saw the other students entering the room, that she should have brought some notebooks, too.

Longingly, Candra looked at the nylon book bags most of the students had slung casually over their shoulders. Wouldn't it be wonderful to have something like that? Or even a purse, she thought, noticing that some of the girls carried them. Candra kept her few dollar bills in her pocket, along with her new key to the Drayers' back door and a plastic black comb that was missing a few teeth.

The girl who took the seat across from Candra had an oversized brown purse *and* a book bag. She had a glowing ebony complexion and wiry hair that was smoothed back in a wide headband, emphasizing enormous dark eyes and high cheekbones.

"Hi," she said, catching Candra looking at her. "I'm Kim Williams. You're the one who just moved here from Jamaica, right?"

Startled, Candra immediately recognized the girl's familiar, lilting accent.

"Yes," she said. After a pause, because she knew it was expected, she added, "I'm Candra Bowen."

"Nice to meet you. I just moved to the States from Montego Bay three years ago."

Candra nodded. She hadn't expected to meet anyone from home here. She hadn't *wanted* to.

"What part of the island are you from, *mon?*" Kim asked causally, resting her chin on her fist and looking at Candra.

Reluctantly, she said, "Outside Ocho Rios."

"So how come you talk like that?"

"Like what?"

"Like everyone *here.*" Kim swept a hand around to indicate the kids who were filling the chairs around them.

Candra just shrugged and looked away, toward the front of the room where Mrs. Birch was standing in the doorway, herding people through and urging them to take their seats.

Beside her, Kim said, "You know what else?"

Irritated, Candra glanced at her.

"I didn't expect you to be white."

Again, Candra shrugged and looked away, hoping the girl would get the hint and leave her alone.

Just then, a piercing, high-pitched tone blasted into the room from somewhere above.

Candra clutched the sides of her desk, startled. "What on earth is that?" she blurted, turning toward Kim.

The girl stared at her, then grinned. "The noise? It was the bell."

It hadn't sounded like any bell Candra had ever heard. She noticed that Kim was still wearing that pleased little smile.

Is she laughing at me? Because if she is . . .

Candra scowled across the aisle. "Is something the matter?"

The girl looked unfazed. "Nope. But you *do* have an accent, don't you? It came out as soon as you were caught off guard. How come you're trying so hard to hide it?"

Candra didn't bother to reply. Instead, she faced forward, set her jaw firmly, and thought, *I'll have to be more careful.*

And keep my distance from Kim Williams.

Meg checked the rearview and side mirrors, then looked over her left shoulder as she merged onto I-95. It was six-thirty and traffic was still heavy heading out of New York and along the coast to the Connecticut suburbs.

She didn't have to be at Mirabelle's until seven, and Wainwright College was in Spring City, only a ten-minute drive up the interstate. Still, she had left the house a half hour early. In the back of her mind was an idea that had taken hold last night while she was trying to fall asleep. She had debated and discarded it repeatedly all day.

Now, as she pulled out into the middle lane and zoomed past the slower traffic, she found herself considering it again.

Should I?

No!

She would be asking for trouble, particularly in this car. Her mother and Lester had bought her the gleaming black Honda Accord for her last birthday.

It has "carjack me, please" written all over it, Meg told herself. *You'd only be asking for trouble.*

But the part of her mind that had come up with the idea in the first place was growing more insistent, overruling her common sense side.

She passed a sign that said *Spring City, Next 3 Exits*.

She edged the car into the right lane again, just ahead of a dusty old Buick with a Mississippi license plate. In the rearview mirror, she could see the tanned, silver-haired man behind the wheel.

And for a fleeting moment, she thought, irrationally, that it was her grandfather.

But of course it wasn't. Grandpa hated heat and humidity. He had probably never been to Mississippi in his life . . .

And besides, he's dead.

Somehow, the realization took Meg by surprise, as it always did. After almost two years, you'd think she'd have accepted it by now. But she kept forgetting that she would never again see that unruly shock of white hair or those piercing blue eyes.

She bit her lower lip and tried to force back the image that tried to fill her mind—of Grandpa as she had last seen him. His eyes had faded and were clouded with pain. And his hair had all fallen out from the chemotherapy.

She could see him pointing to his bald head, hear him saying, "See this, Megan? No man in my family has ever lost his hair. My father had a full head of it when he died at ninety-five." Then he would sigh and squeeze her hand with surprising strength. "Whenever you're around, Megan, I feel like I'm going to make it to ninety-five myself."

But he hadn't.

Elmont Avenue, Spring City—1/4 mile.

Automatically, Meg flicked on the right turn signal.

No, her grandfather was gone. And Meg hadn't been there to say goodbye.

Stop thinking about it!

Lately, the painful memory of his death seemed to be on her mind more than ever. She tried to push it away, to think of something else, but she couldn't.

After all those nights spent in the hospital at his bedside, hearing him call her "Megan the Miracle Worker," hearing him say that just seeing her stopped the agony his body was enduring, she hadn't been there for him when he needed her most.

At Lester's insistence, she'd been helping her mother chaperon twenty seventh-grade girls at Carrie's birthday slumber party.

If I had been there with him, he never would have died.

No! Don't think about that!

The part of her mind that always shut out that horrible night took over, and she shifted her thoughts to Grandpa when he'd been alive. He had been fighting cancer for months, and the doctors had said it was a miracle he'd lasted as long as he had. When they'd first discovered the cancer, they had said it was so far gone he had a month to live. He'd lasted a year.

Megan the Miracle Worker.

He'd started calling her that right after he'd gotten sick. She remembered the first time he'd said it. He had been lying on the couch at home, nauseous from a chemotherapy treatment, and she had been sitting next to him, sympathetically rubbing his still-chubby belly and fervently wishing that she could make his pain go away. And after a while, he had said, "You know, it's the strangest thing—I suddenly feel a hundred percent better! What kind of medicine do you have in those hands, Megan?"

She glanced in the rearview mirror to get another look at the man in the Mississippi car, but he was gone.

Startled, Meg realized she was on the exit ramp. She slowed for the red light ahead, and glanced at the green street sign at the intersection.

Elmont Avenue.

How had this happened? She had warned herself not to do this, and somehow, she had done it anyway.

She looked around for a familiar blue and gold sign that would indicate the on ramp where she could get back on 95. There it was, off to the left.

But when the light changed, something compelled her to turn right.

What are you doing?

She had no idea. It was as if she had no control over her actions.

She drove down the broad avenue, looking around, looking for . . . what?

Block after seedy block, she scanned the boarded-up storefronts, the weed-choked lots, the knots of shifty-eyed people on the sidewalks. She knew, from the way they were examining her and the car, that she was a fool to keep going. But somehow, she couldn't seem to stop herself.

She stopped for a light and realized she was at the intersection of Twelfth Street. She looked over to the right. Rivera's Newsstand was on the corner.

Above it, she knew, was the apartment where Dalila Parker lived. The woman's words drifted through Meg's mind.

You'll come back to me.

Abruptly, she made a right hand turn onto Twelfth and pulled into the first parking lot she saw.

She U-turned so fast that her tires squealed, and pulled back out onto the street. At the intersection with Elmont, she made a hurried left as the light was changing from yellow to red.

Then, her heart beating wildly, she drove as fast as she could back down Elmont Avenue and sped up the ramp onto 95.

Candra slipped into her room in the Drayers' basement, closed the door quietly behind her, then turned and pushed the button on the knob.

Not that she thought anyone might barge in on her. Since they had been here, the Drayers hadn't set foot down here. And Grandmother was upstairs, clearing the supper dishes. Candra had eaten at the kitchen table with her while the Drayers ate off gold-rimmed china plates in the dining room.

It had been the same in Jamaica—Candra and her grandmother separated from the people whose house they shared, not only by invisible class lines, but by actual walls or floors.

Mabel, whose parents were also employed by rich Americans, had told Candra she was lucky to be eating the same food Rosamund cooked for the Drayers. Where she lived, that wasn't allowed.

I'm lucky to be living in a house where I'm reminded, every minute, that I don't belong here? That nothing around me is mine?

Someday, she promised herself repeatedly, whatever she wanted would belong to her.

Especially now that she was in America. Everyone knew that here, a person could become something—become a *somebody*, instead of a nobody, like Candra had been all her life.

All a person needed was dedication and motivation. Eventually, those things would pay off.

But Candra didn't have the patience for *eventually*. She was tired of waiting.

Today was Thursday, and Thursday was ruled by Jupiter, whose influence was associated with riches and ambition.

She crossed the room to the chest of drawers under the high cellar window. Reaching into the top drawer, she took out the familiar carved mahogany box and set it on the bed beside her.

She opened the lid and began removing the items she would need. Once they were assembled on the chintz bedspread, she cleared off the top of the dresser.

It'll make a perfect altar.

That thought had crossed her mind the first time she had seen this new bedroom.

In the Drayers' Jamaican home, her room had only had a cupboard with shelves where she kept her clothes. There was nothing to use as an altar. She'd had to slip away, into the woods, and use a wide, flat rock to perform her rituals.

She placed two white candles at the back of the dresser, with an incense burner in front of them. In the forward right-hand corner, she placed the holy water.

Then she picked up the remaining candle on the bed. It was green, symbolizing prosperity. She reached for the small vial of oil she had brought with her from Jamaica. It had been mixed with a money-drawing formula: frankincense, myrrh, sandalwood, and bayberry herb.

Now Candra used it to anoint the green candle, rubbing it carefully over the wax surface while she concentrated on the thing she coveted, the thing that mattered to her more than anything in the world.

Wealth.

"Hi, Meg—you're right on time!" Mirabelle drawled, standing in the doorway of her dorm room. She was wearing sweatpants and a tee shirt, and her hair was caught back in a rubberband. "Come on in."

"Thanks." Still feeling shaky from her experience in the car, Meg stepped over the threshold and looked around. She had never been in a dorm before.

The room was simple, with white painted walls and wooden floors. There were two twin beds, with matching desks and dressers on opposite walls.

"My roommate went over to the library," Mirabelle said, closing the door behind her. "She's real nice. From someplace out west—Montana, I think. Or Wyoming. One of those states that has ranches and cowboys."

"That's nice." Meg chewed her lip and moved over to the chair in front of one of the desks. Her legs were a little wobbly.

"Go ahead, sit down," Mirabelle offered. She settled herself on the edge of the bed beside the desk and looked at Meg. "Are you all right? You look a little odd."

"I'm fine."

From the way Mirabelle was looking at her, Meg knew she didn't believe her. But thankfully, she didn't push it.

Instead, she just said, "Why don't you tell me more about what's been happening to you, Meg."

"I told you everything. About Chasey, and Dalila Parker. . . ."

"The fortune-teller?"

Meg nodded. "Mirabelle, I need to know what you meant when you said a person could be in two places at once . . ."

"Astral projection."

"What?"

"Astral projection. That's how you could have done it."

There was a pause.

Meg could hear an old Pearl Jam song playing somewhere down the hall. From the floor above, there was a thumping sound, and then a girl giggled and squealed, "Jason, cut it out!"

"What's astral projection?" Meg asked Mirabelle at last.

"It's real simple. Every living body has an astral double that's with him all his life here on earth. After death, the double parts with the body and moves on to the next plane."

"You mean it's like a soul," Meg said.

"Sort of. Sometimes, even here on earth, the astral double parts with the body. During dreams, for example. And other times."

Meg shook her head. "I don't get it."

"Look, Meg, I already told you that I could tell you have certain . . . capabilities. Even if you're not yet consciously aware of them, it's possible that some part of you is. You may be astral projecting while you're asleep, and not even realizing it."

"You mean some part of me is . . . what, lifting itself out of my body and zooming all over town?" Meg asked incredulously. "That's crazy."

"No, it isn't. I've done it myself."

Meg blinked. "You have?"

"Mmm hmm. Deliberately, and probably in dreams, too. It's done through concentration—you *will* your astral self out of your body, and then you make your consciousness step into that double. It takes a long time to get the hang of it, but once you do . . ." She shrugged.

Meg stared. Mirabelle was sitting here acting like she was giving instructions on how to program a VCR. This was insane.

She shifted on the hard wooden chair and started to get up.

"Meg, wait, don't go," Mirabelle said, laying a hand on her wrist. "I know it's hard to believe—I thought so, too, when Cecile first told me about it. But think for a minute. Two people have seen you in places where you couldn't possibly have been. There must be some explanation. What else is there?"

Meg hesitated. There was something in the back of her mind . . .

Something she should remember.

No!

She forced it away and shook her head. "I don't know. But there *must* be something else, because I just can't believe this."

She was about to get up again when suddenly, the thing that had been nudging at her crashed into her mind and made her freeze.

The thing that had happened to her two years ago.

The thing she had struggled to block out until now, because it was just too scary—too impossible.

"What is it, Meg?" Mirabelle asked quietly. "What did you just remember?"

"How did you . . . ?" She stared at the girl.

"Tell me, Meg. What happened?"

"It was the night my grandfather died," she blurted. "He had been sick for months, and I went to the hospital to be with him every single night, after dinner. But this one night, I couldn't be there—it was my younger sister's birthday. I was in the kitchen, putting candles on her cake, when all of a sudden, I just . . . wasn't *there*."

She heard her own voice growing more high-pitched as the memory took hold.

"One second, I was in our kitchen, and the next, I was in the hospital room. I could see Grandpa lying there in the bed. Oh, God, he was gasping for air," she said on a sob. "He couldn't breathe, and he was really afraid, and I couldn't help him this time. I tried to touch him—he always said that when I touched him he felt better—but it was too late."

She closed her eyes and hugged herself, rocking back and forth as grief overwhelmed her again.

Mirabelle reached out and squeezed her hand. Meg clung to her cool fingers and took a deep breath, then let it out slowly.

"I saw him die, Mirabelle," she said softly, opening her eyes again. "I couldn't have been there, but I *was*. I know I was. Two seconds later, I was back in our kitchen, lighting the candles. But when the phone rang a little while after that, I *knew*. I *knew* it would be Grandma, and I knew why she was calling."

For a long time, Mirabelle just held her hand, stroking the top of it with her thumb. Then she asked quietly, "You never told anyone what had happened?"

"I never *remembered* it had happened until now."

"You blocked it out," Mirabelle said. "You couldn't handle it. But now you're ready to deal with it."

You're ready to deal with it.

No.

No, she wasn't ready to deal with whatever Mirabelle was talking about.

Abruptly, she pulled her hand from the girl's grasp and stood up.

"What are you doing, Meg?"

"I'm leaving, that's what I'm doing." She headed for the door.

Mirabelle came after her. "Wait! Meg, stop . . . we should talk about this. I know how you feel, and—"

"No, you *don't* know how I feel, and I've got to go," Meg bit out.

She threw the door open and rushed down the corridor, past open doors of other rooms and, no doubt, past curious stares.

But she ignored them, ignored Mirabelle's shouts of "Wait!" behind her, ignored the startled R.A. who looked up as she flew past him toward the front door.

She ran to her car, fumbled in her purse for her key chain, pushed the button that turned off the alarm, and slid behind the wheel.

And for the second time that night, Meg drove as though the demons of hell were nipping at her heels.

Five

Friday afternoon, Candra was walking along Soundview Avenue through pouring rain on her way home from school when a dark green BMW pulled up beside her.

"Hey, Candra," called Craig Drayer from the driver's seat.

She saw that there were two other guys in the car with him. Even from where she stood on the sidewalk, she could tell that both of them were good-looking. And rich, no doubt.

She hugged her books against her chest, feeling her wet hair plastered against the top of her head, her clothes clinging uncomfortably to her body.

"Get in. I'll drive you the rest of the way." He said it the way he always spoke to her. Like it was an order.

"No, thanks," she said coolly, and kept walking, stepping around a puddle even though her sneakers were already soggy.

The car followed alongside her, at the curb. "What, are you nuts?" Craig called. "You're getting soaked. You don't even have an umbrella."

She shrugged.

So did he. "Suit yourself."

She heard a quiet whir as the window rolled up, and then the BMW peeled away from the curb.

She glanced up and saw the car turn into the Drayers' driveway a block ahead.

She hadn't known Craig was coming home from boarding school for the weekend. Now she would have to put up with both him and Jane, who wasn't leaving for her own school until Monday night.

She clenched her jaw as she splashed her way down the road to the huge white house. The BMW was parked in the circular driveway in front, behind Monica's black Mercedes.

Candra walked through the marshy yard to the back door and paused just inside to take off her sneakers. She could hear voices in the kitchen, off to the right through the pantry. It sounded like Craig and his friends were rummaging through the refrigerator.

Clutching her muddy shoes in her hand, she was about to head down the stairs when out of the corner of her eye, she glimpsed someone watching her from the doorway between the pantry and the kitchen.

She turned her head and looked directly at him, and her stomach made a curious little cartwheel.

"Hi," he said. "Guess you like walking in the rain, huh?"

She just stared for a moment, looking him over. The guy was about six feet tall, with wavy dark hair that brushed the collar of his oxford. His shoulders were broad beneath the light blue cotton fabric, and he had on jeans, faded ones that were soft and broken in and hugged his hips and muscular thighs.

She heard an unfamiliar male voice call, "Hey, Landon, catch."

Someone tossed the guy a cellophane package. He caught it effortlessly. "Thanks, Jack," he said over his shoulder.

He held the package up, and Candra could see that it contained two chocolate cupcakes. "Want one?" he asked her.

She shrugged.

He put the wrapping between his teeth and with a quick motion tore it away. "Here," he said, and offered her one of the cupcakes.

Candra took a few steps toward him, still clutching her muddy shoes in her left hand. As he put the cupcake into her right one, his fingers brushed hers.

"Thanks." She noticed that his eyes were an unusual color—not quite blue, not quite green, not quite gray.

He grinned. "I love these things. Pure sugar and fat—the best." He devoured most of his cupcake in one enormous bite, finished the rest, and licked the cream off his fingers.

Candra just stood there, still holding hers.

"Aren't you going to eat it?" he asked.

She took a small bite of the moist cake and slowly licked the sugary cream off her lips.

"I'm Landon Keller," he said, watching her.

She swallowed the chocolately sweetness and tilted her head. "I'm Candra Bowen."

"I know. Craig told me who you were when we saw you on the street."

Right. Craig had told him that she was a nobody, the housekeeper's granddaughter.

"Hey, Landon, what are you doing over there?" A moment later, Craig was standing in the doorway, too, wearing his usual insolent expression.

"Go downstairs and change into dry clothes," he said, as his sharp gaze slid over Candra. "Do you realize how indecent that outfit is?"

She frowned and looked down at the white tee shirt she was wearing. The wet cotton was nearly transparent now and molded to her body. The outline of her low-cut bra was clearly visible.

She looked Craig in the eye and shrugged. "So?"

He rolled his eyes. "Leave it to Candra not to care."

Landon's dark gaze met hers. What she read in it bore no resemblance to the contempt in Craig's. He stared at her intently, and a faint shiver slid down her spine.

It was Craig who broke the connection, punching Landon in the arm. "Hey, come on, before Jack eats all those sandwiches himself."

Candra took a step back, toward the stairs. "See you," she said, tossing her head so that her long, damp hair swung around and hung down her back.

"See you." Landon followed Craig back into the kitchen, but she could feel him glancing back at her over his shoulder.

Candra went down to her room and slowly finished eating the cupcake, wearing a bemused smile.

Meg was in her room, getting ready to go out with Shea. They were doing what had become their usual Friday night thing—pizza and a movie. Since there was only one theater in town, the Dumont, there wasn't much choice about what to see. Tonight a new action movie, *Return of the Exterminator*, was opening. Meg wasn't crazy about car chases or gun battles, but Shea really wanted to see it.

She stood in front of the mirror and ran a brush through her long black hair, then pulled it back from her face in a wide black headband. She dabbed on some kiwi-flavored lip gloss, then used a charcoal liner and mascara to make her dark eyes stand out more.

She didn't wear much makeup at this time of year. As much as she tried to stay out of direct sun, her olive skin always seemed to take on a tan after five minutes outside in the spring. Chasey, whose fair complexion freckled and burnt easily, was always telling her how lucky she was.

There was a knock on her bedroom door, and then her mother was opening it and peeking in. "Meg?"

"Yeah?"

"You going out with Shea?"

"Yeah."

"I figured. Carrie's spending the night at Lindsey's."

"I know." She had seen her sister leaving an hour ago, an overnight bag slung over her shoulder. They hadn't exchanged a word. Carrie was still mad at Meg for not letting her borrow the treasured pearl drop earrings her grandfather had given Meg when she turned thirteen. Carrie had wanted to wear them to school. Now, Meg knew, she would be given the silent treatment for a week, at least.

Her mother took a few steps into the room. Meg could tell she was in one of her chatty moods. That usually meant something was bothering her. Great.

"Lester and I just got back from 4C," Giselle informed her.

That was the local slang for Crawford Corners Country Club, where her parents went every Friday afternoon for their golf game.

"We were out on the course when that big rainstorm came out of nowhere," Giselle said, shaking her head. "One minute, it was warm and sunny –the next, we were hightailing it back to the clubhouse."

She still had on the pink and green print romper she had worn out on the golf course. Meg knew her mother liked to get as much sun as possible on her arms and legs.

Unlike Meg, she had light skin and had to work at becoming bronzed. In winter she was always going to the local tanning salon or zipping off to Florida for weekends at the beach. Giselle wasn't the type to worry about UV rays or skin cancer. Or anything else, for that matter.

Now she drifted across Meg's room and plopped herself down on the bed, leaning back on her elbows and lifting one of her legs in the air to examine it. Meg could see her mother reflected in the mirror, and thought, as always, of how her friends were always telling her Giselle looked, acted, and talked like a teenager.

"See this?" Giselle asked, pointing to the lean, bare shin she was holding straight in the air.

"What?" Meg turned around and looked at her.

"This . . . *thing*. I just found it. It's the beginnings of a varicose vein."

"Where?" Meg walked closer and peered at her mother's perfect leg. "I don't see anything."

"Look closer. See it?"

Meg sighed and straightened. "No, Mom, I don't see anything."

"Well, it's there. You need better light to really see it. I'm getting old, Meg."

Old. Yeah, right. Her mother was thirty-three. She'd had Meg at sixteen, something Giselle, for all her liberal breeziness, didn't like to discuss.

"Mom, you're not old."

"After it started raining, Lester and I went in to the clubhouse for drinks. That wench Tara Cunningham asked me if I'd gone to the reunion last weekend."

"What reunion?"

"Adamson-Swift's twentieth. She acted like she thought I was in my *late thirties*, Meg. Then she made a point of asking me, in front of the Maines and the Lowells, when I *had* graduated. Can you imagine?"

Actually, Meg could imagine. She knew exactly what Zoe's mother was like.

Tara Cunningham would know, just as everyone else in Crawford Corners did, just how old Giselle was—and that she'd had a baby out of wedlock.

In fact, Meg had first heard about the circumstances of her own birth through her friends. How her teenaged mother had been running wild, doing drugs, dating older boys. And how rumors had flown when her grandfather, who was a bigwig in S.N.E. Development, had taken the family to the Caribbean for over a year on an assignment.

Everyone knew Harry McKenna hated heat and humidity—despite the late-seventies boom in island tourism and rapid building of resorts, he had steadfastedly refused jobs that would move him south, even temporarily. People said he had finally gone just to get fifteen-year-old Giselle away from her long-haired, marijuana-smoking, twenty-one-year-old boyfriend, Stu Kingman.

When Giselle came back to Crawford Corners with infant Meg, another, far more scandalous rumor had been confirmed. As far as everyone was concerned, Harry McKenna had taken his family to the islands so that his daughter could go through her pregnancy away from the local gossips.

The Kingmans had moved someplace out west shortly after the McKennas left town, and as far as Meg knew, her mother had never had further contact with Stu.

When Meg had been younger, Meg had tried to find out more about him. But to her frustration, the Kingmans hadn't left a trace. Meg had frequently asked where her real father was, and who he was.

Giselle had never given her a straight answer. All she ever said was, "All that matters is that Lester is your father now, Meg."

But he had never treated her with affection. And he had never adopted her. Meg had been given her mother's maiden name at birth, and still had it. The fact that she was a McKenna, when her half sister and even her mother were Hudsons, like Lester, had always made her feel like she wasn't one of them—like she didn't belong in her own house.

The one place she had ever felt like she belonged was with Grandpa McKenna, and now he was gone.

Her mother got off the bed and walked over to the carved antique cheval mirror. She gazed at her reflection with a critical eye and said, "Your mother's getting old, Meg. How does that make you feel?"

Her attitude made Meg feel like throwing something at her, and she hated herself for that. Lord knew she should be used to Giselle's obsession with age and beauty. She was used to these conversations, and knew what her mother was waiting for her to say.

So she sighed inwardly and said it.

"Oh, please. You're beautiful, Mom. Everyone is always saying we look like we could be sisters."

Giselle's face brightened. "They are?" she asked, as though she'd never heard that before.

"Sure. All my friends are jealous because their mothers are middle-aged frumps."

"Yeah, well, I'll bet *Zoe's* jealous, having that old battle-ax Tara Cunningham for a mother. The woman's old enough to be *my* mother. In fact, when I was in the ladies' locker room at the club, I overheard her talking to Monica Drayer about their school days. And Monica is fifty if she's a day, not that *she* looks it."

"Who's Monica Drayer?" Meg sat on the edge of her bed and slipped her feet into her favorite black leather flats.

"You remember . . . oh, maybe you don't," Giselle said, leaning closer to the mirror and prodding the skin around her eyes with her index fingers. "Jonas Drayer worked with Grandpa at the development firm. He's been living in Jamaica for the past twenty years or so, working on resorts. But I heard Monica—she's his wife—insisted on moving back. Supposedly, she had been spending a lot of time at their apartment in New York over the past couple of years, having an affair with some wealthy Manhattan businessman. But rumor has it that he dumped her last year. Now she's back in town, the whole family is, living out on Soundview Avenue in their old house. It's good to see the place finally getting some use after being empty all those years."

Meg nodded, bored. She couldn't understand why her mother was always fascinated by local gossip when she herself had once been the hottest topic in town.

She walked over to the mirror and stood beside her mother to check her outfit. She was wearing slim black leggings and a short-sleeved cashmere top. Her only jewelry was the jade baby ring on its slender chain around her neck.

"You look pretty, Meg," her mother said, studying their side-by-side reflections. "Sometimes, when you tilt your head like that, I think you look a little like me."

"Yeah?" Meg acted like she believed her, even though she knew there was no resemblance between them.

Everyone was always commenting that her sister, Carrie, was identical to Giselle's high school photos. Both Meg's mother and sister were petite and green-eyed, with silky blond hair.

Meg fingered the jade ring, then found herself asking, "Mom, why did you have this chain soldered around my neck?"

Was it her imagination, or was there a fleeting flash of . . . something—alarm?—in her mother's eyes?

Why would she be alarmed by such a simple question?

It must have been my imagination, Meg told herself.

Because now Giselle shrugged and casually said, "I didn't want you taking it off and losing it. You know how you're always fiddling with things, losing things. That baby ring is very special. I gave it to you the day you were born. Why? Don't you like wearing it anymore?"

"Sure. I like it." She hesitated and was about to ask her mother why the ring was jade.

But Giselle slapped her hands against her thighs and said abruptly, "Well, I'd better go get changed. We're going over to the Lowells' for dinner. When is Shea picking you up?"

"Any second now." Meg moved away from the mirror as her mother walked toward the door.

Giselle looked back at her and said, "Have fun tonight, Meg."

"I will."

She thought, for a moment, that her mother was going to say something else. But Giselle just tossed her blond head and left the room.

Candra examined her reflection in the mirror. Now that the rain had stopped, the September evening was warm and muggy. She was wearing cut-off denim shorts she'd made from a pair of old jeans that were ripped in the thigh. She'd had to cut them pretty short to get past the frayed hole, and now they hugged the tops of her long, slender legs.

Candra was wearing a faded pink half tee shirt, its hem brushing her flat, dark stomach a few inches above the waistband of her shorts.

She brushed her long black hair and let it fall, loose and shining, down her back. She had already put on her makeup—eyeliner, brown shadow, and mascara to bring out her already enormous eyes, deep wine-colored lipstick to define her full lips, and foundation and blush to enhance her exotic complexion.

She studied herself in the mirror, pleased with the effect. She looked sexy, but the pastels of her clothes gave her an innocence, too.

Perfect.

Candra turned away from the mirror and left her room. She walked swiftly past her grandmother's closed door. Rosamund would be asleep by now. She always went to bed by nine o'clock, and it was half past now.

Candra went upstairs and noticed that the house was quiet and empty.

The Drayers had gone out to dinner tonight, but Craig and his weekend guests had eaten here, and so had Jane and two giggling girl-friends of hers.

From her spot at the table in the kitchen, where she and Rosamund were eating, Candra had heard the girls in the dining room, making fools of themselves, trying to impress the three boys.

She had heard something else, too.

Craig, Landon, and the other guy, Jack, were discussing their plans for the evening. They were going into town to see the new action movie that had just opened tonight.

There was only one local theater, the Dumont, on Broad Street.

Candra knew exactly where it was.

She didn't have the money to buy a movie ticket.

But that didn't mean she couldn't happen to be walking by the theater when the movie got out.

"What'd you think of the movie, Meg?" Shea asked as they inched up the aisle of the theater after the lights came up.

"It was all right," she said around a yawn. In truth, she'd had a hard time concentrating on it. It wasn't just that the movie had no plot. It was more that she was preoccupied after everything that had happened to her lately.

She and Shea stopped to let several people out of the row to their left. The theater was jammed with people, and they'd been lucky to find seats together, though they'd had to sit in the front row. Now Meg's neck was sore from straining back to see the screen—and it hadn't even been worth it.

"Hey, isn't that Carrie?" Shea asked, nudging Meg and pointing to a familiar blond figure a few steps ahead of them. From the back, the girl looked like her sister. She was hanging on the arm of a boy Meg vaguely recognized. He had graduated from Adamson-Swift a good two years ago.

Meg frowned. "It looks like her, but she's supposed to be sleeping over her friend Lindsey's house tonight."

"Uh-oh."

"Uh-oh is right." Meg watched as the tiny blonde stood on her tiptoes to whisper into the ear of the guy she was with. As soon as she turned her head sideways, Meg recognized the profile. It was definitely her sister.

"Carrie!" Meg said sharply, and the blonde turned around.

Her eyes widened at the sight of Meg and Shea, but she recovered her aplomb with remarkable speed. "Hi," Carrie called brightly, waving. "Did you guys like the movie?"

"Excuse me, can I get through here, please?" Meg said to the couple in front of her.

They stepped aside to let her through.

"Carrie," Meg said in a low voice, moving forward to stand right next to her sister, whose eyes looked suspiciously bloodshot. "What are you doing here?"

"Watching the movie . . . among other things," her sister said suggestively, and she and the guy laughed.

Meg caught a whiff of liquor on Carrie's breath. "You've been drinking," she accused.

"So?"

"So you're not supposed to be drinking, and you're not supposed to be out with some . . . *man.*" Meg shot a meaningful glance at her sister's date.

"Who're you, her mother?" he asked lazily, brushing his shaggy blond hair out of his eyes.

Shea had reached them now, looking uncomfortable, his hands tucked in the back pockets of his jeans.

As though they were gathered on the church steps after Sunday services, Carrie started making introductions. Her voice was more high-pitched than usual, and her words were slurred. "Hi, Shea. This is Eddie. Eddie, this is Shea Alcott. And this is my half sister, Megan."

Half sister. She always said it that way. Just as Lester always made it a point to say that he was Meg's *step*father.

"Carrie, where are you guys going now?" Meg asked, shoving away the little twinge of hurt. She should have been used to this by now.

"I have no idea."

"Are you really sleeping at Lindsey's tonight?"

"Sure," Carrie said, shooting Eddie a glance.

Yeah, right.

"Come on," Eddie said, tugging on her sister's arm. "Let's go."

The crowd in the aisle was thinning. Before Meg could say another word, her sister waved and said, "See you guys." Then she and Eddie hurried toward the exit doors ahead.

Shea and Meg looked at each other.

"Where'd she find that loser?" he asked.

Meg sighed. "Who knows? I'm sick of worrying about her."

"She's pretty trashed, isn't she? Are you going to tell your mother and Lester?"

"My mother probably wouldn't think it was that big a deal, and Lester wouldn't believe me. Carrie would just tell him I'm lying again, like she did the time last month when I told them about her being the one who stole that hundred dollar bottle of scotch from Lester's liquor cabinet. He blamed that on me. He'd find a way to make this my fault, too."

Shea shook his head. "What's the deal with Carrie, Meg? She used to be so . . ."

"Innocent?" Meg shrugged. "She's spoiled rotten, that's what's wrong with her. As far as her daddy's concerned, she can do no wrong."

They were moving up the aisle again, slowly, trailing behind the last of the crowd.

As they made their way through the doors into the red-carpeted lobby, Meg suddenly felt a stab of trepidation.

She frowned and looked around, half expecting to see something amiss.

"What's wrong?" Shea asked.

"Nothing . . ."

She scanned the crowded lobby. Here and there, she saw a familiar face from school or from her neighborhood. There were a lot of people she didn't recognize, which wasn't unusual. Some of the local kids went to the public high school, and Meg didn't know any of them. Also, a lot of city people had weekend houses around here and came into town to go to the movies on Friday nights.

Meg kept looking around, scanning the strangers' faces, looking for . . . she had no idea who.

She only knew that all of a sudden, she had the overpowering feeling that someone was lurking nearby. . . .

"Meg? You okay?"

"I . . . Yeah. I just—I'll be right back," she told Shea, spotting the ladies' room sign off to the side.

"I'll wait for you out on the sidewalk. It's too hot in here."

"Okay." Meg hurried through the crowd and pushed her way into the rest room. There was a line of women waiting to use the two stalls.

"Hey!" someone said as Meg hurried past them. "Wait your turn."

Meg ignored her and went straight to the sink. She was trembling, suddenly, from head to toe. She gripped the edge of the white basin and stared at her reflection in the mirror. She looked pale and frightened.

What is wrong with you? she asked herself. *Why do you keep freaking yourself out like this?*

She turned on the water and splashed some on her face.

I can't go back out there yet.

She didn't know *why*, only that she couldn't.

She opened her leather purse, took out her brush, and started methodically running it through her long, black hair.

"Candra! What are you doing here?"

"Oh, hi," she said casually in her American accent, looking from Craig to his two friends. "I'm taking a walk. What are you doing?"

"We just saw a movie," Landon told her. He gestured at the marquis above their heads. "*Return of the Exterminator.*"

"Was it good?"

"It stunk," said the other guy, the one she hadn't met yet. He had straight, dark hair and tanned skin. "I'm Jack Keller," he said, offering his hand to Candra.

She shook it, hiding her surprise. Few people offered handshakes, especially to her. "I'm Candra," she said, and then she realized something. "Did you say your name was Keller?"

"Yeah." Jack grinned and pointed at Landon. "We're cousins."

"You don't look alike," she noted, studying both of them.

"That's because—"

Craig interrupted Landon with an abrupt, "Come on, you guys, let's get going."

"Take it easy, Drayer," Landon said. "What's with the big rush?"

Candra noticed the way his eyes slid eagerly from Craig back to her. Landon Keller was definitely checking her out. She ran a hand through her long hair, combing it with her fingers.

"Where are you going?" she asked, focusing her attention on Landon.

"To this party out at some park near Craig's house," he said. "Want to come?"

"She can't," Craig told him, jangling the keys to the BMW. "She wasn't invited."

"Who cares?" Jack asked. "Neither were we."

Candra glanced at Craig.

He shot her a warning look.

She ignored it. "I'd love to come to the party," she told Landon and Jack.

"Cool. We're parked back in that lot around the corner," Landon said, pointing.

Craig stalked off in front of them.

Jack stared after him. "Geez, what's with him?"

"Drayer's always moody," Landon said. "No big deal. Come on."

As they rounded the corner, they nearly bumped into a couple that was leaning against a tree, locked in a passionate embrace.

The girl, a petite blonde, broke it off and glanced in their direction. As soon as she saw Candra, she narrowed her bleary-looking eyes and said in a slur, "God! What are you doing, following me around?"

She tugged the shaggy-haired boy's hand, and the two of them hurried away, weaving unsteadily.

"Who was that?" Landon asked.

Candra narrowed her eyes and watched the girl until she had vanished around the corner. "I have no idea."

"It seemed like she was talking to you," Jack said.

Candra shrugged. "I never saw her before in my life."

"She was pretty wasted," Landon observed. "She must have thought you were someone else."

"Yes," Candra said, nodding slowly. "She must have."

For the first time ever, when Shea turned the car down Soundview Road, Meg wished he hadn't.

She knew they weren't necessarily going out to Moseby to park. At least, not this time. Tonight some of the seniors at Adamson-Swift were throwing a big party there, in one of the pavilions. A lot of their friends were supposed to be there.

But Meg just wanted to go home after the unsettling experience at the theater. First Carrie—then that weird feeling of foreboding. And before that, she had been too distracted to pay much attention to the movie—or Shea.

Now the last thing she wanted was any kind of intimate connection to him.

She needed to be alone.

She glanced across the front seat and looked at his profile in the dim light of the car. She studied his familiar, strong jawline, his masculine-but-not-overly-big nose. The way his short, dark hair stuck up slightly over his forehead, no matter how he tried to comb it down.

Shea drove the way he did everything else. Carefully, and obeying the rules. He kept the speedometer exactly at forty-five, which was the limit out here, and his hands were positioned precisely at one o'clock and seven o'clock on the steering wheel, the way they had been taught in driver's ed.

Just being with him, just noticing those little things about him, should have reassured her. This was good old Shea, who cared about her.

Sometimes, lately, she felt like he was the only one in the world who did. Maybe that was why she was always so frustrated when he pulled back, unwilling to make their relationship as intimate as it could be. She *needed* to be close to him.

But not tonight.

Tonight, her instincts wanted to push him away. Physically and emotionally.

He must have felt her gaze, because he looked over at her. "You okay?" he asked.

"Mmm hmm."

"Are you sure? Because you didn't look that great back there at the Dumont. You were pretty shaken up about your sister."

Meg nodded.

Maybe it *had* been seeing Carrie sneaking around, drunk, with that scumbag Eddie.

Who wouldn't be upset about something like that?

But she knew it was more than that.

She knew that the feeling that had come over her in the lobby had had nothing to do with running into her sister.

"Maybe you should have a talk with your mother about this, Meg."

"About what?"

"About Carrie. What else are we talking about?"

"Oh. I was just . . . My mind was wandering, I guess."

Shea studied her for a moment before turning his eyes back to the dark country road. "Meg, you know, when I think about it, you've been acting kind of—detached—all week. What's going on at home? Is Lester getting to you again?"

"Lester *always* gets to me."

Distracted, she turned her head and stared out the window. The uneasiness she'd felt at the theater hadn't left her. It was as though some nameless, faceless thing was closing in on her.

"Aren't he and your mother going away soon?"

"What?"

"You said something the other day about your parents leaving."

"Oh, yeah." Meg forced her attention back on the conversation. "They're going on vacation in a few days. To Fiji."

They went to the South Pacific every September. Giselle claimed a few extra weeks of basking in the sun was the only way she could make the transition into autumn in New England.

Meg had heard Lester asking her mother why they couldn't go to the Caribbean this year. It was closer, and cheaper. But Giselle had been adamant, without giving a reason. And whatever Giselle wanted, she got, from Lester, her parents—anyone.

Meg knew her mother had never been back to the Caribbean since she had been born, and Giselle never discussed the year she had lived there while her father was working on a resort. Obviously, she wanted to avoid being reminded of the experience. And obviously, she hadn't told Lester any more than she had told anyone else.

"Well, maybe before your mother leaves, you should sit her down and tell her about Carrie," Shea suggested.

"What would I tell her?"

"Come on, Meg. Everything you've been telling me lately! That she's been running around with a rough crowd, doing drugs—"

"I only said I *think* she is, Shea—I'm not positive."

"Yeah, well, if I remember right, her pal Eddie was a dealer back when he was still in school. He's a few years older than us. At first I didn't recognize him. He used to be all wholesome and clean-cut. Right before he graduated, he wrapped his Porsche around a tree, and everyone started talking about what a waste case he was. He had just managed to hide it until then."

Meg remembered that incident, too. She knew Eddie had been a dealer—probably still was—and she *knew* Carrie was doing more than drinking these days, too. Still . . .

"I'm not saying anything to my mother," she told Shea, shaking her head.

"Why not?"

"Because every time I try to tell her anything, she just shrugs it off and says that when *she* was in high school, she wasn't exactly a saint. Then she laughs and tells me some crazy story about something wild she had done, and says those days were the most fun she ever had."

"Well, I'm sure your mother's good old days didn't include drugs."

"Yeah? I wouldn't be surprised if they did."

Meg felt Shea look at her sharply, but she didn't turn her head. She just said, "I have a feeling my mother did a lot of things other people's mothers didn't do."

"You're kidding."

Meg shrugged. "You don't know my mother."

And neither do I, she thought. *Not really.*

Suddenly drained, she turned and looked at Shea. "Listen, would you mind just taking me home? I'm really exhausted."

"I had a feeling you were going to say that."

"I'm sorry, I just—"

"It's okay. I'm not really into a party tonight anyway. I have to be up early in the morning."

She was about to ask why when she remembered that he was going to New York to visit his father and his new wife. He wouldn't be back until Sunday night.

Meg found herself relieved that Shea wasn't going to be around for the next few days. She didn't feel like explaining herself to anyone.

"Can you help me look for a place to turn around?" he asked, slowing the car and peering into the darkness. "This guy in the car behind me is right on my tail. Geez, his lights are blinding. I think he has his high beams on. Jerk."

Meg looked ahead. "There's a driveway right up there on the right. See it?"

"Yeah." He put on his right signal and pulled in between the two pillars at the foot of the driveway. The car that had been following them whizzed past. "Good, this is a circular drive. I can just pull around."

Meg glanced up at the large white house. Somehow, she felt more acutely aware of the anxiety that had been dogging her ever since they'd left the theater.

"Hey, this is that place that's been empty for years," Shea said, steering past the large front door. "Now it's all lit up. Wonder what the deal is?"

"Oh," Meg said vaguely, remembering. "I know where we are. My mother was just telling me tonight that the people who live here have been away for years. The guy works for S.N.E."

"Around here, who doesn't?" Shea braked at the other end of the driveway, checked both directions, and then pulled out onto Sound-view again.

Meg looked back at the house as they passed it again.

There was something about it that bothered her.

She tried to shrug it off.

Lately, what doesn't bother you? she asked herself, half-irritated, half-anxious.

"Hey, who was that pulling into your driveway?" Jack asked Craig over the blasting radio as they sped past the Drayer house.

"Some idiot who can't drive, that's who it was," Craig said, looking in the rearview mirror. "Probably some friends of my parents or something."

In the backseat, Candra looked over her shoulder.

"Do you know who was in that car?" Landon asked, beside her.

"Get real. Who would Candra know around here?" Craig asked, steering around a bend in the road.

Landon and Jack ignored him.

Candra glanced back again, though she could no longer see the house or the other car. She couldn't shake the odd feeling. The whole time they had been following the car and Craig had been cursing the driver for going too slow, she had felt—well, the same way she had been feeling, on and off, all week.

As though there was an elusive *something* just beyond the realm of her consciousness that kept beckoning to her.

"Have you ever been out to Moseby Park?" Landon asked, beside her.

"Not yet. Have you?"

He shook his head. "I'm not from this area. My parents live in Rhode Island. So do Jack's."

"Where is that?"

In the front seat, Craig made a snorting sound. "Don't forget, Landon, Candra's not an American, even though she's doing her best to sound like one."

She narrowed her eyes at the back of his head.

Jack glanced over his shoulder and his gaze met Candra's. She saw sympathy there. It should have irritated her—she hated pity—but instead, it was oddly comforting.

Beside her, Landon said, "Yeah, well, Rhode Island's so small half the people around here seem like they haven't heard of it."

"Oh." She turned toward him in the darkness. She could smell the spearmint gum he was chewing, and the clean scent of his clothes. "I guess we have that in common."

"What?" Landon asked. He reached out and settled a warm hand on her bare knee. His self-assured attitude and the look he sent her made Candra shiver.

"That you come from an island, too," she told him, keeping her voice throaty.

But Craig had turned the radio down, and he instantly gave a mocking laugh. "Sorry to ruin your big romantic moment, Candra, but Rhode Island isn't an island."

"How's she supposed to know that?" Jack asked sharply.

Craig didn't reply, just reached down and raised the volume again.

For the next few minutes, the only sound in the car was the music blasting over the tape deck.

Candra stared straight ahead, through the windshield, hating Craig Drayer.

Someday, he would be sorry. She would make him regret the way he had treated her.

She would make him regret the day he had ever been born.

Six

Meg woke up Saturday morning and discovered that she had the house to herself.

Her mother and Lester were out shopping for new luggage for their trip, according to the note Giselle had left on the kitchen table.

Carrie still hadn't come back.

And Sophie, the housekeeper, didn't work weekends.

Meg took a shower and hastily braided her damp hair to get it out of her way. Then she got dressed in jeans and her favorite sweatshirt. It was Nantucket red—a faded, reddish-pink color that suited Meg's dark complexion.

The phone rang while she was crouched on the floor of her walk-in closet, looking for the missing right shoe of her favorite pair of Weejuns. She'd let the machine pick it up. She didn't feel like talking to anyone.

But her mother must have accidentally shut off the answering machine. Giselle was always doing that, whenever she tried to play back messages. She still hadn't figured out how to work the VCR, either. Even the microwave gave her trouble. But Giselle, being Giselle, always laughed off what she called her "total lack of appliance ability."

After all, when she couldn't work something, there was always someone around to take care of it for her.

The phone kept ringing insistently, and Meg finally straightened and hurried over to it.

"Hello?" she said impatiently.

"Meg? Is that you?"

"Yeah. Hi, Zoe."

"Hi. Geez, you sounded so gruff when you picked up, I thought I had the wrong number."

"Sorry. I was just in the middle of something."

"What?"

"Looking for my other shoe."

"Hey, now, *that's* important. No wonder you were upset when I interrupted you."

There were times when Meg found Zoe's sarcasm amusing. This wasn't one of them.

"Listen, Zoe, I have to—"

"Don't worry, I won't keep you hopping on one foot all day. I just wanted to find out if you want to come to the mall with us."

"Who's 'us'?"

"Mirabelle and me."

"No, thanks," Meg said quickly. Too quickly.

There was a moment of silence. Then Zoe said, "You know, Meg, I wish you'd tell me what the deal is. The other day, you were begging me for my cousin's phone number. Now you act like you don't want anything to do with her. Yesterday, when I asked if you wanted to come with me to visit Mirabelle at the dorm, you said no right away, too."

"I already had plans with Shea."

"Did you guys go to that party out at Moseby?"

"No."

"Chasey was supposed to go. I don't know why she wanted to go to some stupid high school party instead of coming with me to the dorms."

Meg didn't reply.

Zoe went on, "So what are your plans now? Is the elusive shoe going to keep you tied up all weekend, or what? Why don't you come with us?"

"Zoe, maybe I'm not in the mood to shop, all right?"

"Since when?"

Meg clenched her jaw. "I *don't* feel like going to the mall. Okay?"

"Okay. Fine. But Mirabelle's going to be disappointed."

"She'll live."

"Okay, I can take a hint. I'm hanging up now . . . but God, Meg, if I didn't know better, I'd say you and Shea were on the rocks."

"What's that supposed to mean?"

"You've been acting so weird and out of it lately, something must be wrong. Trouble in paradise?"

"No. Things with Shea are fine."

"Then what is it? New adventures in Lester-land?" Zoe was no stranger to Meg's situation at home.

"Yeah," Meg said. It wasn't really a lie. Lester was always a problem. "Exactly."

"What's up this time?"

"I don't really want to discuss it." Meg stooped to pick up C-A-T, who was nudging her leg. She stroked the cat's short, smooth black fur and scratched gently under the folds of skin around her neck. C-A-T was beside herself with contentment.

Zoe sighed. "Look at it this way, Meg. Whatever it is, it'll be history soon."

"What?"

"I mean, you'll already be away at college at this time next year. The evil Lester will be out of your hair."

"Yeah, you're right." Meg rubbed her cheek against C-A-T's velvety head. The cat purred even louder.

"I'll let you go," Zoe said. "I've got to go get Mirabelle."

"Okay. Have fun."

"Yeah. Call me tomorrow."

"I wi—oh, I can't. I'll be at my grandmother's all day. I promised I'd help her do some stuff."

"What kind of stuff?"

"Just—I don't know. Stuff. She needs help sorting through boxes, cleaning out the attic, whatever."

"She's not getting ready to sell the house, is she?"

"I have no idea."

"If I owned that place, I'd never get rid of it."

Zoe had frequently visited the McKennas with Meg over the years. The sprawling brick house sat on a hill overlooking the Long Island Sound. It had been built in Colonial times and was surrounded by enormous old trees, gardens, and a low, crumbling stone wall bordering the grounds on three sides. The water was on the fourth.

"Maybe the best thing for her to do right now is sell it," Meg told Zoe briefly.

"Why would she want to do that? She can't be hurting for cash . . ."

"Maybe because the house reminds her too much of my grandfather, okay?"

"God, Meg, you don't have to snap at me. I was only—"

"I'm sorry, Zoe. I know."

There was a moment of silence.

Then Meg said, "Listen, I have to go."

"Yeah, me too."

"I'll talk to you Monday at school."

"Right. See you."

"Bye." Meg replaced the phone in its cradle on her desk and looked down at the cat in her arms.

The animal's pale greenish yellow eyes looked unblinkingly into hers.

"Why does everything seem to be falling apart all of a sudden, C-A-T? What's going on?"

C-A-T only purred.

"I wish you could talk to me," Meg said. "Sometimes I feel like you're the only one who understands."

"Meow," C-A-T said.

"Sorry," Meg told her ruefully. "That doesn't quite cut it."

She put the cat down on her bed and went back to her closet.

Candra followed her grandmother down the three steps off the bus, conscious of the driver's appreciative eyes on her. She glanced up over her shoulder at him.

He was a young, good-looking black man, with a brawny build that strained the fabric of his short-sleeved blue shirt invitingly.

But he was a bus driver.

Candra turned her back on his hopeful expression and caught up with her grandmother on the sidewalk. Behind her, the bus doors folded closed, and it pulled away from the curb.

Candra thought about Landon Keller as she and her grandmother walked briskly along Elmont Avenue toward Aunt Tish's apartment.

The party had been in a pavilion at the waterside park at the end of Soundview Road, a few miles down from the Drayers' house.

The night was cloudy and there were no lights in the place. Candra had scanned the shadowy faces of the crowd of strangers who surrounded her, drinking and laughing and dancing to the music from a portable C.D. player. She wasn't sure what or who she was looking for among them, but nothing triggered recognition. The feeling of restlessness faded, but wouldn't leave her entirely, as the night had gone on.

Candra had been hoping Landon would ask her to go down one of the pitch-black paths that led off through the woods, where handholding couples kept disappearing or emerging. But Landon kept a casual distance from her, and it was Jack who spent more time talking to her, asking her questions about her life in Jamaica.

Candra was no fool.

She knew exactly what was going on with Landon.

Here, surrounded by people of his own caliber, he wasn't as interested in her. Though he was as much a stranger to the kids at the party as she was, he was one of them. She wasn't.

Craig had said they were wealthy locals, according to Jack, and most of them went to the private high school Candra had seen that day outside of town. The Adamson-Swift School.

Craig had heard about the party somehow, though he wasn't a part of this crowd and didn't seem to know anyone beyond nodding a brief hello. He spent most of his time staring moodily into space and drinking whiskey from the bottle he'd stashed in the glove compartment of the BMW.

Landon, meanwhile, had worked the crowd, casually holding a plastic cupful of beer in one hand. Candra had sat on a picnic table bench in the dark fringes of the pavilion with Jack. Occasionally, she glimpsed Landon as he circulated, joking around and getting into long conversations with people he'd never met before.

"I don't know how he does that," Jack had commented at one point, catching her watching Landon.

"Does what?"

"Fits into the scene wherever he goes. He doesn't know a soul here, but he's instantly old pals with everyone. He's always been that way."

"Did you grow up together?"

"Yes. Our fathers are brothers, and we lived next door to each other. When we turned twelve, we were both sent away to the Lawson School."

"Is that when you met Craig?"

"No. We go way back. Our parents are old friends. My dad and my uncle work at the Rhode Island branch of S.N.E.—that's Southern New England Development, the same company Mr. Drayer works for."

"That's interesting," Candra murmured, not so much because she cared, but because she felt an obligation to keep up her end of the conversation. Jack was sweet and attentive—not her type at all, but she was grateful for his company. If it weren't for him, she'd have been sitting there all alone.

Jack had gone on then, talking about growing up in a small town in Rhode Island. Candra had pretended to listen, but she'd kept her eyes searching for Landon. He spent a lot of time talking to a pretty blonde with a smooth pageboy that was an exact duplicate of Jane and Monica Drayer's hairstyles.

Candra had seethed with jealousy as she watched the girl looking up at Landon admiringly. Every once in awhile, he would glance around, catch Candra's eye, and wink as if to say she shouldn't worry, that she was the one he was interested in.

By the time the party was breaking up, she was pretending not to notice him at all.

Jack took the keys away from Craig as the four of them walked toward the BMW, which was parked at the far end of the rapidly emptying lot.

Craig had protested, then promptly passed out as soon as he climbed into the backseat of the car. Jack, who hadn't had anything to drink, got in behind the wheel. Candra wasn't about to get any closer to the slobbering drunk Craig than she absolutely had to, and she opened the front passenger's door without a backward glance at Landon, who had run his hand over the small of her back as they walked to the car.

Now that we're away from the crowd, I'm good enough for you again, is that it? Candra had thought darkly, walking faster to evade his touch.

She wasn't sure whether Landon noticed or not. Suddenly, she had noticed something that made her heart skip a beat.

Just ahead, a car's headlights had briefly illuminated a couple emerging from a path in the woods that rimmed the parking lot.

In that fleeting moment, Candra thought she had seen a familiar face, but the car lights had swung around and plunged the two figures into darkness before she could be sure.

Landon had sat in back and kept up a conversation with Jack the whole way home. Candra had no idea what they had talked about. She had been too preoccupied—with her anger at Landon and with her curiosity over the girl she thought she had seen—to pay much attention.

Unless she was mistaken, it was the same redhead who had stopped her on Broad Street last weekend. She kept replaying the image of the girl's face as they drove the few miles along Soundview Avenue. That, and the memory of the bleary-eyed blonde who had spoken so angrily at her outside of the movie theater earlier.

Both of them had mistaken her for someone—who?

As soon as Jack had pulled the BMW into the Drayers' driveway, Candra had climbed out of the car and slammed the door behind her.

Without a backward glance, she'd headed toward the back of the house, leaving Jack and Landon to get the unconscious Craig out of the car.

When she and Grandmother had left to walk to the bus stop in Crawford Corners at noon, all three of them had still apparently been sleeping upstairs.

Rosamund was giving Candra the silent treatment today. She knew her grandmother was angry that she hadn't come home until well past midnight. She hadn't asked where Candra had been—she never did—but she had been tight-lipped and colder than usual all morning.

Her grandmother crossed Twelfth Street a few steps ahead of her. Candra picked up her pace to get across the street before the light changed.

They were only half a block from Aunt Tish's now.

She stepped around a cart stacked with Sunday newspapers on the sidewalk outside of Rivera's Newsstand on the corner, then covered the few remaining yards along Elmont to the shabby three-family house with its peeling green paint.

It wasn't until they were inside and climbing the steep flight of stairs to the third floor apartment that Candra noticed the bag her grandmother was clutching. It was a doubled plastic shopping bag from the local supermarket, and she was clutching it tightly in her right hand, which was right at Candra's eye level, since Rosamund was above her on the stairs.

She studied the bag through narrowed eyes.

Her grandmother had carried a similar parcel to Aunt Tish's last Saturday afternoon, too. Candra had the feeling whatever was in it was something Rosamund didn't want her seeing. Last week, when Candra had casually asked what it was, her grandmother had said, with a stubborn, closed expression, "Nothing that concerns you, *mon*."

Rosamund arrived on the top step and knocked on the closed door.

Aunt Tish threw it open and greeted them with a smile. "Come in, come in."

She was warmer, friendlier than her older sister, though they looked very much alike—considerably overweight, with the same finely wrinkled black skin and short, curly, salt-and-pepper hair. But Tish was dressed American-casual in navy blue stretch pants and a white sweatshirt, while Rosamund was wearing a flowing fuchsia skirt and turquoise and pink floral top she'd often worn back in Jamaica.

"I have lunch waiting," Aunt Tish said in the lilting accent she hadn't lost after two decades here. "Come on into the kitchen."

She led the way through her small, shabby-but-scrubbed-looking rooms to the table.

"I'll be right back." Rosamund headed toward the bedroom that opened off the kitchen as Candra slid into a chair.

"Where are you . . . oh," Aunt Tish said, as though she had realized something.

Candra frowned, wondering about the look that had just passed between her grandmother and aunt.

When Rosamund came back to the kitchen a moment later, she was no longer holding the plastic grocery bag.

* * *

Meg glanced over her shoulder as though someone were following her, even though that was impossible.

No one was home. Her parents were still out shopping, and Carrie had shown up only briefly to dump her overnight bag in her room, make a few phone calls, and shoot Meg a dark look before leaving again.

Feeling like she was about to do something dangerous, Meg reached out and pushed open the door to the master bedroom. Her heart was pounding.

Don't be ridiculous, she told herself.

You're just borrowing a hair clip from Mom. She won't care.

No, but Giselle *would* care that Meg was sneaking through her things while she was out.

And Meg knew that was the real reason she was in here.

The room was silent and sunny, with its windows on three walls. The master suite took up one end of the second floor of the house, and included a full bath with a jacuzzi, several walk-in closets, and a little alcove Lester liked to call the dressing room.

The decor was designer-perfect, with a floral chintz bedspread that matched the draperies, the fabric on the fainting couch beneath the window, and the wallpaper border. Nothing was out of placc, thanks to Sophie, who dusted and polished regularly.

Meg tiptoed across the thick, cream-colored carpet, as though someone were around to overhear her.

Even as she reached her mother's antique bureau and tugged on the top drawer, she thought, *What the heck are you doing? What do you expect to find?*

She had no idea.

But she had to look.

She didn't know when she had first come up with the plan to snoop through Giselle's things. But after several restless hours spent lying on her own bed, staring blankly at the same page in her new issue of *Sassy*, she had found herself tossing the magazine aside and heading for the master bedroom like a woman with a mission.

The drawer she had opened smelled faintly of the French perfume her mother loved. It contained a jumble of silk lingerie, stockings, lacy panties and bras. Nothing else. The next one down held satin night-gowns, several workout leotards, and four bikinis . . . That was it.

Well, what did you expect?

Meg persisted, working her way downward, sorting rapidly through the contents of each drawer. In true Giselle fashion, everything was tossed haphazardly, unfolded and wrinkled.

No wonder her mother always had a pile of things waiting for Sophie to iron each morning before she got dressed, Meg thought, closing the last drawer.

She stood and looked around the room. She wasn't about to search Lester's armoire. No, whatever she was searching for had to do with her mother.

But what is it?

I have no idea. I just have to look.

Meg went over to the walk-in closet that belonged to Giselle. When she opened the door, she again caught a muted whiff of expensive perfume.

The closet was no more organized than Giselle's drawers had been. Beaded evening gowns were hung beside cotton tennis dresses, and the floor was a jumble of sneakers, satin pumps, loafers . . . every kind of shoe known to woman.

Meg impatiently felt her way along the shelves that lined the top of the closet on three sides. Her fingers slid past the jumble of belts and hats that were tossed up there until she encountered something hard and square.

A book.

Her diary! Meg thought, as she tugged it toward her.

She knew her mother had kept one years ago, because Giselle often mentioned it. Whenever she told Meg some wild story from her youth, she would say, "I haven't told another soul about that since I wrote my diary." Then she'd lay a chummy arm across Meg's shoulders and add, "But I don't mind telling you, honey. You need to know that you might see me as a mother, but once upon a time, I was no fuddy duddy."

She tells me everything except what I need to know, Meg thought grimly.

But maybe there was nothing she needed to know. Maybe Giselle didn't like to talk about Meg's father or her birth simply because of the social stigma of having a baby out of wedlock.

Except . . .

That just didn't fit, considering her mother's casual, liberal attitude about everything else in her life.

She's hiding something from me, Meg thought, remembering her mother's cagey reaction when she'd asked about the baby ring.

And there was only one way to find out what it was.

Meg almost had the book off the shelf when she heard a creaking sound behind her.

Someone had opened the bedroom door.

Oh, my God . . . I'm nabbed.

She let go of the book and spun around, fully expecting to see her mother or Lester staring from the room beyond the open closet door.

But it was C-A-T's yellowish eyes that met hers.

Weakly, Meg put her hands against her mouth and took a deep breath.

"You scared the hell out of me, you know that?" she said to the cat, who *meowed* in response.

Meg moved out into the bedroom and picked C-A-T up. The animal instantly launched into a low, rumbling purr.

"Come on," she said, carrying the cat over to the bedroom door. "You're not supposed to be in here. Lester's allergic to you."

Or so he claimed. He was always making a big deal out of it when he caught sight of the cat, going right into his fake sneezing and wheezing routine. He'd tried to make Meg get rid of her on more than one occasion. Luckily, Giselle was on Meg's side about that particular issue. Whenever Lester started acting up about C-A-T, her mother would say to him, "How would you like it if we threatened to give *you* away?"

If only that were possible, Meg always thought.

Now she set the cat on the hallway floor outside the master bedroom door. "Go wait for me in the kitchen. I'll be there in a minute, and I'll sneak you some of that heavy cream fat old Lester drinks in his coffee."

As if she'd understood, the cat *meowed* and trotted obediently down the hall to the stairs.

Meg closed the bedroom door behind her this time, and hurried back over to the closet.

She reached up and felt along the shelf until she came to the rectangular outline of the book again.

Anxiously, she pulled it down, flipped it over, and stared at the cover.

More Joy of Sex.

She should have known.

Rolling her eyes, Meg put the book back up on the shelf and closed the closet door in disgust.

Well, what did you think you were going to find? she asked herself as she moved across the bedroom floor and opened the door to the hallway again. *Even if you did get your hands on her diary, what could possibly be in it?*

A clue, some part of her mind answered.

Startled, she paused with her hand on the knob.

A clue to my past.

But what are you looking for? What kind of clue?

She didn't have an answer to that.

Chewing her lower lip thoughtfully, she closed the master bedroom door behind her and wandered down to the kitchen to give C-A-T her treat.

Candra slipped into the shadows of the alley beside Rivera's News-stand and waited.

Dusk had settled over Elmont Avenue, and things were quiet in these hours before the Saturday night hustling began.

Candra caught her lower lip beneath her front teeth and watched the sidewalk. Sooner or later, she knew, her grandmother and Aunt Tish were going to emerge from the green house a few doors away.

And when they did, she would follow them.

Something was going on, and she had no doubt that it had to do with the bag her grandmother had brought with her this afternoon.

The day had passed uneventfully. After lunch, Aunt Tish had sug-gested that they go for a walk to the produce market up on Fourteenth Street. There, Candra had been bored while her grandmother and aunt picked over dozens of mangos and bananas and melons, none of it, Candra knew, anywhere near the quality they were used to back on the island. That was when she had realized, with a pang, that she was homesick. Just a little.

She hadn't given it much thought until now.

But when it struck her that she hadn't tasted *real* fruit in weeks— not the ripe, juicy kind that had grown right outside their door back in Jamaica—she had felt a twinge of regret.

She'd gotten over it fast, though.

Because back home, she would have been living the same old exis-tence, dreaming dreams that stood no chance of coming true.

Here, she was going to make them happen.

She was going to be Somebody.

Somebody rich.

And when she had more money than she knew what to do with, she'd buy her own plane and fly fresh fruit in from Jamaica every week.

Hell, every *day*.

From the produce market, she had gone with her grandmother and aunt to the Spanish grocery store down the block. By the time they had gotten back to Aunt Tish's apartment, it was dinnertime. Rosamund had fried a panful of chicken and some plantains, and the three of them had eaten in front of the television set.

Aunt Tish, Candra had noticed, watched and talked about TV a lot. In the few times she had been in her aunt's apartment, the set was always blaring in the background.

Candra and Rosamund had never had a television. The Drayers had had one on the main floor of their house in Jamaica, but seldom watched it. When the Drayer kids were around, they complained that they couldn't get any of the American shows they liked.

Now Candra stared vacantly at the screen as a middle-aged man in a suit sat behind a desk and gave the evening news, about things that had happened in places she didn't recognize, to people who were strangers. Her grandmother, like her, showed little reaction.

But Aunt Tish was riveted. "Did you hear that?" she exclaimed. "They found that little girl who was kidnapped from a park in Spring City last month. A psychic helped the cops locate her."

Candra thought that was surprising. She hadn't thought that occult powers were acknowledged here in the States, much less utilized by the police.

After dinner, Candra had helped wash the dishes. Then her grandmother had handed her several coins and said, "You can take the bus back to the Drayers on your own, *mon*. Aunt Tish and I have to go someplace."

"Where?" she had asked suspiciously. This was a repeat performance of last Saturday night. Her grandmother had ignored her, exchanging a glance with Aunt Tish, who changed the subject, giving Candra detailed directions on how to get to the bus stop down the street.

Now, Candra was determined to find out just what her grandmother and aunt were up to.

It was dark by the time she heard a nearby door open with a familiar squeak out on the street.

She flattened herself against the brick wall of the newsstand and turned her head toward the sidewalk. If they didn't pass by within a few seconds, that meant they were headed in the other direction, and she'd have to hurry after them.

But no, there they were, the two of them, moving past the alley. Candra stealthily moved toward the sidewalk and peeked around the corner of the newsstand, expecting to see her aunt and grandmother crossing Twelfth Street.

Instead, they were only a few yards away, knocking on the door beside the now-lowered security gate that protected the closed news-stand. Candra jumped back, praying they hadn't seen her.

A minute later she heard a door open, and someone joined Rosamund and Tish. She heard the female voice and recognized the accent. Someone else from Jamaica. She must be a friend of Aunt Tish's. As the voices faded down the sidewalk, Candra peeked around the corner again.

From this distance, all she could make out of the newcomer was that she was black and slender.

Candra waited until the three women were well into the next block before she slipped out of the alley and started following them.

She noticed that Rosamund was carrying the plastic grocery bag again. Aunt Tish and the other woman had similar bundles in their hands.

Where on earth were they going?

It's probably nothing, Candra told herself. *They're probably visiting someone. Or maybe they're just taking a stroll.*

But then what were they carrying with them?

And why had Rosamund been so evasive?

Something was definitely up.

And Candra had every intention of finding out what it was.

Careful to stay in the shadows, she moved swiftly and silently along the dark sidewalk behind them.

Meg put down her fork. "May I be excused?"

Her mother, Lester, and Carrie all looked at her.

She realized then that she had interrupted Lester in the middle of some boring story he was telling about something no one cared about.

"That was rude," he said, frowning at her. Meg noticed that his stupid reddish mustache that matched his stupid reddish hair was coated with butter sauce. "The least you could do is wait until I stopped talking."

You never do, she thought sullenly, but only said, "I'm sorry."

"Salmon isn't cheap," Lester said in response. Behind his wire-rimmed glasses, his watery gray eyes were resolute.

"Excuse me?" Meg looked to her mother for a clue to what he meant, but Giselle was busy reaching for the wine decanter in the center of the table.

"Look at your plate," Lester said impatiently.

Meg looked and realized what he meant. She had barely touched her dinner. The chunk of broiled salmon sat intact beside the mound of rice pilaf and asparagus.

"I'm not hungry," she told Lester.

"So you plan to waste all that food. Do you know what it was like for me when I was your age? We had nothing. My mother fed all five of us on less than a dollar a meal. We lived on bread and macaroni. She could have bought enough to last a week for what that one piece of salmon cost."

Meg shrugged. "What do you want me to do? Choke it down to make up for your tortured childhood?"

Her mother had refilled her wineglass and now took a sip.

Lester shook his head at Meg. "You think money grows on trees, don't you?"

It was one of his favorite catchphrases. That, and "I'm not made of money." You'd think the man was working two jobs, struggling to make ends meet, the way he talked sometimes.

Meg thought about asking him how many years' worth of groceries his mother could have bought for the price Lester had paid for a new Vuitton garment bag that afternoon.

Before she could say it, Carrie spoke up. "Come on, Daddy, don't bug Meg. If she's not hungry, she shouldn't have to eat."

Meg glanced at her sister in surprise.

For only the briefest moment did she think Carrie was sticking up for her because she cared. One close look into her sister's green eyes told Meg exactly that Carrie wasn't defending her out of the goodness of her heart. She must be worried, at least a little, that Meg was going to tell her father about her actions the night before.

Giselle took a sip of wine and said, "Oh, Les, you're such a skinflint sometimes. What's one stupid piece of salmon? Go give it to C-A-T, Meg. She'll love it."

Meg caught the gleam of amusement in her mother's eyes as Lester turned red and glared, first at Giselle, then at Meg.

"Then what happened, Daddy?" Carrie asked, touching his sleeve.

"What?" He looked distracted.

"On the golf course that day. You were telling us that story . . ."

Les's face lit up, and he smiled lovingly at his daughter. "Oh, that's right, I was, wasn't I? Well, then I looked off into the distance, and I thought . . ."

As Lester droned on, Meg stood, picked up her plate, and slipped out of the dining room.

In the kitchen, she scraped the chunk of fish into C-A-T's green plastic bowl that Meg had had personalized for her at the Pet Emporium on Broad Street last Christmas.

She straightened and started carrying her plate over to the sink nearly tripping over C-A-T. The cat had been upstairs, asleep, when Meg went down to dinner. Now she had materialized in the kitchen as if she'd somehow known there was a special treat in store.

"What'd you do, read my mind?" Meg asked, staring at C-A-T, who trotted over to her bowl and promptly started munching on the salmon.

Meg watched her for a moment, then shrugged. This wasn't the first time the cat had materialized as if on cue.

"You're just the smartest, C-A-T," Meg said, before she headed up the back stairs, not wanting to walk past the dining room again. She could hear Lester and Carrie laughing together over something.

She made her way along the L-shaped hall that bisected the two wings of the second floor. Her room was right in the middle, between the two that were reserved for guests.

When they had moved into this place five years ago, Meg remembered, she had picked out the big back bedroom as her own. She'd loved it because it had a bay window overlooking the backyard, a window seat, and built-in bookshelves.

But on moving day, Carrie had suddenly decided that *she* wanted the room, and had thrown a tantrum when Meg insisted that it was hers.

Naturally, Lester had stepped in and accused Meg of being "a big bully. For crying out loud, she's just a little kid. Let her have the room, Meg."

So the back bedroom had been Carrie's from that day on.

Meg had grown to like her own room, which had a fireplace and a huge closet. And her mother had let her pick out everything—the dusty mauve carpeting, the crocheted lace bedding, the rose-and-vine wallpaper border. It was a beautiful room.

But still, Meg thought about those built-in bookshelves and the window seat that was a perfect place to curl up with a good novel on a winter afternoon. And she resented Carrie, who hadn't picked up a book since Dr. Seuss, and who had filled the shelves with a stuffed animal collection.

Lester still brought her a new one whenever he travelled on business, taking care to pick it out carefully so that it would reflect wherever he'd been. He'd bought her a velvety beaver from Oregon just a few months ago, and a crimson plush lobster from Maine.

He always came home with something special for Giselle, too—perfume or lingerie, and, invariably, a bouquet of flowers.

Not that he left Meg out. No, he made it a point to treat her equally. In fact, he was always saying, to anyone who would listen, that he treated Meg "as if she were my *own* kid, like Carrie is. Yes sir, Lester Hudson is nothing if not fair and square."

Yeah, right.

When Lester travelled on business, he brought Meg things he had obviously picked up in the airport gift shop at the last minute. She had a collection of coffee mugs, key chains, even ash trays ("You can use 'em for those hairpins you're always leaving all over the house, Meg," Lester had said)—all emblazoned with the names of different cities.

In her room, Meg closed the door behind her and drifted over to the bookshelf her grandfather had made for her a few years back. He had sanded the wood until it was silky, then stained it a soft cherry color that was identical to the woodwork in her room. He had even hired an artist to stencil roses on the sides, to match the floral border on her walls.

Suddenly, Meg was overcome with grief. Her eyes welled with tears, and she swallowed hard, trying to force back the lump that had risen in her throat.

Why did you have to leave me? she asked her grandfather silently, looking upward as though he were right there, watching her. *You were the only one who really, truly cared.*

But even Harry McKenna had never answered Meg's questions about the circumstances of her birth.

He had always grown uncomfortable when she'd asked, and had told her that the only thing that mattered was that she'd been born, because he didn't know what he'd do without her.

Megan the Miracle Worker.

She stared down at her hands, remembering how she had spent hours just stroking her grandfather's stomach, or clinging to his gnarled old fingers, as he lay dying his slow, painful death.

She had spent so many hours willing him to get better, begging him silently not to give in to the disease that was devouring him from the inside.

And there were times when she'd actually thought she could somehow stop the inevitable from happening.

Times—even near the end—when Harry would manage to sit up, then stand up, and tell Megan that she had soothed away his torment.

But only for a while.

Because sooner or later, she always had to go home. And the next time she would see her grandfather, he would be weak with pain again.

Meg ran her fingertips over the surface of the bookshelves he had built for her, and pictured him puttering around in the old potting shed where he had dabbled in woodworking.

Then she imagined him lounging on the sofa in the living room of the big brick house, smoking his vanilla-scented pipe and listening to Billie Holiday records.

Or in the huge country kitchen, telling Meg to "Stand by while I whip you up a Harry McKenna Special."

She would always giggle and say, "What's in a Harry McKenna Special, Grandpa?"

"Why, you know that recipe, Megan." His eyes would twinkle at her, and they would say it in unison—"A little of this, a little of that, and a whole lot of love."

Meg gripped the bookshelves, gulped, and let the bitter tears of grief spill down her cheeks.

Never, in a million years, would Candra have guessed the object that was concealed in the grocery bag Rosamund had carried.

Who would have suspected that it was a white hooded robe?

Or that Candra's grandmother, Rosamund Bowen, had joined a coven of witches?

Candra stood in the shadows of a mass of briars at the edge of the old railroad yard. She had followed her grandmother, aunt, and the third woman as they made their way through the maze of narrow old streets to this spot by the water. An abandoned, crumbling shack was nearby, and even in the darkness, Candra could tell that the rusty train tracks that passed through the area were choked with weeds and debris. The tracks came out of a wooded thicket on one side, and disappeared into more woods on the other. The only access to this spot was an overgrown, winding dirt road that led the quarter of a mile from the gloomy, deserted waterfront warehoue district of Spring City.

In the clearing, Candra's grandmother, Aunt Tish, and the other woman had donned their white hooded robes and joined about a dozen identically attired people. She could tell, from their voices, that there were both men and women in the group. They mingled, chatting, as though they were at a cocktail party, until one robed figure, a woman, emerged from the shack and called out, "Let us cast the magic circle!"

Candra watched, fascinated, as the white-hooded figures clustered together in the center of the clearing. She could no longer distinguish Rosamund from the others.

Around them, the woman traced a room-sized circle in the dirt.

Then she placed four candles, north, south, east, and west, outside the circumference, and lit them. Someone else put a draped box inside the circle, in front of the north-facing candle. On it, the woman placed several other items.

Candra peered through the darkness, trying to see what they were. Moonlight reflected off two of the objects. Candra saw that one was a sword, the other a medallion about six inches across.

She knew, though she couldn't see it clearly, that it was a pentacle.

Candra was no stranger to witchcraft.

Back home, it had taken the form of *obeah*, the Jamaican version of voodoo. Candra had never witnessed an actual ceremony, but she, like her friends and her grandmother and just about everyone she knew, had adapted certain rituals, spells, and charms. And from the time she was little, her grandmother had taught her to listen to her instincts and use what Rosamund referred to as the special "powers" she had been born with.

This, though, was different.

This was a coven, and the woman who had cast the circle was obviously the high priestess.

She took a small bowl, held it aloft, and Candra could clearly hear her words. "Oh, creature of water, I bid thee now be exorcised of spiritual impurities . . ."

She then poured a heap of something white from another bowl onto the pentacle, touched it with the glinting blade of the sword, and called it, "Oh, creature of salt . . ."

When she had finished rattling off the prayer, she lifted the pentacle and poured the salt into the water.

Then she walked clockwise around the circle, holding the sword facing down so that it traced the circumference just above the ground. When she reached the altar again, she recited a longer prayer that began, "Oh, circle of power, be conjured now . . ."

When that was done, she walked around the circle again, sprinkling it with consecrated water. She repeated the path with a burning incense holder and, finally, picked up the north candle and carried it around the circle.

Then she picked up the sword, faced east, and held it in front of her. "I beckon thee, Lords of the watchtowers of the East, to witness my rites and summon thee to guard the circle." As she uttered the words, she traced a five-pointed star in the air with the sword, then kissed the blade and held it against her for a moment.

When she turned abruptly toward the south, Candra ducked behind the bush, because the woman seemed to be staring right at her. But the priestess simply repeated the chant, then turned to her right and did it again for the west side of the circle, and then for the north.

Concealed in the shadows, Candra watched the ceremony that followed. She could no longer hear what was being said; the wind had picked up, carrying the voices away from her straining ears.

But as she watched, she saw the circle of robed figures join hands and begin to move clockwise. Faster and faster they danced, until they had become a blur of white.

Candra felt charged with a tingling sensation and realized what was happening. They were raising energy, channelling it through their movement.

She could feel it swirling around her, as real as the breeze that stirred the leaves above her head.

So real that she was frightened by its power.

Slowly, as the circle of witches continued their frenzied dance, Candra backed away.

Then she turned and ran alone along the path through the woods, away from the coven, away from the sizzling energy it had unleashed.

But she couldn't escape the frenzy of emotion and power it had conjured within her.

Even as she ran, she grasped and welcomed the heightened awareness that whatever she had been blindly searching for was almost within her grasp.

She knew that soon, its presence would make itself known to her . . .

And that whatever it was would change her life forever.

Seven

Sunday afternoon Meg drove through the pouring rain to the large brick waterfront house on Gatehouse Lane. She parked around back, beside her grandmother's silver Cadillac.

Her grandfather's black one, she knew, was sitting, silent and abandoned, behind the locked garage doors. It had been there ever since he'd last driven it, two years ago.

Stupid Lester was always urging his mother-in-law to sell it, or at least to drive it once in a while to keep the engine in running condition.

But until now, Gram had refused to even discuss the car. Just as she had avoided making any decisions about the huge old house.

The fact that she's asked me to help her pack things up is a good sign, Meg told herself as she hurried across the wet driveway to the side door.

Hopefully, her grandmother was ready to get on with her life. In the two years since she'd become a widow, she had become more introverted than ever. Hope McKenna had always been a quiet woman, the total opposite of easygoing Harry. She was lost without him.

And so was Meg.

That should have brought her closer to her grandmother, but it hadn't. Hope wasn't close to anyone, not really. Meg couldn't remember ever having a deep conversation with her.

Now, Gram answered her knock on the back door with a half-nervous, half-relieved smile. Meg noticed that she was impeccably dressed, as always, in a raspberry-colored cardigan, a white blouse, slim black pants, and gold-buckled flats.

Hope was built like Giselle and Carrie, small and slender. Her smoothly coiffed hair was the same blond color as theirs, too, although Meg suspected her grandmother had been coloring hers the past several years.

"Come in and dry off, Megan," Hope said, stepping back so that Meg could enter the glassed-in sun room that opened off the kitchen. "Do you want some tea?"

"No thanks." She slipped out of her wet loafers and left them on a mat by the door, then followed her grandmother into the big kitchen.

"It's a raw day out there, isn't it?" Hope gestured toward the window over the sink. Rivulets of rain streamed over the glass, and far above them, Meg could hear the drops pattering on the old slate roof. "I was worried about you driving over here in this weather, Meg."

"It was fine." She shook the water out of her hair.

"But the road has been known to wash out in storms like this . . ."

"No problems today—just a little soggy," Meg assured her.

Her grandmother didn't look convinced. Her light green eyes were lined with worry, and her thin lips, to which she had carefully applied the plum-colored lipstick she always wore, were tight.

"Maybe you should head home before you get stuck out here, Meg."

If Harry were alive, he would be joking around, telling Meg that if she couldn't get back to town, they would make a party of it. On dreary days like this he had loved to light a fire, make popcorn, and take out a deck of cards.

Rainy Sundays at the old house had always been cozy. Now the high ceilings made the kitchen seem drafty, and the raindrops on the windows had a forlorn effect, like the house was crying.

"Don't worry, Gram," Meg said, trying to sound upbeat. "It's fine. Really. Just a little shower. It's supposed to clear up later. So, where do you want to start?"

"At the top, I guess." Her grandmother sighed and started leading the way through the large first-floor rooms. "The attic is crammed with so many boxes I don't know how we'll get through them. Heaven knows, I've only been up there a handful of times in all the years that we lived here. The attic was your grandfather's department. And your mother's. She was always up there when she was little, making forts out of the old boxes and playing dress-up."

Gram started up the stairs, saying over her shoulder to Meg, "It's a shame Giselle couldn't come over to help today."

"I know. But she's busy getting ready for her trip and everything. . . ." Meg wondered why her first instinct was to defend her mother, who probably wouldn't even pack for Fiji until the eleventh hour. When Meg had left the house, Giselle had been cozily snuggling under an afghan in the living room, engrossed in an old movie.

Meg knew her mother's idea of fun didn't include sorting through the junk in her parents' old house.

Like this is my favorite way to spend a Sunday afternoon, Meg thought resentfully, then immediately took it back. *Gram needs me. I promised Grandpa I'd look out for her after he was gone.*

"A lot of what's in those old boxes belongs to your mother," Hope was saying. "I don't even know what she wants to keep, and what she wants to throw away."

"After all these years, it probably doesn't matter to her anymore, Gram," Meg said, following Hope across the second-floor landing and up the next flight.

"Probably not. Giselle never was the sentimental type."

No, she wasn't, Meg realized with a start.

Which made the jade baby ring her mother had soldered around her neck even stranger.

Candra sat on her bed, making tiny, careful stitches to join the edges of the scrap of red flannel. She had been working at it all afternoon.

And as she sat and sewed, she thought about what she had seen last night. She wasn't as much surprised about Rosamund's coven activities as she was startled to find out that such things went on here in America. The West Indies were steeped in black magic and sorcery, but Candra hadn't expected to stumble across it here . . .

Startled, she looked up, hearing a knock on her door. It couldn't be Rosamund—she had ridden to the supermarket with Monica.

And Jonas had left earlier today to drive Jane and all her luggage up to school in Massachusetts.

Only Craig was home, and his two friends. Candra hadn't seen any of them since Friday night, but she knew Rosamund had spent the morning doing their laundry so that they could take it back to school with them later this afternoon. She had heard them in the family room earlier, whooping in front of the television. They had been watching a football game—another American fascination Candra didn't understand.

Maybe I just imagined the knock, Candra told herself, looking back down at the fabric in her hands.

Then she heard it again.

Quickly, she poked the needle through the red flannel and hid the project under her pillow.

She got up, went to the door, and opened it a crack.

Landon Keller stood there.

He was wearing jeans and a thick gray sweatshirt that said "New

England Patriots." He had a rumpled, all-American casual look, and his hair was slightly mussed.

The sight of him brought back how irritated she'd been at him on Friday night. But just as powerful was a renewed sense of attraction. Just looking up into those light, flecked eyes of his made her feel weak.

She didn't say anything to him, just stood waiting for him to speak.

For a moment, he said nothing.

She wondered if he felt the current that was sizzling across the two feet of space in the threshold that separated them.

When he spoke, his voice was low. "Hi. Can I come in for a second?"

She shrugged and stepped back to let him enter.

He walked into the small room and looked around. "Nice," he said briefly, gesturing. He was chewing a piece of gum, and she could smell the familiar spearmint scent on his breath, even from here.

"It's all right." The room was as generic as it had been the day she'd first arrived. Her few personal belongings were tucked away in the drawers and closet.

Landon went over to her bed, sat on the edge of it, and looked at her. "Can you close the door?"

Part of her wanted to say no, that she couldn't close the door, and that he should leave right now.

But Candra reached out, pulled the knob, and shut the door with a quiet click.

Then she folded her arms and looked at him.

"I came down here to find you last night," he said, meeting her gaze head-on. "Where were you?"

I was spying on my grandmother, who was participating in a witchcraft ceremony.

She wondered how Landon would react if she said that.

He was so self-assured, so matter-of-fact about everything, that she couldn't imagine him being all that thrown.

But all she said was, "Out."

"Oh." He paused, still chewing his gum. There was something distinctly seductive about the way he slowly worked it in his mouth. "I was out, too, for a while. But then I came back here, looking for you. You still weren't back after midnight."

At that hour, the bus from Spring City to Crawford Corners ran sporadically. And by the time she'd completed the long walk down Soundview to the Drayers' house, it had been past two A.M.

"Listen, Candra," Landon said, looking into her eyes, "Craig is upstairs packing the car, and we're heading back to school in a little while. I didn't want to go without talking to you first."

"About what?" she asked carefully, leaning against the wall and studying the way his jaw moved subtly, slowly working the gum in his mouth.

"About this *thing* that's going on."

"What thing?"

"You and me," he said directly.

His eyes still hadn't budged from hers. Never before had Candra met someone who didn't seem taken aback by her intense stare—someone who met it with one of his own.

She pushed herself away from the wall and sauntered a few steps closer to him.

"What do you mean, you and me?" she asked in a throaty voice, swinging her hair over her shoulder.

He gave her a faint, pleased smile. "I think you know."

She tilted her head. "Maybe." And shrugged. "Maybe not."

Landon reached out and caught her fingers. He pulled her toward him until she was standing with her legs against the side of the bed, in the vee between his spread knees.

Without saying a word or breaking eye contact, Landon let go of her right hand and let the back of his knuckles brush up her bare arm. Goose bumps prickled her skin, and she fought not to quiver at his touch.

"You must be cold," he said in a voice that was barely above a whisper.

I'm not. I'm on fire.

"Why?" was all she said.

He didn't answer, just ran his fingers over her arm again. He was still holding her left hand in his, and now he pulled her down, slowly, onto his lap.

Her face was only inches from Landon's, and he was still looking intently into her eyes. Candra noted the smooth, tanned skin of his cheeks and jaw, the tiny mole above his lip, the faint scar beneath his right eye, the way his thick eyebrows fanned out near the bridge of his nose.

She wanted to run her fingers through his wavy dark hair, wanted to tug him closer and feel his mouth coming down over hers.

For an endless, breathless moment, they stared at each other.

Then, simultaneously, they leaned forward until their lips collided and clung.

There was nothing tentative about the kiss. It was intense from the beginning—fervent, hot, wet.

It was Candra who first opened her mouth, and she heard Landon let out a groan of pleasure and surprise as she slid her tongue past his lips. He tasted of mint. She located the gum he'd been chewing, tucked into his cheek. Her tongue darted after it, and she took it into her own mouth.

He moaned, and grazed his open palms lightly over her arms, then across the thin cotton fabric that covered her breasts.

She leaned back to give him access, and he moved his mouth from hers, sliding it down, over her jaw, burrowing his lips into the hollow beneath her ear.

Candra closed her eyes and tangled her fingers in his dark curls, stroking his head and leaning gradually back until she was lying against the pillows with him half on top of her.

Her head was swimming, her body was tingling, and the sound that came from someplace above seemed far away . . .

Until she realized that it was footsteps.

Landon pulled back, away from her, and sat up just before there was an abrupt knock on Candra's bedroom door.

They looked at each other.

She was about to ask who it was when the door jerked open and Craig Drayer stood there, angrily looking in.

"What's going on? What are you doing down here?"

"Saying bye to Candra." Landon shrugged and stood up. "You ready to hit the road?"

"Yeah." Craig looked at Candra.

She narrowed her eyes at him, and he looked away, toward his friend.

"Come on," Craig said. "Let's go."

Landon looked at her. "I'll call you from school," he said.

"How are you going to do that?" Craig asked. "She doesn't have a phone."

"What, she can't take calls on your parents' line?"

"They don't like the help tying it up," Craig said pointedly.

Landon looked at Candra.

She was too furious even to meet his eyes, just stood glaring at Craig Drayer.

"See you," Landon said.

"Yeah." She turned away from both of them, went over to the door, and held it open.

As soon as they'd walked through it, she closed it behind them, and pressed the button in the knob to lock it.

Thoughtfully, she reached up and removed the pale green lump of gum from her mouth and looked at it.

Then she carried it over to her dresser, opened the top drawer, and hunted until she found a small plastic container. She put Landon's gum inside, snapped it shut, and closed it in the drawer.

She went back over to her now-rumpled bed and removed the red scrap of fabric from beneath the pillow. She jabbed the needle into the cloth again, so hard it pierced the tip of her pinky finger on the other side.

Candra licked the drop of blood from it and furiously started sewing again.

Meg wearily slid yet another cardboard box over to the spot under the dormer window. There was no electricity up here, and the only light that filtered in from outside was gauzy and gray, too dim to allow her to see much. The rain was still plopping steadily on the sloped roof right above her head, a comforting sound that filled the large room and made conversation seem unnecessary.

Gram was yards away, near the other window, wrapped in silence and in her memories. She hadn't spoken much since they'd come up here, but had worked methodically, emptying the contents of box after box, sorting some of what she found, dumping the rest into a trash bag.

Meg had been assigned to the boxes that contained her mother's childhood clothing. Anything that wasn't motheaten or stained or ripped was to be folded again and kept for the Salvation Army.

She had worked her way through boxes of Giselle's baby clothes, then through play clothes and party dresses, and finally jeans and skirts and blouses and outgrown, outdated versions of Adamson-Swift uniforms.

This new box Meg had opened didn't contain clothing, though. As soon as she realized it, she opened her mouth to tell her grandmother, then clamped it shut again.

She looked back at the outside flap of the carton. Each one had been labeled with magic marker in her grandfather's printed scrawl: *Giselle's Clothes, Age 1, Giselle's clothes Ages 8–9. . . .*

The outside of this box contained three words, and they were carefully drawn in marker, comprised of the cushiony kind of bubble-letters Meg used to doodle on her notebooks.

PRIVATE: KEEP OUT!

Meg stared at the message her mother had written years ago.

She chewed her bottom lip and again looked over at her grandmother.

She caught Hope dabbing at her eyes as she scanned a piece of paper—an old letter?—she was holding up to the window.

Meg quickly looked away, back at the box.

After only another moment's hesitation, she opened the flap again and lifted out the first item.

It was an old Adamson-Swift yearbook. Meg flipped through the pages and saw that it was filled with signatures and messages from her mother's friends. Some of them had written long, rambling notes filled with phrases like *"Remember the time we . . ."* and *"I'll never forget the night you . . ."*

A lot of the signatures were followed by peace signs or initials. R.M.A./I.R.Y.—*Remember Me Always/I'll Remember You.* Kids at Adamson-Swift still wrote that. And even peace signs had made a comeback.

Meg flipped the pages until she found her mother's freshman face staring out at her from a group shot on the stone steps in front of the school.

Oh, my God, that's Carrie, was Meg's instantaneous reaction.

She had seen old photos of her mother on occasion, but not lately. Now she realized that her sister was the spitting image of Giselle. Her mother's hair was in the feathered style that had been popular in the late seventies, but it was the same silky blond as Carrie's. Her lithe body, clad in a tight, striped tee shirt and tight, faded jeans, was as compact as Carrie's. Even the mischievous, defiant gleam in her mother's expression in the black-and-white photo was identical to the one that invariably lit Carrie's eyes these days.

Meg snapped the book shut and set it aside, turning her attention back to the box. She lifted out another yearbook, this one from Giselle's sophomore year. She didn't bother looking through it, just set it on top of the other one and turned back to the box.

She half expected to pull out yet another yearbook, but then she realized that there wouldn't be any others. Her mother had gone away to the Caribbean with her family her junior year. When she had come back to Crawford Corners the following year, newborn Meg had been with her. And Giselle had never graduated from Adamson-Swift.

Meg removed a pair of faded royal blue and white pompoms. The cheerleaders at school no longer used them.

Next she found a rubber-banded stack of color photos. Meg flipped through them quickly and saw that they were mostly of Giselle and her friends on some beach, taken when her mother was about fifteen.

She reached into the box again and took out several wire-bound notebooks. The covers were full of doodles—things like *Supertramp Rules!* and *Disco Sucks!* And there were sketches, too.

Meg vaguely remembered that her mother had once said she'd planned to be an artist.

She hadn't expected to find that Giselle had talent, but the proof was right here. The notebooks, on closer examination, were full of idle pen-and-ink drawings, and most of them were really good. Meg came across several variations of self-portraits, and felt a flicker of amusement. Even back then, Giselle had apparently been self-absorbed.

And not much of a student.

The few class notes Meg found in the notebooks were fragmented and practically illegible. And there was an old report card stuck between the pages. She glanced at it and saw that her mother had gotten nothing higher than a C—and there were two F's. Not only that, but her grandfather's name scribbled on the line above the words *Parental Signature* looked suspiciously forged.

Par for the course, Meg thought, tucking the report card back into the notebook and tossing it onto the attic floor beside her.

There was a layer of art class drawings in the box, each one signed by her mother and mounted on now-faded colored construction paper. Most of them were pen-and-ink views of nature scenes, and there were a few watercolors of the big brick house, too. Meg could see from her mother's depiction that the place hadn't changed much in the past twenty years or so.

Meg carefully lifted the drawings out, one by one, and stacked them beside her. After she had removed the last one, she peered back into the bottom of the box.

What she saw made her heart trip over itself.

A grayish-beige, rectangular metal container.

And even as she thought, *So what?* a voice in the back of her mind was telling her that this was important.

That inside this box was the key to her past . . . and to the strange things that were happening to her in the present.

With trembling hands, she lifted it out and set it carefully on the dusty wooden floor in front of her.

This is it, she told herself as she reached for the lid and pulled upward . . .

It was locked.

She should have known.

Frustrated, Meg looked more closely at the silver keyhole in the top of the box. She stuck her long pinky fingernail into it and twisted, irrationally hoping that somehow, it would work.

It didn't. Her nail broke off, painfully far down. She stuck it into her mouth and sucked away the metallic-tasting drops of blood that oozed from the tip of her pinky.

I've got to get this thing open, she thought desperately.

The key must be hidden somewhere.

Where would Giselle have put it?

That was anyone's guess.

Meg looked back over the pile of things she had removed from the box. There was no place a key could possibly be concealed—unless her mother had taped it to the page of a notebook or a yearbook.

Meg spent the next fifteen minutes checking everything carefully, running her fingers along the seams in the bottom of the carton, even as the voice in the back of her mind told her that she wasn't going to find the key.

At least, not here. Not now.

"I think we've done enough for one afternoon, Meg," her grandmother said abruptly, shattering her concentration.

Meg looked blankly at her. Hope was still across the attic, standing up and brushing off her slacks.

"How did you do with those boxes of clothes?" her grandmother asked, walking toward her.

Meg quickly moved a green garbage bag she'd filled closer, obscuring the metal box she held in her lap. "I found quite a few things you can give to charity," she said, pointing at the boxes she'd refilled.

Hope glanced idly through the stack of her daughter's old garments in one of the boxes. She held up a tiny white eyelet dress. "It's amazing that Giselle was ever a tiny little thing I held in my arms," she said wistfully.

"I know," Meg murmured.

"You were, too," she said, shifting her attention to Meg. "I used to give you your bottle every morning when you were a baby."

"You did?"

"And I gave you your nightly baths, too. You were so . . ." Hope trailed off.

Meg watched as her grandmother's face took on the familiar closed expression.

"So what?" she asked. "I was so what?"

"So sweet," her grandmother said briefly. "You were a sweet baby. Are you ready to come downstairs?"

"I guess," Meg said, wondering, as she always did, why no one liked to talk about this.

"We won't lug any of those cartons or bags of clothes down today," her grandmother said, pointing. "Just leave them here for now."

Meg was still holding the metal box on her lap. She couldn't leave it here. She had to bring it with her.

But her grandmother would want to know what it was. And Meg had the feeling that even if Hope had never seen the box before in her life, she wouldn't want Meg snooping through it. Obviously, whatever was inside was something Giselle had wanted to keep to herself.

On the other hand, maybe it was nothing. Maybe it was just another stupid bunch of old pictures, or a prom corsage, or something.

Or maybe it's her old diary.

But even if it was, what did Meg expect to find there?

Probably nothing that mattered.

Still, she had a feeling about this box. Something told her that whatever was in it mattered a lot.

"Meg?" her grandmother said expectantly.

"You go on down, Gram. I'll finish putting all this stuff away—I don't want to leave it spread all over the floor."

"What have you got there?" Hope asked, bending over for a closer look at the items on the floor beside the open box. "Are those Giselle's old yearbooks?"

"Uh, yeah. And her pom-poms from when she was a cheerleader, and some old photos—stuff like that."

There was a flash of something—worry?—in her grandmother's eyes. Then Hope said somewhat stiffly, "Just leave it there, Meg. I'll take care of it later."

"But . . ." What was she going to say? Obviously, her grandmother didn't want her snooping through her mother's old things.

Obviously, Hope was worried that Meg would find something. What?

Why wouldn't anyone answer her questions? Why didn't anyone seem to care that her whole life Meg had been haunted by a sense that something was missing—something she couldn't put her finger on?

The time had come for her to fill in the blanks, and no one was going to stop her.

"Come on, Meg," her grandmother said. "Let's go down and have some tea."

"Okay." Still holding the garbage bag in front of her, Meg stood up. She kept the box concealed under the folds of dark green plastic. "I'll carry this one bag down, as long as we're going. Why waste a trip?"

"Fine," her grandmother said with a shrug. She wasn't even looking at Meg. Her sharp eyes were focused on the things Meg had left on the floor—the notebooks and the rubber-banded stack of photos.

Meg headed for the stairs, keeping the box hidden behind the bag full of her mother's old clothes. She started down, with her grandmother right behind her.

"I'll bring this bag right out to the garage, Gram," she said. "That way, it won't be in your way in the house."

"All right." Hope's voice sounded preoccupied.

When they reached the kitchen, her grandmother went over to the stove, turned on a burner, and moved the red tea kettle over the flame.

"I'll be right back," Meg said, and hurried toward the door.

She half expected her grandmother to stop her, but Hope just said, "All right."

The rain was still pouring down in torrents, and the wind was gusting harder now than it had been before. Meg glanced over her shoulder at the kitchen window as she walked swiftly across the driveway to her car. Good. Her grandmother wasn't looking out.

She opened the driver's side door and tossed the metal box on the floor, kicking it under the seat before closing the door again.

She carried the garbage bag to the garage and tried to open the door. At first she thought it was locked.

Then she realized what was wrong. "Darn thing sticks in damp weather," she remembered Grandpa saying.

Isn't that the truth, Meg thought, shoving hard against it until it gave.

She entered the musty room that had once been a carriage house. There were still faint marks on the walls where the stalls had been. Meg set the garbage bag down just inside the door and glanced around.

There were Grandpa's gardening tools, lined up neatly on the pegs he'd attached to the far wall. There was the old hand mower he had refused to throw away.

"The thing's an antique," he always protested when Gram had gotten on his back about it.

"It's junk, Harry," she would say, shaking her head.

And her grandfather would say, "One man's junk is another man's treasure, Hope."

Meg forced her eyes away from the mower and made herself look at Grandpa's car. It had always been clean and polished when he was alive. Now it looked dull and forsaken—like Meg suddenly felt.

She turned her back on it and left the garage, tugging the door closed firmly after her.

Then she ran back through the rain to the house. In the kitchen, the tea kettle was whistling and rattling on the burner, and her grandmother, with a faraway look in her eyes, was too lost to notice.

Eight

On Monday morning when the homeroom bell rang, Candra jumped as usual.

Across the aisle, Kim Williams said, "It takes a while to get used to, doesn't it?"

Candra noticed that today her wiry black hair was separated into dozens of cornrows, each with a colorful bead on the end. Candra hadn't seen anyone wearing that hairstyle since she'd left the island two weeks ago. Some part of her was drawn to Kim, if only because they were from the same place. But Candra knew she couldn't make friends with her. Hanging around with another outsider was the last thing she needed.

Kim wasn't part of the in-crowd at Crawford Corners High. Candra had pin-pointed, right from the start, which kids were part of the popular clique. Pert, pretty Sheila Givens. Freckle-faced Danny Taylor. Carla Goldblum and Jason Arnold, a look-alike couple, both tall and pale and slender, who were practically joined at the hip. And there were a few others. Not all of them were white, and not all of them were attractive; but they had one thing in common: a casual, confident air of belonging.

Kim Williams, for all her friendliness and warmth, lacked that. It wasn't just her accent, or her taste in clothes, which ran more to the style of the outfit Candra had worn on what was supposed to be her first day. No, she was just not the type of person who blended into the crowd. She seemed too eager—that was what set her apart from the others. They talked to her. It was impossible for anyone not to; the girl never stopped asking questions and making comments. But she wasn't one of them.

All last week, Kim had done her best to strike up conversations with Candra, and Candra had done her best to ignore her.

To her frustration, Kim didn't seem put off by her attitude. In fact, nothing fazed her, as far as Candra could tell. Kim was in several of her classes, and she was always smiling and joking around, especially with the teachers, who seemed to love her.

She was as cheerful as ever this Monday morning. As soon as Mrs. Birch was finished taking attendance, Kim reached across the aisle and tapped Candra's arm. "What'd you do all weekend, *mon?*"

Candra didn't even look at her, just kept pretending to look through her textbook for a particular page. "Not much."

"It was my birthday. My dad took me to New York to see a Broadway show, my first one. We saw *Phantom of the Opera*. It was incredible!"

Candra nodded, barely feigning interest.

"I'm going to be a singer someday. I have a great voice—at least, that's what Mr. Langdon tells me. He's the choir instructor—have you met him yet?"

"No," Candra said, because it was impossible not to respond.

"He's great. Very cute—looks kind of like Denzel Washington. Do you like Denzel Washington?"

"Who?"

"He's an actor. I guess you didn't go to the movies much back home, huh? Here, it's different. If you want, you and I could go sometime."

"To the movies?"

"Sure. How about next weekend?"

"I . . . I'm busy," Candra said, and looked away from Kim's open, friendly gaze.

"Doing what?"

Kim didn't seem as though she were questioning Candra's excuse—more like she was genuinely interested.

Either way, it didn't matter. Candra didn't need or want anyone snooping into her life.

"I'm just busy, okay?"

Kim shrugged. "No problem, *mon.*"

Candra nearly winced at the familiar phrase. How many times, since she'd arrived here, had she caught herself on the verge of uttering it? *No problem, mon.* It was the Jamaican mantra.

Candra picked up a pen and turned away from Kim again.

Around her, people were chatting with each other, talking about what they'd done over the weekend.

Candra pretended to be busy writing something in her notebook. She was actually copying her own name over and over again, but no one needed to know that.

"What'cha writing?" Kim asked from across the aisle in her lilting accent.

Candra fixed her with a beady stare. "Nothing."

"Something private, huh, *mon?*"

"Exactly."

"You're a private person, aren't you?"

"Yes."

For a moment, Kim just met her gaze. Then, just when Candra expected the girl to grow uncomfortable under her own dark glare, she tilted her head and said, "How come you're so private?"

Candra was so taken aback that she forgot to look menacing. "Because I don't think that what I do is anyone's business."

"That makes sense . . . *if* you don't mind having no friends."

"Who says I don't want friends?"

"It's just the way you've been acting ever since you got here, I guess. You don't talk to anybody . . ."

"Nobody talks to me."

"I do."

You're not the kind of person I want as a friend, Candra thought.

But she couldn't say it. No matter how irritating she found Kim Williams, she couldn't, for some reason, deliberately hurt her.

"Yes. You do talk to me," Candra acknowledged grudgingly.

"I thought you were just shy at first. That's why I kept trying to draw you out. But now that I realized you don't *want* to talk, I won't bother you anymore. Okay?"

Candra hesitated.

She hated herself for the pang of regret she felt at Kim's words. Of course she wanted the girl to stop talking to her.

Of course she didn't want to be bothered.

But something made her say, "You're not bothering me."

As soon as the words were out of her mouth and Kim had broken into a huge smile, Candra wanted to take them back, but it was too late.

"In that case," Kim said, "why don't you have lunch with me today? I've seen you eating alone in the cafeteria. I always sit with my friends from choir."

"Okay," Candra said, because she was on the spot. But she promised herself that after today, she'd go back to ignoring Kim Williams.

When Meg got to Government class late Monday morning, Shea was already there, sitting in the seat across from hers. He was turned around, talking to Andy Dorner, who was sitting behind him.

She slid into her chair and tapped him on the shoulder.

His face lit up when he turned and saw her. "Hi," he said, grinning. "I missed you all weekend."

"I missed you, too," she said, even as she realized it wasn't exactly true. It wasn't that she *hadn't* missed him—more that she'd been too preoccupied to give him much thought. "When did you get back last night?"

"Almost midnight. I wanted to call you but figured Lester wouldn't be thrilled."

"You should have. Who cares what Lester thinks?"

"Next time I will. Did you have a good weekend?"

"It was all right. How was yours?"

"The usual. My stepmother spent the whole time talking about these eighties rock groups like J. Geils Band and Foreigner to show me how 'hip' she is. And I spent the whole time pretending I knew what she was talking about."

"Yeah, well, I wouldn't complain if I were you. I'd take Deb over Lester any day, as far as stepparents are concerned."

"Yeah, I guess you're right. At least she's human. She just tries too hard."

"I know." Meg had met Shea's father's new wife only once, at Shea's birthday party in July. Deb was in her late twenties and looked it, while Mr. Alcott was obviously middle-aged and was probably often mistaken for her father. Shea's mother had shot Deb scathing looks and made catty remarks under her breath all night.

That was the first and only time Meg had ever been glad she'd never known her father or been through a divorce. Shea was always getting caught between his parents. At least Meg didn't have to put up with any bitterness or child support fights.

She just had to put up with Lester.

That, and not knowing who she really was.

But that was going to change as soon as she got the metal box open.

She had spent hours last night working on it in her room, using everything she could think of to try and pick the lock. Nothing had worked. She had thought about searching for the key in her mother's room, but then realized that knowing scatter brained Giselle, it could have been thrown away or lost years ago. If her mother had left the metal box in the attic of her parents' house, Meg didn't think it was likely that she had kept the key in any particular place for all these years.

And, on the off chance that she had, how was Meg supposed to find it? A search of the master bedroom had already failed to turn up anything unusual.

There was only one way to get into that box.

Today after school, Meg was going to bring it to the locksmith she had looked up in the Crawford Corners yellow pages this morning. She pictured him opening it with an easy turn of some master key. He would lift the lid, and she would peek in and see—

"Hey, did you have that talk with your mother?" Shea asked.

Startled out of her reverie, Meg said, "What talk?"

"The one about Carrie and what she's been up to lately."

"Oh. No, I didn't say anything about it."

"I think you should."

"I know you do. But my mother and Lester are leaving first thing tomorrow for Fiji. I don't want to spring it on them now. Maybe Carrie will settle down."

"Yeah, and maybe Lester will be transformed into the father of the year." Shea shook his head. "Come on, Meg."

"I know, Shea. But I'm really tired of worrying about everyone else—especially Carrie. I'm just going to take care of myself for a while."

"Meg, is everything all right with you?"

She hesitated for only the briefest moment before saying, "Yeah. Shouldn't it be?"

"Are you sure?"

"Sure I'm sure." She studied his face. "Why?"

He shrugged. "Just something Zoe said to me this morning in Trig."

"What did she say?"

"She wanted to know if I thought you'd been acting strange."

"What did you tell her?"

Shea didn't answer right away, and before she could prod him, she heard Andy Dorner say to someone, "Meg was there—ask her."

"Hey, Meg," Kyle Bennett called from his seat across from Andy. "Did Chasey really hook up with Wes Emory on Friday night?"

She looked at him. "What?"

"Friday night, out at Moseby."

She gave him a blank look.

"At the *party*, duh," Andy said. "You *were* at the party, talking to some guy in the corner all night, weren't you?"

"No," Meg said slowly, "I wasn't."

She could feel Shea's probing eyes on her.

She thought wildly back to Friday. She'd spent the night watching a Meg Ryan filmfest on cable: *When Harry Met Sally* and *Sleepless in Seattle*.

"You were so there," Andy protested. "I saw you."

"I was not!" she snapped. "I was home."

Andy and Kyle exchanged a glance.

Then a knowing grin slipped over Andy's features, and he said, "Oh, I get it. She wasn't there, Kyle." He tilted his head slightly in Shea's direction. "She was home."

"Oh. Right," Kyle said.

The two of them went back to their discussion of Chasey.

"What's the deal, Meg?" Shea asked coldly.

"There's no deal, Shea. Those two idiots don't know what they're talking about. I wasn't at Moseby Friday night. I was home on the couch, watching TV."

He didn't reply.

She felt a twinge of desperation. "Come on, Shea, don't listen to Andy. You know how wasted he gets. He probably thinks Gwyneth Paltrow was at the party, too."

After a moment, Shea's expression relaxed. "I guess."

The teacher, Mrs. Spelling, had closed the door to the hall and was standing in front of the room. "All right, everyone, notebooks out, pens ready for notes," she said abruptly.

Meg fumbled with the zipper on her book bag. Her mind was racing.

It had happened again.

What was going on?

Could she actually be *astral projecting* herself without being aware of it?

She heard Mirabelle's voice again in her mind, thought of what she had said that night in Zoe's room.

Some people are born with certain powers.

Meg *had* to get into Giselle's metal box. Somehow, she knew without a doubt, now, that whatever was in there would lead her to the answers she sought.

"This is Candra Bowen," Kim said to the three girls who were sitting at her lunch table. "Candra, this is Nedra, Ellen, and Mary Beth."

Candra nodded at them as she slid into the chair Kim had pulled out for her.

These girls were just what she had expected. Nedra had sharp, pointed features and was reading a textbook as she ate. Ellen was enormously fat, with a flushed, red face and several wobbling chins. And Mary Beth shot Candra a skittish glance before blushing and focusing on her fidgeting hands in her lap again.

"We're all in choir together," Kim told Candra, as she unwrapped her straw and stuck it into her open bottle of cranberry juice.

"Oh," was all Candra could think of to say.

She cast a longing gaze at the clique seated around a long table across the room. She noticed that Carla and Jason had their arms draped casually across the backs of each other's chairs. For some reason, that made her think of Landon.

And the way he had kissed her, touched her . . .

She hated the desperate feeling of longing that settled over her every time Landon crossed her mind during the past twenty-four hours.

She hated knowing she had no real control over the situation—that whether or not she saw him again was up to him.

Or was it?

Candra thought about the object she'd pinned to her bra, over her heart. She was wearing a baggy shirt to camouflage it.

Things weren't entirely out of her hands. . . .

"Do you have a boyfriend back in Jamaica, Candra?" Kim asked.

Candra looked at her sharply, for a moment wondering if Kim had somehow read her mind. But then, Landon wasn't her boyfriend. And he certainly wasn't in Jamaica, either.

"No," she said shortly, "I don't."

"That's good. When we moved here, I had a boyfriend I had to leave behind. It was really hard. He's married now."

"He's *married?*" Ellen said incredulously, her chubby hand poised with a fork halfway to her mouth. Mary Beth was peering up at Kim from beneath her lashes, and even Nedra was momentarily distracted from her book.

"Yeah, *mon*. He's older."

"How old?"

"Twenty-three . . . no wait, twenty-four, now," Kim said.

Candra looked at her with begrudging new respect. "You went out with someone that much older?"

"Uh huh. But since we moved here, I haven't had one date."

"Well, I've never had a date in my entire life," Ellen said wistfully, shovelling the forkful of mashed potatoes into her mouth.

Candra found herself jarred by an unexpected stab of sympathy for the girl, and forced it away.

No. Stop it! You don't want to feel anything for any of these people.

She silently bit a tiny corner off her tuna sandwich and chewed methodically.

Across the cafeteria, Sheila Givens and her best friend, LaWanna Mapes, were giggling together over something.

Candra watched them.

Then she noticed that Jason was whispering in Carla's ear, and she was nodding and smiling up at him.

Candra thought again of Landon.

And of everything else she wanted.

Soon, she told herself, trying to calm the sense of urgency that was welling up inside her. *Soon, you'll have it all.*

She reached up and brushed her fingers against the thing that was pinned over her heart, feeling reassured.

The address Meg had scribbled on the scrap of paper led her to an older brick building in the heart of Crawford Corners.

On the first floor were a children's shoe store and a dress boutique that Giselle frequented. The double doors in the alcove between the two shops bore a sign with a vertical arrow and the words *Upper Level of Businesses Ahead.*

Clutching the metal box, Meg climbed the flight of stairs up from street level and started down the long hall of glass-front doors, some of them doctors' and dentists' offices, others businesses she had never known existed in Crawford Corners—a kite shop, a tattoo place, a store that sold religious items.

When she reached the door lettered *Jerry's Lock and Key*, she stopped. Through the glass, she could see a heavy-set man in a flannel shirt standing behind a counter, talking to a well-dressed, bouffant-headed woman on the other side.

Meg hesitated, then pushed the door open and stepped in.

The conversation halted, and both of them looked curiously at Meg.

"Hi," said the man behind the counter. "Let me guess. You're looking for the portrait studio—getting your senior picture done, right? It's two doors down."

"Portrait studio?"

He nodded.

"Um, no," Meg said. "Actually, I was looking for Jerry's Lock and Key."

"Yeah?" He looked surprised. "This is it. Sorry—I get a lot of high school kids in here by mistake, looking for the photographer. His name's Gary—Gary Leggins. Mine's Gerald—Gerald Berry—but people call me Jerry. That's why people get confused. When the kids come in here, I tell 'em, 'you want Gary Leggins, not Jerry Berry.' Not many high school kids around who need a locksmith, you know?"

He and the woman eyed Meg and the box curiously.

She said, "Well, I have this box, and I lost the key, and I need it opened. Can you do that?"

Jerry Berry looked dubious. "Probably, but wait just a minute here. Where did you get the box?"

Meg tried to ignore the frantic feeling that was edging over her. *Stay calm*, she told herself.

But what if he won't do it?

You'll find someone who will.

What if he confiscates the box and insists on calling your parents or something?

What, are you crazy? Why would he do that?

Because he's looking at you suspiciously, like he thinks the box contains some little old man's life savings, and you stole it, that's why.

Somehow, she managed to think quickly and say evenly, "Where'd I get the box? At Home Depot—a few years ago. I keep stuff in it— you know, private stuff. My little sister's always snooping around my room," she added for good measure.

Something did the trick, because Jerry Berry looked convinced. "I have a daughter about your age," he said with a grin. "She's always in her room with her door locked. Her mother and I say to her, we ask her, 'Missy, what are you doing that's so private?' She's a good kid, you know?" He was half talking to Meg, half to the older woman near the counter, who was starting to look impatient.

The woman cleared her throat with a gentle *ahem*, and Jerry Berry said hastily, "I'm sorry, Ms. Blake, I'll be right with you." He looked at Meg. "Let's see that box."

She handed it over.

He gave it a brief inspection, then stuck it on a shelf under the counter and slid a form across the counter to her. "Here, fill this out. I'll call you in a day or so."

"But I was hoping you could—"

"Sorry, but I'm in the middle of something right now," he said, looking at his watch. "Ms. Blake, here, has locked herself out of her car. And after I help her get it open, I have to get going. My son's play-ing quarterback on his midget league football team and the game's about to start."

Meg didn't want to leave the box, but she had no choice. She didn't want to risk taking it someplace else and having to answer another batch of suspicious questions.

Reluctantly, she took a pen out of her book bag and started filling out the form.

Candra was leaving school by the front doors when she heard a voice behind her. "Hey, Candra, wait up!"

She looked back among the crowd in the lobby and spotted a familiar face. Kim Williams, and Nedra was with her. They were both carrying books and jackets and hurrying toward the door with everyone else.

Candra hesitated on the step. She could hardly run away from them, could she?

"Which way are you going?" Kim asked as they reached her.

She could hardly ask Kim, first, which way she was going and then say the opposite, could she?

Wordlessly, she pointed in the direction of Soundview Road.

"Hey, we're heading that way, too," Kim said. "But only for a few blocks. I live on Baker Lane. Nedra lives on Carter, which is the one right before it."

Candra had passed those streets every day on her way home. Both were treeless, with a lot of close-set one-story homes, chain-link fences, and patchy lawns.

Back in Jamaica, middle-class people lived in ugly cinderblock houses that made these small suburban ranches look like palaces. If Candra and her grandmother hadn't lived with the Drayers, they'd have been relegated to the city slums.

But now Candra realized that she'd grown used to the American standard of living. The homes on Baker Lane scraped the bottom of the barrel for Crawford Corners.

Kim and Nedra fell into step beside her. Candra hugged her textbooks against her stomach. She had brought home a whole stack of them tonight, planning to read ahead in every class. She would have to if she didn't want to fall behind. The school system here was far more advanced than it had been back home, and Candra knew she had a struggle ahead if she was going to keep up.

Kim chattered about the Christmas program the choir was already putting together.

Every so often, Nedra interrupted to contradict something she had said.

Candra decided she didn't like Nedra. It wasn't just the girl's severe looks or styleless clothing. There was something unsettling about the way Nedra's humorless, watery blue eyes studied her from behind those thick glasses.

"How about you, Candra?" Kim was asking.

"What?"

"Have you ever been out west? California, Nevada?"

"Oh . . . no," she said, amazed at the way Kim effortlessly darted from one topic to another. She shifted her heavy load of books.

"Hey, I think you just dropped something," Kim said, stopping and pointing to the sidewalk.

Candra glanced down and froze.

"What's that?" Nedra asked.

Candra hurriedly reached down, picked it up, and tucked it back into her sweatshirt pocket.

She glanced at Kim and saw that she looked thoughtful.

"What was that?" Nedra repeated.

"Nothing," Candra said.

"It looked like a little red bag. And it had a safety pin—"

"Hey, Nedra, did you ever find out what you got on that quiz this morning?" Kim cut in, and started walking again.

Candra knew exactly what she was doing. And she didn't want to be grateful, didn't want to owe this girl any favors. Still, there was no denying that Kim was trying to help her by distracting Nedra.

"I already told you, I got a hundred."

"Oh, I didn't mean on the chemistry quiz," Kim said. "I meant in English."

"That's not until tomorrow."

"It's not?"

"No."

"I thought you said you had taken it today."

"Well, I didn't."

Candra could feel Nedra staring at her again.

She turned her head and looked the girl in the eye. It worked. Nedra glanced away after a moment, looking uncomfortable, though not entirely intimidated.

Kim chattered on, flitting from topic to topic, until they reached the corner of Carter Lane. Nedra made her exit after mumbling a brief goodbye.

As soon as they had crossed the street and resumed walking, Kim said, "What's the conjure bag for?"

Startled, Candra halted on the sidewalk. "What?"

"You know—the little red felt bag you dropped back there."

"What about it?"

"Look, *mon*, I know a conjure bag when I see one. Little red drawstring thing, a few inches wide, a few inches long. You fill it with an odd number of items—herbs, roots, whatever—and anoint it on an altar. Then you keep it close to you and concentrate on willing it to bring you whatever you want . . . or keep something away. Which is it, for you?"

Candra didn't reply.

"I have one myself," Kim said nonchalantly, patting her jacket pocket. "Mine's for health. My mother made it for me the other day, when I had a sore throat. She had to go to Spring City to get the right stuff for it. There's this store she goes to on Elmont Avenue, next to the Mystic bookshop. Have you been over there yet?"

"Been where?"

"To Elmont. It's kind of a red-light district after dark, but there are a lot of Caribbean transplants, like us, in that neighborhood, and you can find just about anything there—astrological suppliers, occult bookstores and herbalists, whatever. You haven't been there?"

Candra shook her head.

If Kim realized she was lying, she didn't let on. "I'll take you over sometime," was all she said.

They walked for a few more seconds in silence before Kim said, "So what's the bag for? Or would you rather not tell me?"

Candra fixed her with a dark look.

"Okay, no problem, *mon*." Kim shrugged. "You don't have to tell me. Here's where I turn off. See you tomorrow."

With that, she headed off down Baker Lane, the multicolored beads at the ends of her braids bobbing brightly as she went.

Candra walked more slowly, thinking about the conjure bag she'd pinned over her heart.

In it was a teaspoon of dried passion flower, a pinch of love-drawing powder, and a heart-shaped lump she'd made by melting down a red candle.

Embedded in the wax was a lock of her own silky black hair and the now-hardened, teethmark-riddled wad of spearmint gum she'd stolen from Landon Keller's mouth.

"Meg?"

"Yeah?" She turned from her desk, where she was going through the motions of doing her homework, and saw her mother standing in the doorway of her room.

Giselle was holding two dresses on hangers. Now she held first one, then the other, against her with the hooks of the hangers clasped to her chin, and said, "Which one do you like better?"

"That depends," Meg said, fighting back a sigh. This was the third time her mother had popped into her room for advice.

Giselle was in the middle of packing for Fiji, at the last minute, as usual. Lester was insisting that they leave for the airport by four A.M., and it was after ten now.

"What does it depend on?" Giselle asked.

"Where you plan to wear them."

"To the manager's reception at the resort on Wednesday afternoon."

"The ivory one," Meg said, pointing at the dress in her mother's right hand.

"Why?"

"I don't know . . . it looks like something you'd wear in the afternoon."

"You think?"

"Yes." Meg chewed the end of the pen she was holding.

"Carrie thought the black one," her mother said, indicating the dress in her left hand.

"Then go with that."

"But maybe you're right. Maybe the black is too—after dark. I don't know. I'm so confused now," her mother said, looking distressed.

"Take them both," Meg suggested.

"Lester will have a fit. The garment bag is already jammed. I guess I'll take the ivory one."

"Good."

Giselle smiled. "Thanks for the advice, Meg. What are you working on now?"

"Trig."

"Still?" Her mother shook her head. "They really load you guys down with homework these days, don't they?"

"Kind of." Meg wasn't about to say that she'd have been done with the two pages of problems hours ago if she'd been able to concentrate.

But she kept thinking about how yet another person had seen her someplace where she hadn't been.

And about the metal box she'd left at the locksmith's.

And about Giselle herself.

She looked at her mother, whose biggest crisis right now was trying to squeeze extra dresses into her luggage.

Was it really possible that behind that pretty blond face and those clear, unconcerned green eyes Giselle was full of secrets?

That from her mother, or from the absent Stu Kingman, Meg had inherited some type of magical powers?

It was totally far-fetched. Meg told herself, for the millionth time, to stop thinking such bizarre thoughts.

She had to stop dwelling on the metal box, too—stop thinking of it as the answer to the questions that filled her mind.

But she couldn't seem to help it.

Every time she had almost convinced herself that Giselle was just what she appeared to be—a flightly, self-absorbed person whose darkest secret was that she had her upper lip waxed monthly—she thought about the way her mother had always evaded her questions about her past.

And about the tiny jade ring her mother had had permanently fastened around her neck.

And about the fact that something had once been so important, so private, to Giselle that she'd kept it locked away.

Now, as she watched her mother standing in the doorway, holding those dresses, Meg longed to say, *Who are you, really?*

And who am I?

"Well," Giselle said with a shrug, "I'm going to go finish packing. If I don't get to bed soon, I'm going to look like a wreck tomorrow morning."

She drifted across the room, and Meg smelled the French perfume that always clung to her mother.

"Give me a hug," Giselle said, leaning over Meg.

She reached up and squeezed her mother, suddenly feeling emotional and clingy.

"Meg!" Giselle said in surprise, pulling back slightly.

Meg half expected to be scolded for crushing the dresses, but her mother said, with concern that was very unlike her, "Are you all right?"

"Yes . . . why?"

"Just the way you were hugging me . . . You haven't done that since you were a tiny little girl. Whenever I had to go someplace, you would throw your arms around my neck and say, 'Please don't leave me, Mommy,' almost as if . . .'' Her mother trailed off.

Meg looked sharply at her. "As if what?"

Giselle didn't meet her gaze. "As if, you know . . . you wanted to come with me," she said lightly, and Meg knew that wasn't what she had been about to say.

"Well, I can't blame you," Giselle went on. "After all, who wouldn't want to go to Fiji?"

Meg studied her mother's smile, realizing it was forced.

What? What is it? What aren't you telling me?

The words were so loud in Meg's head that she half expected her mother to hear them.

But Giselle only planted a quick kiss on the top of her head and said, "Take care of Carrie for me while I'm gone, okay? And you know Sophie and Grandma are around if you need anything."

"I know."

"Are you sure you don't want Grandma staying here at the house with you and Carrie, Meg?"

"I'm positive." She had vetoed that idea weeks ago. Her grandmother would drive her crazy, the way she was always so anxious about everything.

"We'll be fine," she assured her mother. "Don't worry about us."

"I never do," Giselle said, and headed for the door. "I've never been the type to sit around wringing my hands."

No, Meg thought. *You haven't, have you?*

In the doorway, Giselle transferred the white dress to her left hand and waved gaily. "See you in two weeks, Meg."

"Bon voyage, Mom," she said.

Giselle closed the bedroom door behind her, and Meg was left alone.

Nine

Candra stepped off the bus on Elmont Avenue Tuesday after school and looked around to get her bearings.

She started off along the sidewalk, heading in the direction of Aunt Tish's. She knew there was no chance of running into her aunt. She would be working in Greenwich right now, and Candra knew she didn't get home until early evening.

Candra's hair hung straight down her back, swaying back and forth as she walked. She was wearing a tight black tee shirt and faded jeans that were threadbare and clung to her long, lean legs.

Her eyes, concealed behind the expensive black sunglasses Jane had left lying around the house, darted from side to side, looking for the shops Kim had said she would find here.

A small, pleased smile played over her lips whenever she attracted whistles and catcalls from the men who lounged in doorways and stood in groups on corners.

They were nobodies, but Candra liked knowing they desired her.

They weren't the only ones.

Landon wanted her, too.

And soon, she would have him all to herself.

Today she had tucked the red flannel conjure bag in the crevice between her breasts to conceal it, and the elastic at the bottom of her bra would keep it from falling out.

She had done her best to avoid Kim and Nedra all day, not wanting to answer any more questions. She'd even skipped lunch so that she wouldn't have to sit at that table with them. She'd spent the period in the school library, reading about American history in her Social Studies textbook.

"Oooh, baby, the way you move," called a man who was just coming out of Rivera's Newsstand.

Candra tossed her head and kept going. This was Aunt Tish's block. What would she do if, for some reason, she did happen to run into her aunt?

She could say she was visiting some friend in the neighborhood. But what if Aunt Tish asked who it was or where they lived?

She could—

"I knew you'd come back to me."

It was a woman's voice, deep and with a familiar singsong dialect. Startled, Candra spun around.

An ebony-skinned, middle-aged woman stood on the sidewalk, grinning at her. She was wearing a cotton house-dress and had a scarf wrapped turban-style around her head.

"Excuse me?" Candra said. She studied the woman from behind her dark lenses. A sixth sense was stealing over her—a warning that this meeting wasn't accidental, no matter how it seemed.

I came here to find the herbalist's shop, Candra protested mentally.

But the whisper of a voice in the back of her mind didn't agree.

"I told you, didn't I?" the woman said. "You're looking for me."

Candra frowned as she suddenly realized who this was.

The woman who had accompanied Aunt Tish and Grandmother to the witchcraft ceremony the other night. Candra noticed the two bags of groceries she was carrying. She was obviously on her way home from the market.

"Come on," she said, and jerked her head, indicating the building on the corner behind her. "I live above the newsstand. You passed my place."

Candra reached up and removed the sunglasses she was wearing. She let her dark gaze settle on the woman, who suddenly looked taken aback.

"You're—oh, my God." Her voice was a whisper.

"What is it?" Candra asked.

"I just . . ." The woman shook her head rapidly, as if to clear it. "You're not her. Your eyes—they're different. Hers weren't as knowing—as bottomless."

"Whose? Who are you talking about?"

The woman only stared and kept shaking her head.

Candra took a step closer.

She could scarcely breathe, could hardly find her voice. There was a rushing sound in her head, a roar that drowned out any coherent thought.

She just watched the stranger, waiting. Bracing herself for whatever was coming.

Finally the woman said, "She was telling the truth. She'd never been here before. It was you."

"What was me? Who had never been here before?" Candra realized she somehow sounded demanding, even as her heart pounded in trepidation.

"The other girl—the one who came to me at the carnival. The one who looks exactly like you."

Meg had rushed home from school, hoping to find a message from Jerry Berry, only to discover that the answering machine was turned off.

"Damn!" she said, banging her fist against the desk. Giselle must have struck again. Her mother had probably turned the machine off by accident last night before she'd started packing for her trip.

What if Jerry had tried to get in touch with her? Meg decided to call him, just in case.

But what if he didn't try to call, and thinks you're being a pain in the butt?

Well, who cared what some stupid locksmith thought of her? As soon as he got the metal box opened, Meg would never have to worry about him again.

Meg opened the desk drawer and took out the local business directory. She looked up the number for Jerry's Lock and Key and dialed it.

One ring . . .

Two rings . . .

"Hello, this is Jerry speaking."

She cleared her throat. "Uh, hi, Jerry, this is Megan McKenna. I left a box there with you yester—"

"Right, can you hang on a second?" he interrupted.

"Yes." There was a click and she was put on hold. Some song was playing in her ear—"Moon River." Grandpa used to hum it while he worked in the kitchen.

Would she never stop being reminded of him at every turn?

There was a click, and the song was replaced by the locksmith's voice. "Hi, thanks for holding. I was just about to call you, Megan . . ."

"You were?"

She waited for him to say he hadn't been able to open the box, or that it had been stolen, anything but what he said next.

"Yes. I opened your lock for you—it's all set here for you to pick up."

"It is?" she asked, gripping the receiver.

"It is. But if you want it, you'd better come down and get it now, because I'm leaving in a few minutes to go on a call. Some woman just found out her husband is cheating on her, and she wants me to change the locks before he gets home from the office tonight."

"I'll be right there—please don't go anywhere before I get there, okay?"

"Yeah, yeah, just hurry up."

Meg hung up the phone and grabbed her car keys and her purse, then raced out of the house.

"My name's Dalila Parker," the woman said as she led Candra up the stairs toward her apartment over Rivera's Newsstand.

"I'm Candra Bowen."

"Candra," she repeated. "That's a variation of the ancient word *chandra*. It means moon."

"I know." She still felt numb, though she shouldn't have, not really. Not after twice before being mistaken for someone else.

But she had been too preoccupied with school and Landon and everything else to dwell on those odd incidents. Now reality came rushing at her, and she felt overwhelmed.

Out on the street, the woman had said, "Are you all right? You look ill."

Candra had stammered something, and the next thing she knew, here she was, being ushered into the woman's building.

They stepped from the dark hall into the bright apartment. Not *bright* just because of the summer sun that streamed through the three narrow-paned windows that ran almost from floor to ceiling along the far wall, but—well, *bright*.

The walls were painted stark white, and the floors were plain, light wood; but everywhere Candra looked were splashes of color—aqua and coral and fuchsia and yellow—colors you wouldn't expect to see in this dingy urban neighborhood; tropical colors that reminded Candra of home.

She eyed the gaily patterned fabric covering the couch and chairs. The jungle of plants, some of them flowering. The bubbling aquarium on a shelf, where exotic fish swam lazily, their iridescent scales glittering in the sunlight. The squawking parakeets in the cage by the window. The framed posters that lined the walls—cheerful, almost childlike pictures of fish and fruit, and people who were no more than crude outlines of males and females, like symbols on restroom doors.

Then she turned and looked at Dalila Parker. The woman was carrying her bags of groceries toward the kitchenette in one corner. "Sit down," she called over her shoulder. "I just want to put the meat and milk into the refrigerator."

Candra sat on the edge of the couch and noticed the cat for the first time. The sleek black animal had been curled up on the floor in a patch of afternoon sunlight that streamed through the window. Now it stood, placed its front paws on the floor and stretched, then looked up, unblinking, at Candra.

The cat approached her and jumped up onto the couch, settling with a purr against Candra's hip.

She reached down and absently stroked the soft fur, becoming lost in thought.

So there *was* another girl. Someone who looked exactly like her.

Somehow, some part of Candra had known she was out there all along. She remembered the feeling that had come over her on the plane before landing in the States that night. The voices in her mind were telling her to "find her."

She remembered how she had been drawn to wander the streets of Crawford Corners, not knowing what she was looking for, only that it was out there, beckoning her.

All her life, really, Candra had been seeking something or someone intangible, something she needed but couldn't put her finger on.

Oh, there were other things she needed, wanted desperately. Money. Power. Landon Keller.

But this was different.

And ever since coming to Crawford Corners, her vague unsettled feeling that something was missing had grown more pronounced.

"Here, this is for you," Dalila said, coming back into the room with a glass of ice water. "It will make you feel better."

"I'm fine."

The woman shrugged and held the glass out anyway.

Candra took it, held it in both hands, and waited.

"I see you've met Erzulie."

"Erzulie?"

"I named her after the voodoo god."

Candra knew all about Erzulie, but she didn't stop Dalila Parker when she launched into an explanation.

"Erzulie is the god associated with wealth—jewels and riches. The day I brought this cat home, she climbed onto my dresser and poked her nose into my trinket box. She still loves to play with necklaces, dangling earrings, things like that."

"Oh . . . that's unusual."

"It is." Dalila Parker sat down on a chair across from her. "Your accent is Jamaican."

"So is yours."

"That's right. I came here from Port Antonio ten years ago. There are a lot of Jamaicans in this neighborhood."

Candra nodded.

"You don't live here, though."

"No." She paused. She wasn't in the habit of offering information about herself to strangers, or anyone else, really. But some instinct made her want to open up to this woman. "I came to this country a few weeks ago, with my grandmother. We're living in Crawford Corners—my grandmother is housekeeper for a family there."

"But I've seen you on Elmont Avenue before. Do you have a friend here?"

She hesitated. "My aunt," she said reluctantly. "She lives down the street from this building. Letitia Bowen."

The woman merely nodded. Then she asked, "Where are your parents?"

"My father died right after I was born. I never knew either of them. His mother—my grandmother, Rosamund—raised me."

"And your mother?"

Candra took a small sip of water and studied the glass in her hand. "She died in childbirth. She was white." She shrugged. "That's all I know about her. I don't know her name, or anything else. My grandmother refuses to discuss her."

She looked up. Dalila Parker had a faraway, thoughtful look in her eyes.

"Tell me about the girl you saw—the one who looks like me," Candra demanded.

The woman focused on her again. "I do readings—they insist on calling it fortune-telling—at carnivals. I don't like to use my . . . talents that way, but I need the extra money. My husband died three years ago and left me with nothing."

"I'm sorry," Candra said briefly. She ran her fingertip along the outside of the glass, trailing a path through the frosty condensation.

"A few weeks ago, at the carnival here in Spring City, a girl came into my tent. I thought she was you—I had passed you on the street here only a few days earlier, and I . . . remembered you."

Something about the way the woman said it made Candra look up sharply. "Why?"

Dalila Parker leaned forward. "You have powers, Candra, don't you." It wasn't a question. "I can feel an energy force from you even now. It's far stronger than it was that day in the tent, with Meg."

The name came at Candra with a whoosh of recognition that vanished as abruptly as it had come. "Meg?" she asked blankly.

"She had a friend with her. I heard her say the name. You didn't know about this person? She's your double. Exactly."

"No."

"Give me that bracelet you're wearing," the woman said abruptly.

"Why?"

Dalila just held out her hand, palm up.

Candra shrugged and reached down, unclasping the string of tiny shells from around her wrist. She dropped it into the woman's hand.

Dalila Parker closed her fingers around it, leaned back, and closed her eyes.

Suddenly, Candra understood. The woman was psychic.

She watched intently while Dalila held her bracelet and concentrated. The room was silent except for the sleeping Erzulie's gentle snoring on the couch beside Candra. Out on the street, a siren approached, then went screaming into the distance.

Finally, Dalila began to speak.

Meg hurried up the steps and down the hall to *Jerry's Lock and Key*. As soon as she reached the glass-fronted door, she saw Jerry Berry stand up behind the counter and set aside the newspaper he'd been reading. He was wearing a navy blue nylon jacket and a New York Yankees baseball cap.

"Hi there," he said, and reached beneath the counter. "I've got everything right here."

"Thank you," Meg told him as he set the familiar metal box on the counter. She was jittery with anticipation, but tried to keep her voice steady. "How much do I owe you?"

"The bill's right here," he said, sliding a sales slip in her direction.

She glanced at it, unzipped her purse, and hurriedly dug out a fifty dollar bill. She probably had the right amount in bills and change, but didn't have the patience to count it out.

Jerry took the money and went over to a register behind him. He quickly counted out Meg's change and handed it to her. "There you go."

She tossed the money into her purse, not bothering to find her wallet and put it away. Then she picked up the metal box.

She couldn't wait another minute to see what was in it. As soon as she walked out into the hall, she'd sit down on the top step and open it.

"I'll walk out with you," Jerry said, picking up a ring of keys and a toolbox and tucking his newspaper under his arm.

"Okay." She would just have to wait until she got to her car.

"So, where do you go to school?" Jerry asked as he locked the glass door behind them.

It took a second for her to focus. "Oh, Adamson-Swift."

"I kinda figured. What grade?" They started down the stairs.

"Senior," she said briefly.

"My Missy's a junior. Wants to be a doctor."

"That's nice."

"I told her, 'Missy, you want to be a doctor, you better win a scholarship or the lottery, 'cause your mother and I are going to have a tough time paying college tuition for all three of you kids.' My wife, Doreen, she's a nurse, and they don't make much."

"No, they don't," Meg murmured, though she had no idea about nurses' salaries.

They had reached the bottom step, and Jerry held one of the double doors open for her.

"Well, I have to go this way," he said, pointing toward the municipal lot around the corner.

So did Meg, but she didn't think she could take another moment of idle conversation. She clasped the box against her with one hand and pointed in the opposite direction with the other. "I go that way," she told Jerry. "So, thanks very much for helping me out."

"No problem. You have a good one."

"You, too."

He headed down the street.

Meg walked swiftly away, glancing over her shoulder until she saw Jerry Berry round the corner toward the parking lot.

She ducked into Burlington's Drug Store and spent five anxious minutes wandering aimlessly up and down the aisles, clutching her precious box.

When she thought enough time had passed and Jerry Berry would be safely on his way, she left the drugstore and scurried along Broad Street and around the corner to the municipal lot.

The Honda was parked at the far end, and Meg practically ran to it. She fumbled with her key chain, pressed the button that disengaged the alarm, and opened the door.

Settled in the driver's seat, she took a deep breath, let it out, and whispered, "Here goes."

Then she lifted the lid of the metal box on her lap.

* * *

"Things are not the way they seem—not the way you have been led to believe they are," were the first words out of Dalila Parker's mouth after her long silence.

Candra frowned. "What do you mean?"

"There are lies all around you. Your whole life is a lie." The woman's voice was matter-of-fact yet distant, detached.

"How is my life a lie?" She found herself wanting to be skeptical, yet waiting breathlessly for whatever information Dalila Parker was going to give her.

"You aren't who you think you are. The woman you know as your grandmother isn't who you think she is."

"What are you talking about?"

"Rosamund isn't your grandmother. Her blood and your blood—there is no relation."

Candra stared. She wanted to deny it, to tell this woman she didn't know what she was talking about, but she couldn't.

She couldn't, because somehow, she knew that Dalila spoke the truth. Some distant part of her mind acknowledged it. Rosamund Bowen was not her grandmother.

But if that was true, it meant . . .

"What about my father?" she asked, and her voice came out hushed, small.

"The man who gave you life was not Rosamund's son. She has never born a child, though I see her helping many children into the world."

"She's a midwife," Candra said quietly.

"Yes. She was there when you were born. You . . . and your sister. . . . And . . . I can't tell . . . are there . . . ?"

As the woman's voice murmured on, faint and questioning, Candra sat there, frozen, unable to breathe, unable to speak.

In her mind, Dalila's words were echoing, screeching, blocking out everything else.

You and your sister . . .

"No. Just two babies . . . ," Dalila whispered. Then her eyes snapped open. "Two babies. You—and your sister. Your twin. Meg."

The first thing Meg saw when she opened the box was a sketch pad. She lifted it out with shaking hands and opened it to the first page. There was a rough charcoal drawing there. She would have recognized the style even though there was no signature in the lower right-hand corner. The scene and bold geometric lines were typical of the stuff Giselle had done in high school. Nothing unusual—just a house on the water, and some trees. Palm trees.

Impatiently, Meg set the sketch pad aside and looked back into the metal box.

"What the . . . ?" She lifted out a little red felt drawstring bag. Someone had made it by hand, judging by the wide, uneven stitches along the seams.

Meg shook it. Something rattled.

Frowning, Meg fumbled with the knot on the string and pulled the bag open. A musty, pungent scent filled the car. It was vaguely familiar.

Meg realized that whatever was in the bag smelled sort of like the inside of the shallow spice cupboard at her grandparents' house.

She peered inside and saw some kind of powder or dust and a small, round greenish stone. There was something else, too. . . .

Gingerly, Meg reached into the bag and pulled out a clump of fine black hair that was tied with a ribbon.

It's your hair, your baby hair, she told herself incredulously.

She held it up to her head and tilted the rearview mirror so she could see herself. The strands of hair from the bag blended with her own, the same shade and texture.

What was the significance of this little bag? What had Giselle been doing?

Perplexed, Meg stuck the hair back in the bag and set it on the passenger's seat, next to the sketch pad.

She reached back into the box and took out the stub of a light blue candle. After glancing at it, she set it aside.

Only two things remained in the box: a piece of paper that was folded several times, and a small bundle wrapped in a handkerchief.

Meg picked up the paper and unfolded it. There were several lines scribbled there in her mother's familiar handwriting.

> *Charm of protection, I do make*
> *for my baby daughter's sake*
> *to the child's aura, we*
> *will give protective energy*
> *Keep her safe, my sacred charm*
> *from he who means to cause her harm*
> *Protect her, through this little doll*
> *from evil spirits he doth call*

Shaking her head in disbelief, Meg set the paper aside and reached for the last object in the box.

Carefully, she unwrapped the white linen handkerchief, then stared at the thing she was holding.

A small, crude clay doll. It was dressed in a scrap of pale pink printed fabric that had been fashioned into a dress of sorts, sewn together with jagged stitches similar to those that held the red bag together. Meg looked closely at the fabric and saw that it was flannel, and the pattern was tiny bunnies and ducks. Something a baby would wear.

And stuck into the doll's clay head was another clump of fine dark hair. Meg's hair.

Was this some sort of voodoo doll? Were the rhyming lines Giselle had scribbled on the paper some sort of spell? Was the little cloth bag the "charm" mentioned in the poem?

Meg's thoughts were swirling.

She dropped the doll, closed her eyes, and pressed her palms against her temples.

She thought of what Dalila Parker had said about her—that she had some sort of powers, an aura of some mysterious energy.

She remembered what Mirabelle had told her about how powers were inherited.

Good Lord.

Was Meg's own mother some sort of witch?

It didn't seem possible.

But . . .

She opened her eyes and stared at the weird assortment of objects she'd found in the box.

Here was the evidence. Giselle had been involved in some kind of black magic.

And it involved Meg herself.

She grabbed the paper again and scanned the words. This was a spell, no doubt about it. Giselle had been trying to protect her from something.

From some*one.*

From he who means to cause her harm . . .

From evil spirits he doth call. . . .

Meg shuddered and shook her head, frightened.

Who was *he?*

"I have a twin sister?" Candra repeated, shaking her head as if to deny it.

"Meg," Dalila Parker repeated.

"But how . . . ?"

"Two babies. One went to the mother. One to the father . . ." She hesitated, closed her eyes for a moment as though she were concentrating, then opened them again.

"What? What is it?" Candra asked.

"I just . . . nothing. I thought—but never mind. Never mind."

"I have a twin sister." This time it wasn't a question.

"Yeah, *mon*."

"My mother took her, and not me?"

Dalila looked as though she didn't want to answer that. Candra waited, willed her to say it. Finally, the woman shrugged. "That's right. Your mother chose your sister."

Candra forced back a lump in her throat. She would *not* cry. She never cried. She swallowed hard.

"Why?" she asked in a strangled-sounding voice. "What made her do that?"

There was no answer.

"What did you see, Dalila? Tell me. *Everything*."

The woman sighed. "I saw a beautiful, young American woman. Blond, green-eyed. She was torn. She didn't want to choose, but she *had* to—one for her, one for him."

"For my father."

"That's right."

"And she chose to give me away and keep my sister." The pain over the realization sliced through Candra's gut. She squeezed her eyes shut against it and bit down on her lower lip so hard she winced.

"It's all right," Dalila Parker said softly.

No, dammit! It's not all right. My mother gave me away. She wanted my sister. She didn't want me.

She had to stop thinking about it, had to stop the hurt . . .

She clenched her fists, took a deep breath and let it out shakily.

She did it again.

That was better.

She and Dalila Parker looked at each other. The older woman's eyes were sympathetic.

"If he wasn't Rosamund's son, who was he?" Candra asked suddenly.

For a moment, Dalila looked reluctant to acknowledge the question. Then she said slowly, "Who? Your father?"

"Yes."

"He was. . . ." She hesitated, then tried again. "Your father was . . ."

"What is it? Who was he?"

"He was just . . . a man. Just a man who lived on the island."

"There's more—what aren't you telling me?" Candra's voice was high-pitched. "Tell me *everything*. I need to know."

But Dalila's eyes had taken on a hooded expression, and she shook her head. "That's all I know," she said staunchly.

"No," Candra said. "That's all you're willing to tell me. But that's all right, because I'll find out the truth sooner or later."

"For your sake, I hope it's later," the woman said softly.

Meg reached for the sketch pad on the seat again and opened it to the first page. She glanced at the simple drawing of the house on the beach, and at the palm trees.

Is this where you lived in Jamaica? she asked her mother silently. *Is this where I was born?*

She flipped the page. Another scenic sketch, this one of a craggy mountain that jutted against an overcast sky. Meg didn't like the mood her mother had captured. It was dark, somehow foreboding. . . .

The picture on the next page stole her breath away.

It was a portrait.

A man.

He was bare-chested and black-skinned, with sharp features and a lean, sculpted torso. His face was expressionless, but his eyes . . .

His eyes were dark and piercing, staring out at Meg from the plain white paper.

Who was he?

She turned the page again, eager to get past the portrait, to no longer be faced with the image of that glare.

On the next page was another sketch. The same man was in this one, but his eyes were closed. He was standing on his tiptoes, his arms stretched above his head. He was holding something—it looked like some sort of pendant, shaped like a five-pointed star. Around him, Giselle had depicted crude outlines of people—just figures, no distinguishing features. They seemed to be standing in a circle around the man.

Meg chewed her bottom lip and flipped to the next drawing. It was a variation of the scene before, only in this one, the man was crouched, lighting a candle that sat on a flat, rectangular rock. In the picture after that, he was shown in motion, his hands joined with others in a circle, as if they were dancing around. Again, the other figures in the scene were mere outlines.

She turned to the next page. A seascape, with rough, churning waters and again, an overcast sky. She turned again, to the next page, and the next . . .

They were all landscapes, showing mountains and the sea and the same house. Some were dreamy, soft-focus scenes with smudged lines; others had been drawn in sharp, jagged strokes, the charcoal marks bold and black. It was as though the sketchbook encompassed a long period of time in her mother's life, and the different styles reflected her changing moods.

When she came to the last page, Meg gasped.

Her own eyes stared out at her. She was an infant in the picture, but there was no mistaking the fact that it was her. Her mother had captured her angular face and full lips perfectly.

In fact, she'd done it twice.

There were two images of Meg, side by side.

She frowned, wondering why her mother hadn't simply turned the paper over to do the second drawing.

There was something odd about the portraits, something she should be noticing . . .

She stared at the page for a long time, but she couldn't put her finger on what it was.

Shrugging, she closed the sketchbook and set it on the seat beside her. She had better get home.

She started the engine and pulled out of the parking lot onto Highland Boulevard. As she drove along the quiet streets of Crawford Corners, her mind was on what she had found.

It was hard to believe that her mother had been involved in anything remotely mystical, but what other explanation was there for the spell, or the little doll? And those drawings of the man . . . were they of some type of ritual ceremony her mother had witnessed while in the islands? Was the man some type of voodoo priest?

Meg focused again on the nagging memory of those drawings of herself as a baby. What was it that she should be noticing?

She was almost home when it hit her.

Only one of the baby portraits had shown the jade ring.

Either Giselle had inexplicably decided to draw her without it for the second portrait . . .

Or she had been drawing two different babies.

Ten

Meg pulled into the parking lot of Adamson-Swift on Wednesday morning to see Shea waiting there, leaning against his car, his arms folded against his chest.

Great, she thought, turning into her usual spot and putting the car into Park. *Just great.*

She glanced in the rearview mirror as she gathered up her books and purse from the seat beside her. He was walking up to the driver's side door, and the look on his face was grim.

She opened the door and swung her feet out, then busied herself bending over and taking an imaginary pebble out of her loafer.

"Meg, where were you last night? I tried calling three times and left messages for you to call me back. The last one was at midnight. Didn't you get them?"

She'd gotten them, all right. She had been sitting right by the phone in the dark, screening the calls, hearing the growing anxiety in Shea's voice but unwilling—unable—to talk to him.

She looked up at him.

"What the—Meg, what's wrong? What happened?"

"What do you mean?"

"You look. . . . Did you get any sleep last night? There are huge circles under your eyes."

"I slept," she lied.

"Where?" The innuendo in his voice was so unexpected, so unlike him, that her jaw dropped.

"What's that supposed to mean?"

"It means, you weren't home, so where did you sleep? That's all I'm asking you."

She reached back, slammed the car door, and started striding toward the school.

Shea was right at her side, saying, "We need to talk, Meg," and grabbing her arm.

She spun on him and said, "How dare you accuse me of—"

"Of what? I didn't accuse you of anything. Maybe your guilty conscience is getting to you."

She just stared at him, hating the look on his face.

"Meg, do you think I'm an idiot? Three different people have told me they saw you out at Moseby late Friday night, sitting in a dark corner like you were trying to hide. No wonder, since you were all cozy with some prep from out of town. And now it makes sense that you wanted me to drop you off early after the movies. What'd he do, pick you up right after I drove away? Did you think I wouldn't find out about it?"

She couldn't answer him. She was too exhausted, too overwhelmed, too furious.

Shea didn't trust her. That was what it boiled down to. And if Shea didn't care enough about her to trust her. . . .

"Listen, Meg, if you're going to screw around behind my back, then at least do it where everyone at school won't see. You're making a fool out of me. They're all talking about it."

She found her voice. "That's what matters to you more than anything else, isn't it? What other people think of you."

"You know that's not true."

"Oh, yes it is, Shea. And that's a shame. Because you know what *I* think of you?"

She paused, staring at him, unable to grasp that it had come down to this—that it was going to end like this.

"I think you're a cold, heartless son of a bitch."

With that, she turned, ran back to her car, and screeched out of the parking lot, leaving him standing there looking shocked.

Candra walked briskly along the sidewalk toward Adamson-Swift, her jaw set and her eyes narrowed behind her black sunglasses. Her long black hair was tucked underneath a baseball cap, and she was wearing a shapeless barn coat she'd found in the back of an old metal wardrobe in the basement.

It wasn't the best disguise, but she didn't want anyone who happened to see her to mistake her . . .

For Meg.

She forced herself to say the name in her mind.

Fury boiled up inside of her.

Meg.

The one her mother had chosen over her.

Meg, who, according to Dalila Parker, lived in Crawford Corners, and judging by the clothes she had been wearing at the carnival and the purse she had been carrying was well-off.

Meg was well-off.

Candra had nothing.

She clenched her fists so hard her nails dug into her palms painfully.

Ever since she'd left Dalila's, her anger had been building. But it wasn't until she was lying on her bed in the middle of the night, staring at the ceiling, that she had been struck by the glimmer of an idea.

Now it was an actual plan. There were still some angles she had to work out, but she was confident she could make it work.

The whole thing hinged on one thing.

Finding Meg.

That was the first step.

And Candra had decided that the private school to which she had been drawn that day last week was a good place to start.

Meg drove along winding Long Neck Road clenching the steering wheel so tightly that her knuckles were mottled white. She automatically propelled the car along the curves, blankly staring through the windshield with no clue where she was headed, except that it was away—away from the school, away from Shea, away from home.

She wondered, briefly, whether Carrie was still back at the house, sleeping. Meg had heard her sister sneak in well past one A.M., and Carrie hadn't gotten up for school this morning by the time Meg left the house. She herself had gone through her own morning rituals and headed for Adamson-Swift only because she hadn't been able to think clearly enough to come up with an alternative plan.

Now she was still unfocused, her mind whirling.

What Shea had just told her in the parking lot had forced her to acknowledge a truth she didn't want to face, a truth she had tried to deny all through the long, sleepless night.

There was someone lurking nearby, someone who looked so much like her that no one questioned that it was Meg.

She had a double.

And her mother had sketched two babies, identical except for the ring on one's chubby finger.

That meant only one thing . . .

She had a twin sister.

There was no other explanation. It was the only one that fit, that made sense. It had to be the reason her mother and grandparents had always been so secretive whenever she had asked questions.

But this discovery hadn't made the puzzle fall neatly into place. It had only opened the door to a whole new mystery, and now Meg had more questions than ever.

What had happened to her sister? Why hadn't she been brought up by Giselle? Why hadn't anyone ever told Meg?

Only two things were certain: whoever she was, she was nearby.

And somehow, Meg had to find her.

Because now she realized why she had always had the vague sense that her life was incomplete—that she should be searching for something.

She had a sister—a *real* sister. The only person in the world who had the exact same bloodline as Meg.

She and her twin had been spawned from a single egg, had shared their mother's womb for nine months, had grown side by side, had been brought into the world one right after another.

And then, for some reason, they had been cruelly wrenched apart. Why? How could Giselle have done something like that? And how could she have kept it from Meg?

Meg wondered if her twin knew about her existence. If not, had she always felt the same nagging sensation that her life wasn't complete?

No wonder Meg had sensed that something was missing from her life. She would only be whole when she found her other half.

She had to find her sister.

And, she realized, as she turned toward the on ramp for I-95, there was only one person who could help her do that.

Candra made her way up the wooded slope behind the sprawling stone school. The grounds were deserted—it was past eight-thirty now, and everyone would be inside.

She reached the edge of the large back parking lot and scanned the rows of cars, most of them expensive. Candra forced aside the prickle of jealousy and concentrated, waiting for something to strike her. But nothing happened.

Either none of these cars belonged to Meg, or Candra was too distracted by her resentment and hostility to focus intently enough.

You have to calm down, she told herself, willing the anger to subside.

But she still felt tense—there was no getting past it. And maybe that wasn't such a bad thing. Maybe she could channel the negative energy so that she could use it to help her locate the elusive Meg.

One way or another, I'm going to find you.

And when I do, you'll be sorry that you were the one who got everything while I got nothing.

You'll be sorry you were ever born.

Meg had only been here once before, but somehow, she had managed to find her way back. She pulled into the visitor's parking lot behind the dorm and hurriedly got out of the car, so anxious she forgot to set the alarm and had to run back to do it.

There were a few students strolling on the tree-lined sidewalk, but no one paid any attention to Meg. She made her way into the lobby of Billington Hall and glanced at the security station off to the side. The girl sitting there seemed to be deep in conversation with a tall, good-looking guy who was leaning against the desk, mostly blocking Meg from her view, had she bothered to glance in her direction.

She didn't, and Meg hurried by, not wanting to take the time to sign in.

She went up the flight of stairs straight ahead and along the hall toward Mirabelle's room, remembering that it was the next-to-last door on the left. There, she paused for only a second before knocking.

You have to involve her. You don't have a choice, she reminded herself.

While she waited, she studied the pink, pig-shaped memo board stuck to the door. A black magic marker dangled from an attached cord. Scrawled on the board were messages to Mirabelle and her roommate.

M.—Meet me at the library at 4:00—Belinda

Char, I stopped by—where are you???—Todd

Mirabelle—I borrowed your blue jacket. Thanks!—D.

As Meg looked over the board, she felt suddenly as though she were cut off from the real world—the world where people hung around with their friends and laughed and listened to music. . . .

For the past few weeks, Meg had been out of touch, preoccupied with her past and battling these strange feelings that had wrapped around her and wouldn't let go.

Would her life ever be the same again? Would she, next year at this time, be away at college, living in a dorm like this one? Would she have forgiven her mother for deceiving her? Would she have a close relationship with the twin sister she had never known existed?

Maybe they could even go away to the same college, be room-mates, Meg thought fleetingly, and knocked again on the door in front of her. Maybe they could share clothes, and books, and—

The door opened, and a bleary-eyed girl stood there, looking bewildered. She was wearing a long football jersey nightshirt, and her short brown hair was puffy and sticking up. "Hi," she said around a yawn.

"Hi . . . I'm looking for Mirabelle," Meg said.

"What's today, Wednesday? She must be in class." The girl had a western twang.

"Oh . . . do you know where?"

"What time is it?"

Meg checked her gold watch. "Nine-forty."

"She should be in psych right now. Over in Gaspar Hall."

"I really need to catch up with her. Do you know when that class gets out?"

"Ten of," the girl said, then frowned. "Why don't you know that?"

"I, um, forgot," Meg said, and turned and started down the hall before the girl could ask any more questions.

Candra clutched the hammer she'd found in the janitor's closet in the school basement and slipped up the dark stairs to the main floor. She hesitated at the door and put her ear to it, making sure there were no voices or footsteps in the hallway on the other side.

Carefully, she put her hand on the knob and pushed the door open, just a crack so that she could poke her head through and make sure the corridor was empty.

Her fingers tightening on the hammer, Candra moved stealthily along the hall to the glass door that led out to the shaded cobblestone courtyard at the back of the school. She glanced out and figured that if she moved fast, she would be able to make it across the courtyard to the woods before anyone saw her.

Satisfied that the plan was foolproof, Candra raised the hammer and held it poised for only a moment before bringing it down forcefully.

Her ears were greeted by the pleasing sound of shattering glass. Swiftly but carefully so that she wouldn't cut her wrist on the jagged shards, she reached into the red box and jerked the lever upward.

The air was pierced by the ear-splitting jangle of the fire alarm.

Still clutching the hammer, Candra darted through the door and sprinted across the courtyard, before the first students spilled out into the cool, sunny September morning.

It wasn't until she had concealed herself in the trees that she realized she'd lost her baseball cap as she was running, and her hair had tumbled down her back.

She saw the hat lying on the ground just outside the school doors and, for a fleeting moment, worried that somehow, someone would connect it with her and come looking in the woods.

Don't be ridiculous, she told herself. *No one saw you.*

Candra concentrated on scanning the crowd that collected on the cobblestones, searching for a familiar face—her own face.

Teachers tried to keep order as the students milled around, obviously glad to be freed from their classrooms, if only for the moment. Inside the school, the alarm was still ringing, and Candra heard sirens approaching out in front.

After one last careful check to see that she hadn't missed someone, she made her way furtively through the trees, around to the front of the school. Just as many students had exited through the main entrance, and now they were standing around in groups, chattering, oblivious to the teachers who barked orders and tried to get them organized into lines.

Candra peered from her shadowy refuge, still searching.

There . . .

She saw a familiar face. But it wasn't the one she was looking for.

Through narrowed eyes, she watched the cute redhead who had stopped her on the street that Saturday night—the same girl who had emerged from the woods with a boy at the party this past Friday.

Was she a friend of Meg's?

Candra remembered what the girl had said before jumping into the convertible on Broad Street that night.

See you in school. . . .

That meant that even though Meg wasn't among the students who were standing around outside right now, she did go to Adamson-Swift.

All Candra had to do was be patient, and eventually, she'd find her.

"Excuse me, but do you know where Gaspar Hall is?" Meg asked a guy who was riding by the dorm on his bike.

"Across the quad," he called back to her, lifting a hand off the handlebars and pointing diagonally ahead. "It's the brick building with the arched entrance."

"Thanks." Meg checked her watch and scurried in that direction. She had seven minutes before Mirabelle got out of class.

As she approached Gaspar Hall, she was dismayed to see that it was sprawling and three stories high. How was she even going to find Mirabelle? She didn't know which end of the building the psych class was in, or even what floor.

Meg stopped walking and looked at the building, studying it. *Where are you Mirabelle? I need to find you.*

Her instincts told her to go toward the right. She did without thinking about it, and sat down on the concrete ledge that bordered the steps up to the entrance on that side.

She realized that if she was wrong, if Mirabelle came out the center doors, or the ones way down on the other side, she would miss her. But some inner voice told her to relax and wait right here.

Was this what Mirabelle had been talking about when she'd said Meg had powers? Was this a premonition—or just a guess?

You'll soon find out, Meg told herself, checking her watch again. *Any minute, now . . .*

The doors behind her opened, and she turned to see first one, then a few, then a horde of students coming out. She scrutinized the people who passed her, and was just about to admit she had picked the wrong door when she saw a familiar face.

"Mirabelle!" she called, standing and waving.

The girl looked around and focused on Meg. She looked startled. "Hi," she said, hurrying over. "What are you doing here? How'd you find me?"

Meg hesitated only a moment before shrugging and saying, "Lucky guess."

Candra walked into the back door of the Drayer house and went down the stairs to her room. She heard a familiar voice calling her name from the kitchen, and then someone descended the steps and approached her door.

Her grandmother opened the door without knocking and stood in the doorway, her hands on her hips. "What are you doing home?" she asked Candra suspiciously in her heavy Jamaican accent. "It's not even noon. Why aren't you at school?"

Candra shrugged. "There was a fire. So they let us go home."

"A fire?"

"Yes." She looked levelly into Rosamund's eyes, daring her to ask questions.

If she did, Candra wouldn't answer them. She didn't owe this woman anything. Rosamund had lied to her all her life, had made her think she was her grandmother when in reality, she was nothing to Candra.

In a way, it had been a relief to discover that the woman wasn't her own flesh and blood. It lessened the hurt Candra had always felt over Rosamund's lack of warmth and affection. Now that hurt had been replaced with resentment—and cold indifference.

The woman in the doorway said, "As long as you're home, *mon*, you can help me with the cleaning. I'm doing the upstairs bedrooms this afternoon."

Candra was about to refuse when it dawned on her that it wasn't worth it. Why have a big confrontation with Rosamund now? In a few days, Rosamund wouldn't have any control over her.

In a few days, Rosamund, the Drayers, household drudgery, this tiny basement room—all of it would be history.

"Meg, what's up?" Mirabelle asked. "You look really upset and tired, like you haven't been sleeping."

"You're not the first person who's told me that today," Meg muttered. She forced the thought of Shea from her mind and looked around. They were sitting on a bench in a grove behind Gaspar Hall. There were a few other students around, studying or sitting and talking, but no one was in earshot.

"Mirabelle," Meg said, turning back to her, "I need your help."

"I know."

"How do you . . . ?" Meg trailed off and shook her head. "What, are you reading my mind or something?"

Mirabelle seemed unfazed by her sarcasm. "No. It's obvious. Why else would you be here in the middle of the morning when you should be in school?"

For a moment, Meg wished she had never come here, had never decided to involve someone else in this craziness. But then she realized that she couldn't do this on her own—she needed help. She wouldn't trust Zoe or Chasey to keep their mouths shut, Carrie and her grandmother were out of the question, and now she'd alienated Shea.

Mirabelle was the only one she could turn to.

So she took a deep breath and started talking. None of it was in order—she kept going off on tangents, getting sidetracked. But Mirabelle seemed to follow her, only stopping her once in a while to clarify something.

Meg talked about her mother, how Giselle had always dodged questions about the past. And about her grandfather, and his death, and how much she missed him. She told Mirabelle about Lester, and about Carrie, and about Shea, who, like the others, had accused her of being someplace she wasn't.

Before Mirabelle could bring up astral projection again, she said, "I've found out what's been going on, and it's not what you're thinking. I am *not* propelling a part of myself out of my body without being aware of it."

"I never said you were."

"You said—"

"That it was possible," Mirabelle interrupted. "It's something you *can* do."

Meg shrugged and went on with her story. Finally, she got to the metal box. She described finding it, and taking it to the locksmith, and how she'd finally opened it yesterday afternoon in the car.

"What was in it?" Mirabelle asked intently.

"A bunch of stuff. Some of it was really strange, and that's why I thought you—I mean, you know about voodoo, right?"

Mirabelle nodded.

"So you might—there was this little red drawstring bag, and—"

Mirabelle cut her off and said something Meg didn't quite catch. It sounded like *gree-gree*.

"What?" she asked. "What did you say?"

"It was a gris-gris bag," Mirabelle said, nodding. "At least, that's what they're called in New Orleans. In other places they're charm bags, conjure bags . . . What was in it?"

"Some powdery stuff and a stone and a clump of hair that looked like mine."

"The powdery stuff was probably herbs."

"What was the thing used for?"

"It's a charm. People fill them with different things, always an odd number of items that reflect their purpose. Then they consecrate the gris-gris bag in a ritual ceremony at an altar, and wear it to help attract something—or help keep something away."

"You mean, like evil spirits?" Meg thought about the spell she'd found in her mother's handwriting.

"Sometimes."

"There were other things in the box, too, Mirabelle. A light blue candle—"

"Light blue. That symbolizes protection."

"Oh." Meg felt a familiar little stab of fear. Why had her mother felt she needed to protect her?

"What else did you find, Meg?"

"A little clay doll—I think it was a voodoo doll or something." She described it to Mirabelle, who looked thoughtful.

But before Mirabelle could comment, Meg rushed on, telling her about the sketch pad. She described the scenes, including the ritualistic depictions of the man with the blazing black eyes.

Mirabelle listened intently but said nothing.

Finally, Meg told her about the last picture in the sketchbook—the babies. And she told Mirabelle the conclusion she had drawn: that she had a twin sister.

It was the only thing that made sense—the only explanation for what had been happening lately. And it would explain Meg's life-long feeling that something was missing.

There was silence for a long time after Meg stopped talking. She was drained from going back over the whole unsettling story, and Mirabelle looked lost in her own thoughts.

Finally, she looked at Meg and said, "What do you want me to help you do?"

"Find my sister," she said immediately.

"Are you sure you want to do that?"

"Of course. I *need* her, Mirabelle. She's a part of me."

"But, Meg, your sister might not be the person you've imagined. I'm afraid you might be getting yourself into something that——"

"I want to find my twin," Meg broke in sharply. "Are you going to help me, or aren't you?"

"What do you think I can do?"

"You said you have powers . . ."

"Yes, but Meg, so do you."

She said nothing to that.

"Your mother was obviously dabbling in some form of black magic when she lived in Jamaica, when you were born. She must have passed whatever powers she had to you."

I knew you were going to say that . . . I've thought of it myself— but somehow, I just don't see it. If you had ever met my mother, you'd know why."

"What do you mean?"

"I told you before—she's not the . . . *deepest* person in the world."

Mirabelle shrugged. "You may not think so, but things aren't always as they seem." She glanced at the watch on her arm. "Uh-oh. Listen, Meg, I hate to do this to you, but I have to run now. I have a test that I can't miss."

"But—"

"I'm sorry, Meg." Mirabelle hurried to her feet. "But listen, I'm not deserting you. We'll talk about this some more. Just give me a day or so to figure out what we should do next, okay?"

"I thought you could help me. You said you would!" Meg hated the petulant tone of her own voice. She sounded like Giselle, spoiled and whiny.

"All I can do is show you how to help yourself, Meg."

"But what can I do?"

"I don't know yet. I'll call you when I figure it out," Mirabelle repeated, and picked up her book bag from the bench. "I've got to go."

Meg watched as Mirabelle hurried away down the path through the trees.

Then she stood up and reluctantly headed back toward the dorm parking lot.

Nothing to do now but go home.

And wait.

Eleven

"Hey, where were you yesterday, *mon?*" Kim Williams asked, sliding into her seat across from Candra.

"Sick."

"What was wrong with you?"

Candra turned and gave her a level look. "I had a cold."

"You don't sound like it."

Without answering, Candra turned away.

The bell rang, and she saw Mrs. Birch standing in the front of the room, holding her clipboard, taking attendance. The teacher looked pleased to see Candra and flashed a warm smile in her direction.

Candra didn't return it. She looked down at the open Social Studies book on her desk and stared unseeingly at the text, pretending to study.

Why was she even here today?

Because you need to keep up a routine so no one will get suspicious, she told herself firmly. *It's only for a few more days.*

In a few more days, her problems would be over, for good. She would have everything she'd always wanted. Everything she should have had, all along.

Everything Meg had.

Except for one thing—

Landon Keller.

She thought again of the way he had looked at her that first day in the Drayers' pantry, and of how it had felt to lie in his arms. He was handsome, and rich, and confident, and American—everything Candra had ever wanted.

And he wanted her, too. Maybe not enough to forget about the fact that she was an immigrant, a housekeeper's granddaughter. Not yet, anyway. . . .

She thought about how he had treated her that Friday night—one minute, all cozy with her in the car, and the next, mingling with his own kind at that party. It was as if he had automatically turned on some inner mechanism that propelled him into his rightful place, that reminded him exactly who he was, and who *Candra* was.

Little did he know that all that was going to change very soon.

And when it did, Candra meant to have Landon Keller. There was no doubt in her mind that she would. Just as soon as the rest of her plan was in place, she would go after him.

But for now, she would keep dreaming about him—about their future.

And she would stay focused on her final objective.

With a secret little smile, she reached up and patted the conjure bag that was once again pinned to her bra, directly over her heart.

Out of the corner of her eye, she saw Kim Williams watching her.

Candra shot her a dark look and turned her back.

On Thursday morning, Meg was twirling the combination on her locker when Chasey Norman materialized beside her.

"Meg! I can't believe you're, like, here today," she said in a low voice, looking around furtively.

Meg opened her locker door. "Why not?"

"Because of yesterday."

Uh-oh. "What about it?" she asked Chasey, trying to act nonchalant.

"Well, for starters, everyone's talking about how you and Shea had this huge fight in the parking lot before homeroom, and how you got back into your car and tried to run him over! When I heard that, I—"

"I tried to *what?*" Meg stared at her in disbelief. "Don't believe everything you hear, Chasey."

"I don't believe everything I . . . Meg, come on. I'm your friend. I mean, did you or did you not break up with Shea yesterday morning before classes?"

Meg shrugged.

"I'll assume that means yes. But you didn't try to run him over?"

"Is that what he's telling people?"

"*He's* not saying anything about anything. But, like, a million people saw you guys out there in the parking lot, so . . ."

"Chasey, would you do me a favor? Tell those *million* people that this is none of their business." She took off her coat and hung it on a hook, wondering why she was even here today.

She hadn't planned on coming, but the alternative was sitting around the house, waiting to hear from Mirabelle. And after another restless night, she wasn't in the mood for that. She needed to be distracted.

Besides, she couldn't stay away from school forever. If you missed three days in a row, Adamson-Swift's policy was that you came back with a doctor's excuse. Meg didn't want to risk that, just in case she needed to take tomorrow off after she'd spoken to Mirabelle.

"Meg," Chasey said, sounding tentative, "there's something else, too."

She sighed. "What?"

"The fire drill."

"What fire drill?"

Chasey appeared to be studying her closely. After a moment, she said, "You really don't know?"

"Know what?"

"Never mind."

"Chasey," Meg said, grabbing her friend's arm, "tell me."

Reluctantly, Chasey said, "We had a fire drill yesterday morning—a false alarm. Someone stole a hammer from the janitor's closet, broke the glass and pulled the box on the first floor, by the courtyard exit. The whole fire department turned out—you should have seen the commotion."

"And?"

"And everyone's saying you were the one who triggered the alarm."

"Me?"

"Meg—"

"Why would I do something like that?"

"That's what *I* said. Zoe, too. We were like, 'Why would Meg do something like that?' And everyone was like, 'Who knows?' But they—"

"Let me get this straight," Meg cut in. "They think I tried to run over Shea, and topped it off by *stealing* a hammer and causing an alarm. Right?"

"Right."

She shook her head and grabbed a notebook from the top shelf of her locker. "I can't believe this."

"Meg, it's not like . . . I mean, a few people said they *saw* you."

She froze and looked at Chasey. "Where?"

"Running across the courtyard. They only saw you from the back, but it looked like—"

"Oh, my God." Meg put a hand on the edge of her locker door to steady herself.

"What, Meg? Are you all right?"

Her mind was racing. Was it possible? Could her twin have been *here*, at Adamson-Swift, yesterday morning?

But if it had been her, why on earth would she have caused a fire drill?

It didn't make sense.

Meg looked at Chasey. "Obviously, you'd better stop listening to your sources, whoever they are, because they don't know what they're talking about." She slammed her locker door and stalked off down the hall toward homeroom, with Chasey at her heels, protesting.

Meg ignored her. She had spotted Shea down the hall, coming toward them. He was walking with his head down, his left hand jammed into his pants pocket, his right straight down at his side, holding his books.

Normally, Shea walked the halls with his head up, saying hi to people and occasionally stopping to chat.

As he approached, Meg desperately wanted to go to him, to stop him and say, "Shea, I need you. Please, let's get back together."

But then she remembered how he had practically accused her of cheating on him, how he hadn't trusted her. And when he glanced up as he passed, as though he had sensed that she was nearby, she met his eyes coldly.

They moved by each other without a word.

Chasey, still keeping up with her, said, "So I guess it is true, huh? At least that part of it?"

"What?" Meg looked at her.

"That you and Shea broke up."

"Yes," Meg told her firmly. "It's true. And I'm glad."

As they went into Pfeiffer's classroom and took their seats, Meg's twinges of regret about Shea were replaced by bewilderment, once again, over what Chasey had told her about the fire drill.

And she remembered Mirabelle's warning.

Your sister might not be the person you've imagined.

But of course she was. Her twin was her other half, her soul mate.

Meg desperately needed to believe that.

Candra slipped up the steps to the first floor and paused in the pantry to listen, making sure the house really was empty.

Of course it was. She had come home from school to find Rosamund leaving to walk to the supermarket down the road. Monica was out shopping as usual, and Jonas was at the office.

Candra had the place to herself for the first time in days. She had to take advantage of it before someone came home.

In the kitchen, she went straight to the telephone on the wall and lifted the receiver. After a moment's hesitation, she pushed the 0.

Almost immediately, a voice came on and said, "Operator."

"Yes, may I please have the number for the Lawson School?" she asked politely in her smoothest American accent.

"You need to call directory assistance for that."

"How . . . uh, how do I do that?"

"Dial four-one-one," the operator said impatiently. There was a click, and then a dial tone.

Candra dialed four-one-one.

"City please?"

"Pardon?"

There was a sigh. "What city, please?"

"Oh, it's . . . near New Haven." She forgot to use her American accent.

"*Near* New Haven?" the voice asked brusquely.

"Yes." *Don't let her intimidate you.* "I need the number for the Lawson School."

There was a pause, and then a click. Candra thought the woman had hung up on her, but then she heard what sounded like a robot saying, "The number is five-five-five-three-one-three-two."

Memorizing it, she hung up, then lifted the receiver again and dialed.

"Good afternoon, this is the Lawson School. May I help you?"

It was about time. "Yes, please, I need to reach a student there. His name is Lan—" Candra broke off, hearing the front door open, then close.

Abruptly, she hung up the phone.

Candra scurried across the kitchen and silently fled down the stairs just as a pair of heels tap-tapped toward the back of the house and Monica's voice called, "Yoo hoo, anybody home?"

In her basement room, Candra wrote down the phone number she had memorized.

Be patient, she commanded herself.

But it wasn't easy. She was tired of waiting.

She decided to go back to the Adamson-Swift School tomorrow to look for Meg.

"Carrie, is that you?" Meg called, hearing the front door slam.

"Yeah." Her sister's footsteps started up the stairs.

Meg left the den, where she had been sitting staring at the phone, willing it to ring. In the front hallway, she saw Carrie up on the land-ing.

"Wait a second," she said.

Her sister turned around, her foot poised on a step. "Yes?"

"Where have you been?"

Carrie didn't reply, just stood there wearing a smirk. Meg noticed that she was wearing a ripped pair of jeans and a grungy flannel shirt, and her green eyes were bloodshot.

"I mean it," Meg said. "You have some explaining to do. I know you weren't in school today, because I checked. And when I got home after school, Sophie was all worried because your bed hadn't been slept in."

"How does she know that?"

"Because it was made."

"Maybe I made it."

"Oh, please, Carrie. You've never made your bed in your life. And anyway, I know you weren't home last night because I was here, and I was up all night, worried sick."

At least it was half-true. She had been up all night, though it hadn't been over Carrie's absence. But the housekeeper's distress had rubbed off on her. Now she wasn't only angry with Carrie, she felt guilty for not paying more attention to her sister's whereabouts over the past few days.

"Listen, Meg, you're not my mother," Carrie said. "So don't act like you are."

"Mom told me to look out for you while they're gone. And if you don't shape up, I'm going to call her and tell her exactly what you've been up to."

"You can't call."

"Oh, yes I can. Mom said she'd leave the number on the refrigera-tor for me."

"She did?" Carrie looked amused. "Well, you know Mom. Some-times she forgets to do things."

Meg narrowed her eyes at her sister. "Carrie, you found the number and got rid of it, didn't you?"

"Why would I do that? I told you, Mom forgot."

Yeah, right, Meg thought. She vaguely remembered seeing the number a few days ago, on a scrap of paper stuck under a magnet. If it wasn't there now, Carrie was responsible. And since Meg had no idea what the name of the resort was, there was no way of tracking her mother down.

That left her with an uneasy feeling, not just because of Carrie.

Somewhere in the back of her mind, she realized that she had been thinking of calling her mother and confronting her about her twin. Now that was impossible, and Giselle wouldn't be back for another week and a half.

"Well, I'm sure she'll call in," she told Carrie.

"Since when does Mom call from vacation?"

Her sister was right, but Meg kept right on talking over her protest, "And when she does, I'll tell her that you were out all night, and that you cut school, and—"

"So did you!"

Meg stared at her.

"Come on, I go to Adamson-Swift too, remember? I know you weren't there yesterday. I was a little late myself, but as soon as I got there, I heard all about your fight with Shea, and how you tried to—"

"I did *not* try to run him over!" Meg shouted. "And I didn't set that fire alarm, either!"

Carrie's pale eyebrows shot up. "The fire alarm? Gee, I hadn't heard that one. You're really changing, you know, Meg? I think Mom and Dad will be very interested to hear about what *you've* been up to all week, too."

"Lester Hudson isn't *my* 'Dad,' " Meg said coolly. "Thank God." With that, she spun on her heel and went back to the den to wait for Mirabelle's call.

Twelve

Candra sat on a rock in the woods that bordered the front lawn of Adamson-Swift, peering through a pair of binoculars.

That had been a last-minute idea, one she couldn't believe she hadn't come up with sooner. She had seen them in the same metal wardrobe where she'd found the old barn jacket a few days ago, but hadn't thought to bring them along before.

With them, she could see, with remarkable clarity, the faces of the students who were hurrying toward the big double doors at the front of the school. She'd been here for over an hour now, ever since the first students had started trickling in.

She had seen the short blond who had been kissing the long-haired boy on the street that night before accusing Candra of following her. She had also seen the familiar redhead, who had stepped out of a cream-colored Mercedes in the parking lot.

Candra watched one expensive car after another pulling in, and her anger grew.

What did Meg drive? she wondered bitterly.

She thought about the rusty twenty-year-old car Rosamund had left behind in Jamaica. Candra and Mabel used to sneak it out after dark and practice driving it up and down the dirt roads. A few times, it had stalled on them, and they'd had to push it back to the Drayers' house.

Candra wondered what it would be like to be behind the wheel of a *real* car.

Well, you'll soon find out, she promised herself, and concentrated on looking for Meg.

The Honda was almost out of gas, Meg noted as she drove toward school. She'd have to stop on the way home or she wouldn't make it. Meg had never run out of gas before—she was usually really conscientious about keeping her car in good shape. She'd just been so distracted lately.

She reached up to rub her stiff neck. She had fallen asleep with her head on the desk by the phone last night. When she woke up at three in the morning, she was sore and disoriented, and it had taken a few seconds for her to figure out where she was.

Then she realized that Mirabelle had never called her. The last thing Meg remembered was leaving a message with her roommate at about eight-thirty.

There had been nothing for Meg to do but go to bed.

She had repeatedly tried the dorm before she left the house, but the line was busy. And she couldn't be late for school today—Pfeiffer had asked her a lot of suspicious questions yesterday about her absence. The last thing Meg needed now was for him to give her detention.

She'd just have to call Mirabelle from the pay phone, between classes.

The school came into sight ahead, and Meg felt a sudden prickle of anxiety. She tried to ignore it, but the closer she got, the stronger it was.

You're just nervous about seeing Shea today, she told herself.

But somehow, she knew it wasn't that at all. She recognized this feeling—it was the same one she'd had that night in the lobby of the Dumont. Only this time it was stronger, more urgent . . . more frightening.

She tried to shake it off as she pulled into the long driveway that led up to the parking lot beside the school, but it persisted. As she drove, her eyes darted from side to side, scanning the grounds. She clenched the steering wheel tightly to keep her hands from shaking.

Someone's out there, she thought with inexplicable conviction.

But who was it?

Her twin sister?

No. It couldn't be. Because if it were her sister, she wouldn't have this sudden chilling certainty that whatever, whoever, was lurking meant to cause her harm.

It's her.

Candra knew, even before the sleek black Accord had come to a stop in the parking lot, that her twin was behind the wheel.

Her senses had alerted her to Meg's presence even before the car had appeared on the winding drive. She had known, instantly and instinctively, that she was about to get her first glimpse of her twin.

Her hands gripped the binoculars in front of her eyes. She tried to steady them, but she was trembling all over.

Breathlessly, Candra waited and watched.

It never even entered her mind, as the door of the black car opened, that it might not be Meg who stepped out. There had been only a few times in her whole life that Candra had been this in tune with something, this positive about what the voices in her mind were telling her. This premonition was so strong it threatened to overwhelm her, and she fought to stay calm, to simply observe and not act.

The long-haired girl who stepped out of the car had her back turned, and Candra whispered urgently, "Turn around! Please . . . let me see your face."

As if she had heard, the girl turned suddenly, and though Candra had thought she was prepared for what she would see, she gasped and nearly dropped the binoculars.

It was like looking into a mirror.

Not only that, but . . .

Meg was looking directly at her.

Don't be a fool! Candra told herself, fighting the urge to toss the binoculars and run.

She can't see you, not from that far away. It only seems as though she can.

But as she watched, Meg's face grew more troubled, and she seemed to be looking right at Candra, her eyes wide with . . . fear?

After a moment, Meg shook her head rapidly, as though trying to clear it, and turned back to her car. She took out a book bag, closed the door, and started walking toward the school.

But Candra noticed that as she went, she kept looking around nervously, as though she sensed that she was being watched.

And her eyes kept coming back to rest on the spot where Candra was hiding among the trees.

When Meg had finally vanished inside the school, Candra lowered the binoculars. She took a deep breath, then let it out slowly, to calm herself.

She had never counted on this.

She had never suspected, never *imagined*, that Meg, too, had a keen awareness, a way of knowing things.

How could she have overlooked such an important possibility?

No, not even a possibility—a *likelihood*.

It only made sense. After all, her twin had the same flesh and blood. Like Candra, Meg had obviously inherited intuitive powers from . . . who? From their mother? Or from their father?

It was a question Candra had often asked herself, but right now, it wasn't important.

All that mattered was that Meg was alert to Candra's presence, even from this far away.

It was a complication Candra hadn't considered.

And it meant she had to think of a new plan immediately . . . because the last one had hinged on catching Meg off guard.

"Hello, is Mir—Mirabelle? Is this you?" Meg asked. She was on the pay phone outside the school cafeteria, and she had only three minutes to talk to Mirabelle, then sprint upstairs for her next class.

"Meg? Where are you? What's all that noise in the background?"

"School," she said shortly. "Listen, why didn't you call me back last night? I waited up until three in the morning, and I—"

"Whoa, calm down, Meg. I did call you back. Twice."

"But—"

"Someone was on the phone both times," Mirabelle said, "and when I beeped in on call waiting, she told me she'd give you the message. I take it she didn't?"

"No, she didn't."

Seething, Meg thought, *Wait till I get a hold of Carrie.*

To Mirabelle, she said, "That was my sister, and she must have been upstairs on the extension all night."

"I kind of figured. She didn't sound happy to be interrupted either time. Anyway, I've been thinking about your situation, and I have a few ideas."

"Great. I'm going to have to hang up in a second to get to my next class, though. I'd rather discuss this in person anyway."

"Fine. Do you want to meet me tomorrow morning at my room? We can talk then."

"How about tonight instead? I can come over as soon as I get out of school, and—"

"Can't—I have a date, and since this is my first one since I've been here at college, I don't want to change it. He's really cute, Meg," Mirabelle drawled. "You should see him. He's taking me to dinner, and then we're going to a party."

"That's nice," Meg said briefly.

She made arrangements to meet Mirabelle in the morning, then hung up and hurried up the stairs to her government class.

She probably should have made more of a big deal about Mirabelle's date, she realized belatedly.

But parties and dates seemed so trivial compared to what she was going through right now.

Even Shea was far from her mind . . .

At least, he had been until she walked into Government and saw him sitting there, talking to Andy Dorner as usual. As soon as Andy saw her, he nudged Shea and whispered something, and Meg saw Shea stiffen.

Suddenly feeling miserable, she went down the aisle and slid into her seat, wishing she'd never put herself across from Shea on the first day's seating chart. Now she would have to sit only inches from him every day, half-wistful, half-angry.

Sometimes it seemed that nothing in her life would ever be right again.

The moment she heard the big grandfather clock on the floor above her striking midnight, Candra lit the black candles and incense on her makeshift altar.

Now it was Saturday, the day ruled by the planet Saturn, the day to channel negative psychic energy to do your bidding.

Candra closed her eyes for a long time, concentrating.

Finally, she opened her eyes and reached for the two chicken bones she'd set aside. With heavy black thread, she began tying them together, chanting softly,

> *Forces of evil, I summon thee*
> *to rise and stand before me,*
> *And in the candle's glow*
> *be absorbed into this marrow*

When she was finished, she set the thread aside and held the crossbones over her head, her eyes squeezed shut.

After a moment, she lowered the bones to complete the ritual.

First, she sprinkled them with salt, to represent Earth.

Next, with holy water, representing Water.

Then she passed the bones through the flickering candle flame, to represent Fire.

Finally, she passed them through the incense, representing Air.

When the crossbones had been consecrated by all four elements, Candra slowly unbuttoned her shirt and tucked the crossbones into the left side of her bra.

There, she thought with a faint smile. *I'm ready.*

She would wear the charm over her heart until it had served its purpose.

Thirteen

Meg found Mirabelle still wearing her pajamas at noon when she showed up at the dorm.

"Guess your date was a success," she said with a grin, entering the room. "Did you get in late last night?"

"Yes. I only got about four hours of sleep," Mirabelle said, closing the door behind Meg and rubbing her eyes, "but it was worth it."

"Oh, yeah? Are you going to see him again?"

"I sure hope so. Have a seat, Meg," she said, motioning to the only uncluttered spot in the room—her roommate's bed.

Meg sat and said, "So what do you think?"

Mirabelle smiled. "Nothing like getting right into it, huh?"

"I'm sorry . . . I'm just anxious to know what ideas you have about finding my sister."

"I know. I understand exactly how you must feel, Meg. And I know you'll be willing to try anything to locate her, right?"

Meg didn't like the way she'd said that. Something told her she wasn't going to like what was coming next, either.

"Meg," Mirabelle said thoughtfully, "when I sat down to think this thing through, it struck me that we've overlooked the one real clue you have about your sister."

"Which is . . . ?"

"The psychic you met at the carnival."

"Dalila Parker? Mirabelle, I don't want anything to do with that woman."

"Hear me out, Meg. She's the one who first accused you of being someplace you weren't, right? She said she had seen you, where—?"

"On Elmont Avenue. That's where she lives."

"That's here in Spring City, right? Listen, I can jump into the shower and get dressed, and then you and I can zip over there and talk to her about this thing."

Meg was shaking her head the whole time, and as soon as Mirabelle stopped talking, she said flatly, "No way."

"Why not?"

"Because," Meg started, and hesitated. "Because she gave me the creeps," she finally told Mirabelle.

"So? So did I, when you first met me, right?"

"I never said that."

"You didn't have to. I could tell you were really thrown off when I told you about your powers, Meg. From what you said, Dalila Parker said the same thing. You gave me a second chance. Why don't you give her one, too?"

Meg thought about it.

And she remembered Dalila's words.

You'll come back to me . . .

Some stubborn part of her didn't want to give in, didn't want to do what the woman had said she'd do. Because if she did, that would make Dalila Parker right. And if the woman had been right about that, she could be right about other things, too. Things Meg found too frightening to even think about.

"Come on, Meg," Mirabelle cajoled. "What have you got to lose?"

"A lot," she said bluntly. "The woman is a nut case."

"So? She saw your sister once. Maybe she's seen her again since. Maybe she'll lead us right to her."

Meg chewed her lower lip and stared at the ceiling.

Then she sighed, looked at Mirabelle, and said reluctantly, "All right. Let's go."

Candra and Rosamund were on the bus to Spring City, on their way to visit Aunt Tish as usual. And as usual, her grandmother was clutching the plastic shopping bag that Candra now knew contained her white hooded robe.

Candra had been hoping the bus would be too crowded for them to sit together, but it wasn't. In fact, it was almost empty. Now, with Rosamund sitting next to her, Candra pretended to study the American History textbook she'd brought with her.

Not that Rosamund was very big on small talk. But ever since she'd discovered the woman wasn't really her grandmother, Candra had been so resentful she was afraid she'd accidentally give something away. And a few times, she had caught her grandmother looking at her thoughtfully, as though she somehow suspected that Candra was up to something.

So she had kept her mouth shut and avoided Rosamund as much as possible these past few days.

The only reason she had decided to come to Aunt Tish's today was that she wanted to pay a visit to Dalila Parker. Something told her the woman would be able to help her with her plan.

Whether she'd be *willing* was another story.

Still, Candra had always had a way of persuading people to do things they didn't feel comfortable with. Even things that were against the law.

And now she had the crossbones on her side.

Meg and Mirabelle walked around the corner from the parking lot behind Rivera's Newsstand where Meg had reluctantly left the Honda amidst broken glass and shady-looking loiterers.

"Wait," she said, stopping short as they reached the corner of Elmont.

"Come on, Meg, stop worrying about the car. I told you, as long as it has an alarm, it'll be fine."

"It's not that. I just suddenly have this really weird feeling."

"What kind of weird feeling?" Mirabelle asked patiently.

"I've had it before. In the movie theater last week, and again the other morning at school. It's kind of eerie, like . . . I don't know, like I'm being watched or something."

She scanned the street, which was busy with Saturday afternoon traffic, and people walking or hanging out on corners and stoops, and children on bikes. Nothing unusual. But still . . .

"You're probably just nervous about seeing Dalila," Mirabelle told her.

"No," Meg said resolutely. "I had this feeling the other day, when I was walking into school, and I tried to convince myself that it was because I had to see Shea. But it wasn't that at all. It was really creepy, Mirabelle—this feeling that something sinister was somewhere nearby, like it was coming to get me and I had to be careful. I know that sounds ridiculous, but that's exactly how it was. How it *is* right now."

"It doesn't sound ridiculous, Meg. I believe you. I told you all along, I know you have capabilities other people don't have. If you sense that you're in danger . . . well, you probably are."

Meg stared at her, suddenly oblivious to the noise on the street.

"Meg," Mirabelle said reluctantly, "there's something I haven't told you all along."

"What is it?" she asked, dread creeping over her.

"I've felt it, too. The first time I saw you at that party, you were surrounded by a black aura."

"What do you mean?"

"I could see that something was looming over you, Meg. Something dark. You need to see this Dalila Parker—there might be something she knows, something that can help you. Not just with finding your sister."

"Okay," Meg said quietly, reaching up and touching the jade baby ring on its chain around her neck. "I'll see her."

She started walking again, toward the door leading to the apartment above Rivera's Newsstand.

Candra sat at Aunt Tish's kitchen table picking at her sandwich and listening to her grandmother and aunt talking about people they had known back in Jamaica when they were children.

In the next room, the television set blared, while in the kitchen, a portable radio on the shelf was turned to an all-news station. The noise didn't seem to faze Aunt Tish or Rosamund, but with every minute that passed, Candra was becoming more irritated.

She couldn't hear herself think, and she desperately needed to. She had to be prepared when she spoke to Dalila, had to know exactly what she was going to suggest.

Finally, she knew she had to interrupt the conversation and ask if she could turn the volume down on the radio or turn the television off. If she didn't, she'd go crazy.

She tuned in to what her aunt was saying, waiting for a pause. And that was when she heard something that made her quickly look down again and pretend not to be listening.

". . . was about seventeen or eighteen years ago, when I helped you arrange the adoption. Don't you remember, Rosamund? And then you—"

Aunt Tish broke off suddenly. Candra looked up and saw the warning expression on Rosamund's face. Both sisters glanced at her, and she kept her face carefully vacant, as though she hadn't heard a thing.

After the merest hesitation, Aunt Tish resumed talking. But it was about something else entirely.

Candra forced herself to take a bite of her sandwich, conscious of Rosamund's eyes probing into her. She knew, Candra realized, that something was up. Rosamund might not be her real grandmother, but she did have an intuitive sense. She was the one who had first taught Candra to tune in to her own mental powers.

And right now, Rosamund was aware that she had heard what her aunt had said. Candra fought the urge to look the woman in the eye and say, "I heard, and I know it has something to do with me. Why don't you just tell me the truth after all these years?"

But she couldn't do that.

She sensed that Rosamund had no intention of revealing any secrets.

Had Aunt Tish been talking about arranging *Candra's* adoption? If so, who had adopted her? Rosamund? And why?

She thought back to the weeks before she had left Jamaica, when Jonas Drayer had been forced to pull strings to forge some kind of document that would let Candra leave the country. She hadn't thought twice about it. Rosamund and Jonas had handled the whole thing.

Now she wondered why it had been a problem. What was it that they'd needed? Proof of when and where she had been born—and who her parents were?

And if that was the case, why had they been forced to forge the paperwork?

Dalila Parker opened the door, and reggae music spilled out into the dingy landing.

"Ms. Parker?" Mirabelle drawled.

"Yes?" She glanced at Mirabelle, looking puzzled.

Then her dark eyes slid to Meg. Immediately, the woman opened her mouth to speak, then clamped it shut again. For a moment she only stared, frowning slightly, saying nothing. Then she nodded and said, "You're Meg."

"Yes."

Meg caught her lower lip between her teeth. There was something strange about the way the woman had said it. Not as though she had drawn a blank at first and had been trying to figure out how she knew this person at her door.

No, it was more like she had nearly mistaken Meg for someone else.

And that could only mean one thing.

"You've seen her again," Meg said, taking a step closer to Dalila. "Haven't you?"

"Seen who?"

"My identical twin sister."

At Meg's words, the woman's eyes widened. "You'd better come in," she said, stepping back and opening the door wider.

Meg stuck close to Mirabelle's side as they stepped into the apartment. She glanced around the bright room, studying the bright tropical prints and the plants and aquarium. Somehow, she felt reassured.

She had been expecting . . . what? A dank, cobwebby lair? This looked more like a Florida condominium.

"And who is this?" Dalila asked, gesturing toward Mirabelle after closing the door.

"I'm a friend of Meg's. My name is Mirabelle Moreau. It's a pleasure to meet you."

Dalila tilted her head and studied her. "You're from Louisiana," was all she said.

"Yes. New Orleans."

Dalila nodded. "I recognized your accent. I spent some time there a few years back. I had a friend who—never mind."

Meg was about to ask what she had been about to say when a beautiful black cat trotted into the room and immediately came over to her. She looked down in surprise as the animal rubbed against her legs.

"Erzulie!" Dalila said sharply. "Go away. Leave her alone."

"No, it's all right. I like cats," Meg said, reaching down to pet its sleek fur. The animal rumbled in contentment.

"What did you call her?" Mirabelle asked.

"Erzulie."

"That's the god associated with wealth, isn't it?"

"Yeah, *mon*. How did you know?"

Mirabelle smiled. "I just know."

Dalila shrugged. "Go ahead, sit down," she said. "Would you like anything to drink?"

Meg and Mirabelle murmured "no thanks," and both sat on the couch. The cat continued to nudge its head against Meg's legs, purring.

Meg was thinking that this was the oddest thing she had ever done. Here she was, paying a visit to a fortune-teller in the seediest neighborhood in town, and it was like dropping by somebody's aunt's house for tea.

Dalila took the chair across from them and focused her attention on Meg again. As soon as Meg met the dark gaze, her uneasiness returned full force. This wasn't a casual afternoon visit. She was playing with something that was way out of her league.

Mirabelle spoke. "Ms. Parker, we understand that you have had some contact with Meg's twin sister?"

There was a pause. Then the woman said, to Meg, "How did you find out?"

She wanted to lie and say that she had known all along, but she couldn't get the words out and merely shrugged.

"I didn't realize that there were two of you back at the carnival that day," Dalila said. "It wasn't until—" She broke off, looking uncertain.

"Until what?" Meg asked. "Until you saw her again?"

"Yes. That was when I realized what was going on."

"Where did you see her the second time?"

"Here, a few days ago. On this block."

"Do you know her name?" Mirabelle asked.

Clenching her fists in her lap, Meg waited for the reply.

After what seemed like an eternity, Dalila said simply, "It's Candra."

"Candra," Meg repeated softly. It was a beautiful, exotic name. Hearing it brought her one step closer to finding the sister she had lost.

She should be exhilarated. Or at least comforted. So why was she still feeling tense? And threatened?

"Does she live in this neighborhood?" Mirabelle was asking Dalila.

"No, *mon*."

"Then where?" Meg asked.

"Crawford Corners."

She and Mirabelle gasped simultaneously.

"That's where *I* live," Meg said, bewildered. "Are you sure?"

"Yeah, *mon*. Her grandmother is the housekeeper on an estate. They just came here from Jamaica a few weeks ago."

"Then she really is my sister," Meg said slowly. "That's where I was born. My mother lived there for a year as a teenager. My grand-parents took her there because she was pregnant, and they wanted to save her the embarrassment of . . . what? What's wrong?"

Dalila Parker had been shaking her head. "No," she said, "that is not true."

"What isn't true?" Mirabelle asked over Meg's protest.

"She was not pregnant when she arrived on the island."

Startled, Meg just stared.

Mirabelle said, "She got pregnant there? Who was the father?"

Was it Meg's imagination, or had Dalila Parker just given a faint shudder?

"I don't know," the woman said resolutely, breaking eye contact and looking down at the floor.

Reeling from the knowledge that her mother's dropout boyfriend, Stu Kingman, wasn't her father after all, Meg felt powerless to react.

But Mirabelle did. "Yes, you do know," she told Dalila staunchly. "I know you do."

"No, *mon*. I don't know his name."

"But you know something about him."

Dalila Parker evaded the question, turning to Meg. "Your mother is blond and beautiful, isn't she?"

"Yes. How did you know?"

"Her name—what is it?"

"It's Giselle Hudson—it was Giselle McKenna before. My name is still McKenna. She never told me who my father was—or that I had a twin sister."

"So you didn't know. How did you find out?" Dalila asked.

Realizing she had slipped, Meg looked at Mirabelle for help.

"Meg found some old things of her mother's recently."

"What kind of things?"

"A sketch pad," Meg said. "And some other stuff, too. A doll and a red felt bag . . ."

"A gris-gris bag," Mirabelle supplied.

Dalila nodded. "That's what you call it in New Orleans. I know it as a conjure bag. So I was right."

"Right about what?" Meg asked.

"Right about your mother. She got involved in something that was way over her head. And she paid the price."

The ominous tone in Dalila's voice sent a shiver down Meg's spine.

"How?" Mirabelle asked. "How did she pay?"

But Dalila's expression had become closed once again. "I don't know."

"Yes you do!" Meg said, jumping up. "Please, you have to tell me everything you know. And you have to help me find my sister!"

Dalila watched her intently, then sighed. "After your mother gave her up, Candra was raised by a woman she thought was her grandmother. She wasn't aware of your existence."

"Does she know now?"

"Yes," Dalila said, "she does."

Meg was startled. "She knows about me? You're positive?"

"She knows you exist. I told her what I've told you. I can't speak for what else she may be aware of by now."

"I have to get in touch with her, Dalila," Meg said urgently. "Please. You have to tell me exactly where I can find her."

"How do you know she wants to be found?"

Meg stared, and she felt Mirabelle touch her arm lightly. "I told you, Meg," Mirabelle said. "Your sister might not be the person you imagine she is."

"She's my flesh and blood, a part of *me*," Meg said hoarsely. "I feel as though I know her already. I have to find her. Please, Dalila . . ."

The woman gazed at her for a long time, and her expression was inscrutable. Then she finally said, "I'll try to find Candra, and when I do, I'll tell her that you want to meet her. If she agrees, fine. If she doesn't . . ."

"She will," Meg said with confidence. "I'll call you tomorrow and make arrangements."

"You can't. I don't have a telephone. But you can come by on Monday afternoon."

"All right," Meg agreed. "After school."

"All right." The woman stood up.

There was so much more Meg wanted to ask her. She was certain that Dalila Parker was keeping something to herself. But she also sensed that there was no way the woman was going to reveal anything else. At least, not yet.

"Come on, Meg," Mirabelle said. "Let's go."

Reluctantly, she rose from the couch. Erzulie, who had fallen asleep curled next to Meg's feet, stirred and looked up reproachfully, then closed her eyes again.

Meg and Mirabelle followed Dalila over to the door.

"Thank you," Meg told the woman as she and Mirabelle stepped over the threshold into the hallway. "I really appreciate your help."

"No problem, *mon*." For a moment, the woman was silent. She looked hesitant, as though she wanted to say something more, and Meg fleetingly glimpsed an expression of concern—almost as if she were about to deliver a warning.

But then Dalila's face relaxed, and she said simply, "I knew you'd be back," before closing the door.

Candra had to wait until Rosamund and Tish left to go down to the Spanish grocery store and produce market before she got a chance to slip over to Dalila's.

As she hurried down Elmont, she scanned the street, half expecting to see Meg. She had been nagged, all afternoon, by a vague feeling she now recognized—one that meant her twin was close by. Of course, she knew it was unlikely that a wealthy girl from Crawford Corners would set foot in this section of Spring City.

Still, her instincts were rarely wrong, and she carefully took a last look over her shoulder before opening the door that led to the apartment above Rivera's Newsstand.

At the top of the stairs, she knocked, and the door was opened almost immediately.

When Dalila Parker saw her, she said, "Now what? Did you forget something?"

"What?"

The woman frowned and peered at her in the dim light from the bare overhead bulb. "Candra?" she said, sounding surprised. "Come in." She stepped back to let her enter the apartment.

"Did you think I was Meg?"

Dalila shut the door behind her and motioned her to the couch. "Only until I saw that your clothes are different."

"What do you mean? Was she here?"

"She just left, *mon*, not five minutes ago."

"No wonder . . ." Candra smiled. "I *knew* it. I sensed it, but I didn't—I've been sitting in my aunt's apartment, wondering why I felt like Meg was nearby. I didn't believe it. What was she doing here?"

"Looking for you."

"Looking for *me?*" Candra stared at Dalila. "Then, she knows?"

"She found out. She was going through her mother's belongings and she came across some . . . evidence."

"What was it?" Candra heard a sound behind her and turned.

She saw that Dalila's cat was watching from a doorway across the room. The sleek black animal looked as though she had stopped short, and now she stood staring with her unblinking yellow eyes.

"Here, kitty. Come here, Erzulie." Candra crouched and made kissing noises.

But instead of coming right over, purring, as she had the other day, Erzulie humped her back up, then hissed and darted backward, out of sight.

"What is wrong with that animal?" Dalila asked, raising her eyebrows. "She's never behaved that way before."

Candra shrugged and turned back toward the woman. "What evidence did Meg find?" she repeated.

Still looking distracted, Dalila said, "Just some drawings of both of you as babies, and . . . some other things. She figured out that she has a twin, and she knows that you're in the area. She wants me to set up a meeting."

"That's perfect!"

"You want to meet her?"

"Yes." Candra reached up and briefly touched the crossbones amulet that was concealed under her shirt. "In fact, Dalila, I need you to help me with something . . ."

Fourteen

"Meg, where's Carrie?" Hope McKenna asked as she opened the side door on Sunday afternoon.

"I have no idea. I waited for her—that's why I'm late. She knew we were supposed to come over for lunch today, and to finish helping you with the attic, but she's not around."

Meg didn't want to tell her grandmother that her sister hadn't come home again last night. That in fact, she hadn't seen her since yesterday morning, when she'd poked her head into Carrie's room before leaving for Mirabelle's dorm. Her sister had been sleeping so soundly she hadn't stirred when Meg had called her repeatedly.

"Well, I hope she's all right," Hope said worriedly, leading the way into the kitchen. "I promised your mother I'd look out for you girls while she's away."

"Don't worry, Gram. Knowing Carrie, she forgot all about coming over here today. She's probably at the mall."

The September sun was streaming in through the paned kitchen windows, and outside, the trees had started to turn, their leaves hinting at the dazzling New England autumn that was just around the corner. This had always been her grandfather's favorite time of year, when the hot, humid August days were gone for good and he could putter around, raking leaves and chopping wood for the fireplace.

"Well, then, Megan, you and I will just have to eat lunch without that sister of yours," her grandmother said. "Go ahead, have a seat."

Meg noticed that her grandmother had set the old wooden table in the breakfast nook with the bright Fiestaware plates Meg and Carrie used to fight over. Both of them had always wanted the pinkish-mauve one. Of course, whenever Lester was around, Carrie got it.

There was a big basket lined with blue-and-white-checked napkins in the center of the table. It was filled with fresh rolls, and beside it was a pitcher of lemonade, thin slices of lemon floating with ice cubes on the top, the way her grandfather had always liked it.

"I'm afraid we're only having sandwiches," Hope said, following her gaze. "You know I'm not much of a cook. That was your grandfather's department."

Meg smiled faintly and nodded.

Oh, Grandpa, she thought, *I wish so much that you were here.*

Not just because she missed him desperately.

But because she knew that somehow, she would have turned to him for help by now.

Although, even if he were here, what would Harry McKenna have been able to do for her? Apparently, he had known Giselle's secrets, and, like everyone else, had kept them from Meg. Ever since she had found out about Candra's existence, she had been battling the feeling that her grandfather had betrayed her.

She didn't want to be angry with him. She knew there had to be a reason why everyone had kept quiet all these years. Maybe then she would understand.

"Go ahead, sit down, Megan," Hope said again, removing a plastic-wrapped platter of cold cuts from the refrigerator and carrying it over to the table.

For a while, the two of them made small talk as they ate, with her grandmother asking Meg about school and her friends.

"And how's Zoe?" Hope asked, daintily nibbling on the corner of her sandwich.

"She's fine," Meg said, though she realized suddenly that she hadn't seen much of her friend in the past week. Zoe hadn't called, and they didn't have any classes together.

"Actually," she added, forcing herself to sound bright and chatty, "Zoe's cousin from New Orleans is here, and she's really nice. She's going to college at Wainwright. Her name is Mirabelle Moreau—isn't that a beautiful name?"

"Yes, it certainly is," Hope said, nodding. "And her initials are M.M., like yours."

"Hey, that's right. I never realized that."

"When you were a little girl, your grandfather used to call you M&M," her grandmother added, with a faraway look in her eyes.

"He did? I never knew that."

Hope nodded. "He said you were sweeter than chocolate."

"That sounds like him."

There was silence.

"Gram . . ." Meg found herself suddenly saying, "why did you go to Jamaica to live for that year?"

Her grandmother looked startled, but quickly recovered. "Your grandfather's job, Meg. I thought you knew that. Harry was a developer for S.N.E., and he was working on a resort project. Would you like some more lemonade?"

Meg glanced at her glass, which was still full. "No, thanks. You didn't go because my mother was out of control?"

"Of course not. Giselle was never . . . she was rambunctious, yes, but . . ." Hope shook her head and looked as though she wished she were anywhere else.

"Gram, you can tell me the truth," Meg said, finding that tears had sprung into her eyes. She felt desperate. "I mean, everyone in Crawford Corners seems to know the story except for me. And it's not fair."

"Megan . . ."

For a moment, she expected her grandmother to change the subject, or to tell her it was none of her business.

But Hope said wearily, "Yes, I suppose it was all over town that we went away that year to get Giselle out of here temporarily."

Meg wiped at a tear that had spilled over and trickled down her face. "And it was true?"

"Yes," her grandmother finally said with obvious reluctance. "It was."

Shocked that at last she had been given a straightforward answer, Meg pressed on. Her tears were gone; now she was only eager to get more information. "I know she used to smoke and drink and sneak around with an older boy. Right?"

Hope shook her head. "I . . . I can't remember, exactly, what she did."

"Well, my mother even told me about those things. She's always said she was no angel."

"That, she wasn't," Hope agreed with an unexpected smile.

"But she wasn't pregnant with me when you moved down there, was she?"

There was a pause.

"No, she wasn't," Hope said at last, then looked as though she wanted to take it back. As though she knew what was coming next.

"Well then, if my mother didn't get pregnant here, she got pregnant there," Meg said logically. "Which means that she must have met my father in Jamaica . . . and she must have left him there when she came back to Connecticut. Didn't she love him?"

Her grandmother shoved her chair back and stood up abruptly. "Do you want another sandwich, Megan?"

"No, thanks."

"All right, then." Hope picked up the basket of rolls, and Meg saw that her bony, crepe-skinned hands were trembling. "I'll put these things away, and we'll go up to the attic to finish sorting."

"But, Gram, you have to tell me about my father. Please, I *need* to know," Meg said. She wanted to add that she knew about her twin sister, but something held her back.

"On second thought," her grandmother said in a jittery voice, "I'm not in the mood to do all that dirty work today. I have a terrible headache, and the dust in the attic will only make it worse." She reached up and put her fingertips to her temples and closed her eyes briefly.

"But—"

"Why don't you run along home, Meg," Hope went on in a high-pitched, barely controlled voice. "I'll wrap up some sandwiches for you to take to Carrie." She fumbled with the plastic wrap on the platter of meat.

Meg stared at the older woman silently, longing to ask why no one would answer her questions; why, after all these years, no one, not even Giselle, had told her the truth.

But she sensed that she wasn't going to succeed in anything but pushing her grandmother to the breaking point. And Hope McKenna had been so emotionally fragile ever since Harry's death that Meg couldn't bring herself to pursue it.

So she just sighed, pushed her chair back, and said, "That'll be fine, Gram."

Candra was lying on her back on her bed, staring at the ceiling, when she heard the phone ring upstairs. It was the middle of Sunday afternoon, and no one was home except her and Monica.

A few minutes later, she heard footsteps approaching the top of the cellar stairs, and then Monica was calling, "Candra? Candra, are you down there?"

She got up and opened her door. "Yes," she said.

"Well, you have a phone call."

"I do?" She hurried up the steps, feeling her heart rate accelerating.

When she got to the kitchen, she found Monica Drayer having a conversation with whoever was on the phone.

"No, but just tell him that it would be nice if he called home once in a while," she was saying. "Yes . . . I know you can't make him, but give him the message, all right, Landon? . . . Good. . . . Yes, she's right here, hang on."

Monica held the phone out toward Candra. Her expression was curious and disapproving at once.

"Thank you," Candra murmured, and held the receiver up to her ear. "Hello?"

"Hi, Candra. It's me, Landon Keller."

"Hi," she said, trying not to smile. Monica was still just standing there, watching her.

"I've been thinking about you all week," he said. "All weekend, too."

"You have?"

"Yup."

"Well, uh . . ." Why wouldn't the woman just get out of here and let her have her conversation in peace? Candra cleared her throat and said self-consciously in her American accent, "Uh, what have you been doing?"

"Studying, mostly. And I went out last night."

"Where?"

He hesitated. "To a dance."

"Oh." Since it was an all boys' school, Candra realized, he must have brought a date. Jealousy shot through her, and she tightened her fingers on the receiver. "That's nice," she said curtly.

"No, it wasn't. I brought this girl I know, from home. She spent the weekend here, and by the time she left a little while ago, I was dying to call you, Candra."

"Oh," was all she said to that. She found herself hating the nameless, faceless girl who had spent the weekend with him—the girl he thought was good enough to bring to a dance in front of all his friends, while she, Candra, was obviously not.

"What have you been up to, Candra?" Landon sounded awkward.

"Not much," she said, casting a glance at Monica Drayer, who was no longer standing there obviously eavesdropping. Now she was over by the sink, watering a plant on the windowsill. Candra was well aware that she was still listening in, since the lady of the house never lifted a finger when it came to domestic tasks.

"How's school?" Landon asked.

"Fine."

"I wish I could see you right this second, Candra."

"Why?"

"Because I miss you. Do you miss me?"

"Yes." She lowered her voice and turned her back away from Monica. "When are you coming back here?" she whispered.

"Oh, I get it," Landon said. "Mrs. Drayer is still there. You can't really talk, right? She's eavesdropping?"

"Yes."

"That's a relief. For a second, I thought you were being so short with me because you were upset that I had a date this weekend."

"Of course not," Candra said, forcing herself to sound casual.

"Good, because it wasn't anything. I had asked her before I even met you, Candra."

She nearly sighed with relief.

"And anyway," Landon said, "I wish that we could get together. But Drayer isn't going to be going home for the weekend anytime soon. He's on restricted detention, but don't tell his mother."

"What happened?" Candra asked, feeling a satisfying twinge of pleasure that Craig was in trouble.

"He got drunk and started a fight. Then he cursed at the headmaster. But don't tell his parents, okay?"

"I won't."

"Well, listen, I just wanted you to know I was thinking about you," Landon said. "And I'm going to figure out a way to see you, okay?"

"Yes," she told him, smiling.

You'll be seeing me, Landon.

Sooner than you think.

Meg wandered restlessly through the house, turning on lamps. It was dark out now, and Carrie still wasn't home.

She considered calling a few of her sister's friends to see if they'd heard from her, but decided against it. Even if they knew where Carrie was, they probably wouldn't tell Meg. Those girls had covered for her on more than one occasion.

And besides, Meg wasn't particularly anxious to talk to any of them these days. Carrie's friends were freshmen at Adamson-Swift, too, which meant they had undoubtedly heard the rumors about Meg last week.

Suddenly, Meg missed her own friends. Zoe and Chasey hadn't called her all weekend, which was unusual.

Maybe you should call them, she told herself, glancing at the phone.

But she didn't really feel like talking about school. Or about her breakup with Shea.

Shea.

He was the one she missed most of all.

She pictured his familiar, good-looking face and wondered where he was, what he was doing right this minute. Was he thinking about her, wishing things were different?

Probably not. Not after the way he had accused her, had yelled at her. Not after the way he had believed the worst about her, had refused to trust her.

Still, Meg thought wistfully, hugging herself, he did have a reason for what he'd done.

Obviously, her twin had been at that party, and with another guy. Why *wouldn't* everyone assume it was Meg? Why *wouldn't* Shea be jealous? She had been acting distant from him ever since that party at Zoe's—ever since she'd become obsessed with her own past, with the strange feelings she'd experienced lately.

Why *wouldn't* Shea assume she was involved with someone else?

She reached for the phone impulsively, and punched out the familiar number before she could think twice about it.

As it rang once, then twice, she realized she had no idea what she was going to say to him. Could she tell him the truth? Would he believe her? Or would he think she was crazy?

"Hello?"

It was his mother's voice, and Meg hesitated, uncertain whether to ask for him or to hang up.

"Hello?" she repeated.

"Is Shea there?" Meg blurted.

"No, he isn't . . . Can I take a message?"

"No, thanks," she mumbled.

And as she was hanging up, she heard Shea's mother asking, "Meg, is this you?"

I shouldn't have called, she told herself, setting the phone back in its cradle. *Thank God he wasn't home.*

Now wasn't the time for her to be giving him explanations. She should wait until after she had seen Candra for herself. Then maybe she would even introduce her twin to Shea. Maybe Candra would help her explain what had happened. Then they would all have a good laugh about it, and things between Meg and Shea would be back to normal.

And she would have a sister—a *real* sister. Someone who understood her the way no one ever had before.

Tomorrow, Meg thought, smiling and hugging herself. *Tomorrow's the day my whole life will change.*

Candra slipped into the shadows among the trees that bordered the sprawling property, clutching her binoculars.

She raised them to her eyes and trained them on the big house in front of her. The windows had been dark when she'd first walked by it a few minutes ago, strolling down the street through the September dusk as though she were taking an evening walk like everyone else she passed.

Of course, she was really checking numbers on mailboxes, looking for Meadowview Terrace. She had found the address in the telephone directory. Dalila had given her the last name. She hadn't wanted to, but Candra had wheedled it out of her by swearing she just wanted to glimpse the house where her mother lived.

It was as beautiful as she had expected, a big brick colonial with porches and shutters and flowers and trees dotting the large grounds.

Meg's car was in the driveway, and now lights had gone on in the first-floor windows. Some were hidden behind draperies, but others had only sheer lace curtains over them. Candra focused on those, peering through the binoculars, waiting.

And while she waited, she plotted.

Tomorrow, she thought, smiling to herself. *Tomorrow's the day my whole life will change.*

C-A-T had been lying on the couch, snoozing peacefully. Now, she woke with a start and looked around.

"Hi, kitty," Meg said, going over and patting her.

Normally, the cat would have purred and rolled over on her back so that Meg could rub her stomach.

Now, however, she jumped off the couch and *meow*ed loudly, as though she was trying to tell Meg something.

Meg frowned.

"What is it, C-A-T? Are you hungry?"

The cat looked agitated, pacing the room a few times.

Then suddenly, she took off like a shot, and Meg heard her dashing up the front stairs.

Astonished, Meg looked after her.

And then she realized that it was back—that same nagging feeling that something was wrong.

Come on, don't go getting all scared just because the cat is acting so crazy, she told herself.

She looked around the den, with its big-screen television, leather couches, and bookshelves lined with books no one but Meg had ever bothered to read. Everything was silent, familiar, undisturbed.

But there was something . . .

There was definitely *something*.

And maybe C-A-T had felt it, too.

She glanced at the windows. She had drawn the drapes earlier, when the late afternoon sun was creating a glare on the television screen. She had been trying to concentrate on a movie, but now she didn't even remember how it had ended or when she had shut off the TV. She had been too distracted.

Now she turned on the set again and stood in front of it, clicking the channels with the remote control until she found a "Cosby Show" re-run. There—that was reassuring.

She watched for a few minutes, but the unsettling sensation was so overpowering that she couldn't sit still.

Meg stood up and went into the living room.

Everything seemed normal here, too.

Meg looked around at the framed impressionist paintings on the walls, the chintz flowered couches, the lace curtains her mother had brought back from a trip to Ireland a few years back.

Everything is fine, she told herself. *See?*

But why did she feel a growing sense of panic?

Why did she feel as though something sinister was closing in on her, as though she had to run, to escape?

Her eyes were drawn to the windows.

Someone's out there, she thought wildly, staring into the blackness. *Someone who wants to hurt me.*

It didn't make sense.

Who would want to hurt her?

She fingered the jade baby ring on its gold chain, as though it would protect her.

Fifteen

Candra strolled into homeroom ten minutes early on Monday morning and slipped into her seat.

When Mrs. Birch looked up from her desk, said "Hello, Candra," and smiled pleasantly, Candra greeted her and smiled back.

The teacher went back to correcting papers, and Candra opened her American History textbook and started studying the chapter on the Declaration of Independence.

She kept reading until Kim Williams showed up and said, "Hi, Candra, how was your weekend?"

"Great," she said, looking up. "How was yours?"

Kim looked momentarily surprised, then grinned. "It was fun. I went to my little neighbor's birthday party on Saturday night, and they had a chocolate ice cream cake shaped like a teddy bear. What'd you do?"

Candra shrugged. "Not much," she said. "Hung around."

"Hey, maybe we can go to a movie together next weekend," Kim suggested.

"That sounds like a good idea," Candra told her.

Again, Kim looked surprised. This time, she didn't bother to hide it. "You mean, you want to go?"

"Of course."

"That's great. I kind of thought you'd say no."

"Why would I do that?" Candra asked, enjoying herself.

"Because you didn't seem like you wanted to be friends with me."

"Where did you get that idea?"

Kim shrugged. "I don't know—I guess I was wrong. You want to eat lunch with us today?"

Candra hesitated only briefly before saying, "Sure."

She could put up with Kim—and Ellen and Mary Beth, and even Nedra . . .

She could put up with anything for this one last time.

The bell rang, and Kim turned around to face forward. While Mrs. Birch took attendance, Candra went back to her textbook.

They were having a test on this material in Social Studies on Wednesday. *Too bad I won't be here to take it*, Candra thought smugly. She would have been sure to pass. She knew this chapter inside and out.

Freedom, she thought contentedly.

That was what America was all about.

And in just a few more hours, Candra would be free, too.

For good.

Meg walked down the hall toward Government class, leafing through her notebook, trying to find the take-home quiz she'd stuck there on Friday. She had completely forgotten about it until she'd overheard someone mentioning it just now when she was by her locker.

If she could just find it and finish it before class started, she'd be all right. The last thing she needed now was a failing grade.

There it is! She pulled the folded white paper out and started scanning it, picking up her pace.

"Hey, watch where you're going," someone said, and Meg stopped short just before walking into a water fountain.

The quiz slipped out of her hands and floated to the floor. She bent to pick it up and saw someone else's fingers close over it.

"I got it," a familiar voice said.

She looked up. "Shea."

"Hi, Meg." He handed her the paper. "How've you been?"

"Fine," she said, trying not to look wistfully at him. Suddenly, she wanted to throw herself into his strong arms and pour out the whole story about what had happened.

"Shea, I—" she began, just as he said, "Meg, I—"

They both laughed nervously.

"My mother said she thought you called last night," Shea said. "Did you?"

For a split second, Meg considered lying, denying it.

But she couldn't. She didn't want that. She wanted to be honest. She wanted Shea back.

"Yes," she said, nodding. "It was me."

He tried to hide a pleased little smile. "Oh," was all he said.

"I wanted to tell you something," Meg went on. "I thought I owed you an explanation. But—"

"But now you don't?" he asked warily.

"No, I still want to talk to you. Shea, some stuff has been going on lately that you just wouldn't believe. But I can't tell you right now," she said. "You just have to trust me that I will, as soon as I can."

He nodded. "I trust you."

"You do?"

"Yeah. I know I didn't act like it the other day, but then I realized that I was being stupid. I mean, people have been saying the stupidest things about you, Meg. Someone asked me if you really tried to run me over with your car! And that was when I realized what an idiot I was to have listened to gossip instead of to you."

Meg let out a shaky breath and smiled at him. "Thank God, Shea. Because no matter what you heard, I haven't been cheating on you, and I wasn't at that party last week. I can explain everything."

"Let's get together after school and talk then," he suggested, putting a hand on her elbow.

"I can't. Not after school," she said, feeling a familiar flutter at his touch. "But we can get together tonight. I should be home around seven."

"Home from where?" he asked.

"I can't say. Not yet. That's part of it. I'll tell you the whole story later. Right now, I have to finish this test."

"You didn't do it over the weekend? Why not?"

She paused. "I just forgot. I've been really distracted."

"So have I," Shea told her. "It's like my whole life has been upside down ever since we broke up."

"Yeah," Meg said, nodding. "I know exactly how you feel."

After lunch, Candra went to her locker and put her books on the shelf, then stood there, debating.

After a moment, she reached up and took the American History text back down. This one, she'd take with her.

Luckily, it was a warm Indian summer day, so she hadn't worn a coat to school. Now she closed the locker door and hurried down the hall, carrying only her history book.

As she approached the main entrance, she kept an eye out for teachers, hall monitors, and the principal. All she needed was for someone to see her leaving early and demand to know why.

Her whole plan hinged on arriving at Dalila's before Meg got there.

Luckily, no one was around but a lot of students, chattering and banging locker doors as they got ready to head toward sixth period.

Calmly, Candra walked straight to the double glass doors and pushed them open.

Moments later, she was heading down the sun-dappled street without a backward glance.

Goodbye forever, public school, she thought gleefully, walking briskly along toward the bus stop in the center of Crawford Corners. *Hello, freedom.*

Meg wished Mirabelle had come with her. If she were here, she would be saying, "Don't worry, Meg—relax. Everything's going to be fine."

But Mirabelle was in a biology lab someplace at Wainwright, and Meg was here on Elmont Avenue alone, walking slowly toward Dalila Parker's apartment.

And every step of the way, she was battling a growing sense of panic.

Clenching her hands at her sides, she forced herself to approach the door to the apartment above Rivera's Newsstand.

This is what you want, she reminded herself. *Focus on meeting your sister.*

But somehow, she couldn't think beyond the horrible sense of dread that gripped her.

This was crazy. Why did she feel like a condemned prisoner approaching the execution chamber?

She took a deep breath, turned the doorknob, and stepped into the shabby vestibule. She pulled the door closed behind her and gulped when the reassuring street noise was shut out and she was alone in front of the stairway. It seemed to loom in front of her, taunting her, and she wanted to turn her back on it and run.

But she didn't. She put her foot on the first step and forced herself to start climbing.

And when she reached the top and knocked, the door was instantly flung open.

"Meg," Dalila said, smiling. "Come in."

"Is she here yet?" she asked, stepping into the bright apartment and expecting to feel better.

But she didn't. She felt more panicky than ever. She looked around the room, almost expecting someone to jump out and grab her.

"No, *mon.* She should be here soon, though."

Was it her imagination, or did Dalila look uneasy as she closed the door and locked it, then put the chain on.

Why had she done that? Meg suddenly wondered, staring.

Dalila flashed a white-toothed smile. "Would you like a cup of tea?" she asked graciously.

"No thanks," Meg said.

Stop being ridiculous, she told herself, chewing on her lower lip. *Of course she keeps her door locked. This isn't the greatest neighborhood in town.*

Still, why had she bothered with the chain? Candra would be here any minute, and then she'd have to undo everything.

"Have some tea," Dalila said, heading toward the kitchen. "It will calm your nerves."

"Nerves?" Meg asked, and her voice sounded unnaturally high-pitched. "I'm not nervous."

"You're not? I would be, if I were about to meet my sister for the first time."

"Oh, well . . . maybe I am a *little* bit nervous." Meg took a deep breath and let it out slowly. She couldn't help looking around the room, as though she expected to find something lurking. Why did she feel so acutely threatened?

"I'm going to pour you a cup," Dalila said from the kitchen. "The water is already boiled, and I'm having some, too."

"All right," Meg agreed, noticing that the door to the next room was shut today. The other day, it had been open.

She stared at it uneasily. She could swear she had just heard a faint sound coming from behind it. It must be the cat.

"Where's Erzulie?" she called to Dalila.

"I let her out a little while ago."

"Oh." Meg shook her head and looked away from the door. It must have been her imagination again.

A moment later, Dalila appeared in the doorway with two steaming mugs. "Here," she said, handing Meg the one in her right hand. "Why don't you sit down and relax."

"I'll try," Meg said, going over to the couch and clasping her icy hands around the mug in her lap. The heat felt good.

Dalila sat across from her.

Again, Meg thought she noticed a flicker of anxiety on the woman's face; but then it disappeared, and Dalila smiled and sipped her tea. "Mmm," she said, swallowing. "Is yours too sweet? I put sugar in."

"Oh—I hadn't tasted it yet," Meg said, and lifted the mug to her lips.

The hot beverage was pungent and tasted bitter-sweet. "What kind of tea is this?" Meg asked, swallowing.

"Herbal."

"Oh." Meg didn't really like it, but sipped again to be polite.

"Did you tell anyone you were coming over here today, to meet your sister?" Dalila asked.

"No. Mirabelle knows, of course, but—I didn't want to tell anyone else."

The woman nodded.

Was it Meg's imagination, or did she look relieved?

Dalila took another sip from her mug, and Meg did, too.

"You know, you were right," she told the woman. "This tea is really calming me down."

"I knew it was just what you needed."

"Was Candra excited about meeting me?" Meg asked around a yawn.

"Yeah, *mon*. She was excited." Dalila seemed to be watching her intently.

"Well, I wish she'd hurry up and get here." Meg checked her watch, and found that she had to squint to see the hands clearly. Everything seemed a little fuzzy . . .

"Are you all right?" Dalila asked, standing up.

"I . . . I was just . . ." Meg struggled to focus as the woman came toward her.

For one moment, she knew utter fear as she realized that something was terribly wrong . . .

There had been something in the tea . . .

Her instincts had been right all along . . .

Then a wall of black silence rushed at her and carried her away.

Candra held her ear against the door, listening. After a few moments, she heard Dalila say, "All right, come out."

She pushed the door open and hurried out into the living room.

She halted a few feet from the couch and looked down at the figure that was slumped there.

Meg's eyes were closed, and her body was limp, half sitting, half lying against the cushions.

"I caught the mug right before she let go of it and spilled this hot tea all over herself," Dalila said in a low voice. "She went out just like that."

"Good," Candra said, still standing there, looking at her twin sister. She hadn't expected to feel this sudden twinge of remorse. She found herself wanting to reach out and move the strands of hair that had fallen across Meg's face when she'd fainted.

Why do you feel sorry for her? a voice in her head taunted. *She has everything. You have nothing. Feel sorry for yourself.*

Candra snapped into action and moved forward. "I'll take her arms," she told Dalila, "and you take her feet."

Suddenly, the woman looked reluctant. "I don't know, *mon*," she said, shaking her head.

"You promised," Candra said sharply, narrowing her eyes at Dalila. "Grab her feet."

With a sigh, the woman set down the mug and put her hands around Meg's ankles. Candra went around to Meg's head and hesitated for only the briefest moment before touching her.

As soon as her fingers made contact with Meg's warm flesh, she felt another stab of regret. Quickly, she forced it away. "Lift," she commanded Dalila, and together, the two of them carried Meg into the bedroom.

There, they lay her across the top of Dalila's wide bureau, which had been draped in a black cloth. Meg didn't stir as Candra arranged her arms folded across her stomach so they wouldn't dangle over the edge.

"All right," she said, looking at Dalila. "Go ahead."

"Candra, I don't—"

"It's too late to back out now. Do it."

"But—"

"Do it!" she commanded harshly.

Dalila just looked at her, her lips set in a grim line.

Uh-oh . . . what if she changes her mind?

"I'm sorry for snapping at you," Candra made herself say. "I'm just anxious, Dalila. You said you understood how it is for me. You said you'd help me. You know how badly I want to see my mother."

The woman shrugged. "I know, but—"

"It's only for a week, just like we said," Candra reminded her. "Please cast the spell, Dalila."

"All right," the woman said grudgingly at last. She reached for a match and lit the gray candles and the incense that were placed at the back of the altar.

She raised her arms straight over her head and chanted,

> *You're helpless now*
> *Your hands are tied*
> *And by this spell*
> *you will abide.*
> *You cannot move*

You will not rise
Until I open
up your eyes.

Then Dalila lowered her arms and held her hands out to Candra, who placed one vial in each. The first was filled with a dark powder, the other with murky oil.

Dalila sprinkled the powder over Meg, then the oil, then lowered her head and closed her eyes.

Candra knew she was concentrating, and forced her own thoughts to focus on harnessing the power needed to render Meg completely helpless.

At last, Dalila looked up, met Candra's gaze, and nodded. "It's done."

"Thank you!" Candra said, and reached out to squeeze the woman's arm.

Dalila actually flinched at her touch, as though she had been burned. Candra narrowed her eyes at her. "You're on my side, Dalila. Don't forget that."

"It's only for a week. Don't *you* forget that."

"Don't worry, Dalila," Candra said, smiling sweetly.

The woman didn't reply, just turned around and left the room.

Candra stared after her for a long moment.

Only one week . . .

Sure, Dalila. Whatever you say, she thought, grinning to herself.

Then she reached down to carefully unzip Meg's plaid school uniform.

PART TWO

PART TWO

Sixteen

It wasn't easy to get used to driving on the right-hand side of the road, but Candra managed to make it back to Crawford Corners in one piece. After a day or so of practicing, she should be able to make it to the Lawson School in New Haven with no problem.

She drove the black Honda slowly along Broad Street, careful to stay within the speed limit. The last thing she needed was to be stopped by a police officer. Not that he would be able to tell.

No one would be able to tell.

She turned onto Long Neck Road and headed out of town, anticipation building as she drew closer.

Finally, she reached the intersection and turned onto Meadowview Terrace.

Moments later, she was turning into the driveway beside the mailbox marked 41.

Forty-one Meadowview Terrace—the address even *sounded* affluent.

She stopped the car, put it into Park, and turned off the ignition. Quickly, she opened the door, climbed out, and looked up at the big brick colonial house.

Then, with a tiny, satisfied smile playing at her lips, she smoothed the skirt of the plaid uniform and walked up the front steps.

"Home at last," Candra murmured contentedly, opening the door and stepping over the threshold.

She decided, moments after walking through the front door for the first time, that her birth mother had expensive taste.

Stopping just inside the entrance hall, she looked around in awe. The honey-hued wooden floors were polished and gleaming. The ceiling rose two stories above her head, its centerpiece a delicate crystal chandelier. On the walls were framed watercolors—paintings, not prints—and there was a vase of fresh pink roses on a carved table beside the door. Straight ahead was a graceful stairway that led to a second-floor balcony overlooking the hall.

Candra started to move forward, then stopped short and gasped when she caught movement out of the corner of her eye.

She'd been certain no one was home—

She sighed in relief. She'd glimpsed her own reflection in an enormous mirror on the opposite wall.

"Hello . . . *Meg*," Candra whispered to herself, a faint smile curving her lips as she stepped closer and examined her image.

Her long, straight black hair was hanging loose and parted in the middle, as always. Her dark complexion, almond-shaped ebony eyes, and angular features looked the same as ever.

But the rest of her was different.

She was wearing the navy and green plaid school uniform she'd stripped from her identical twin sister a half hour before. Meg's hunter green and tan leather Dooney and Bourke purse hung over her shoulder, and Meg's silver Tiffany key ring was still clutched in Candra's fingers.

And, she thought giddily, right this moment, Meg was lying unconscious on the makeshift voodoo altar in Dalila Parker's apartment on seedy Elmont Avenue. Meg's lanky body was now dressed in Candra's shabby jeans and the New York Yankee tee shirt that Candra's grandmother had bought for a dime at the secondhand store. Meg's long black hair was fanned out beneath her head, her dark eyes were closed, and her full lips were parted slightly.

She looked like she was sleeping—but of course, she wasn't.

She would remain frozen in that position until Candra decided it was time to let her wake up.

If Candra decided to let her wake up.

Still smiling, Candra moved to the doorway to her right and peeked inside. The living room, obviously. Lots of floral chintz furniture, more paintings, and ivory lace curtains framing the windows and the French doors that led out onto the porch.

And photographs, Candra noticed, glancing at the mantel.

She walked slowly toward them.

Photographs of Meg—as a solemn-eyed toddler, as a grinning schoolgirl with squared-off bangs and missing teeth, and as the pretty teenager she was now.

And Candra realized that in her identical sister's face, she was seeing what she herself must have looked like, growing up. Fascination mingled with renewed bitterness as she studied the images.

Back in Jamaica, there had been no money to pay a photographer to capture Candra's different stages through the years. And even if Rosamund had been able to get her hands on a camera, and even if she'd been inclined to aim it at Candra, there had been no beautiful clothes for Candra to pose in, no carved mahogany mantel where the photos could be displayed.

There had been nothing.

Candra had grown up with nothing.

Meg had grown up with everything.

Candra clenched her fists and forced herself to keep examining the pictures.

In some of them, Meg was posed with a younger blond girl who looked vaguely familiar. Candra's eyes narrowed. A sister? Had Meg's mother had a child with Lester Hudson, the man she had married when Meg was still a toddler?

Candra stared at an obviously recent picture of Meg and the blonde as she tried to remember where she had seen the girl before . . .

Yes, that was it. Last Friday night, on the street in Crawford Corners. Candra had been walking by a couple who was leaning against a tree, making out, and the girl had suddenly broken off and accused Candra of following her.

Now it made sense.

The girl had been Meg's younger sister, though they looked nothing alike. Meg was tall and olive-skinned and exotic-looking with serious eyes; her sister was fair and petite and wore a pouty smile, as though she were flirting with the photographer.

Candra looked from one face to the other, hating both of them—hating, even more, the woman who had given birth to them.

Because Giselle McKenna Hudson had given birth to Candra, too.

Eighteen years ago—almost exactly, since their birthday was in a few days—in Jamaica, when Giselle was just a teenager herself, she had had two babies.

Soon afterward, she had abandoned only one.

Meg had been raised never knowing she had an identical twin sister, just as Candra had. But Meg had grown up here, with everything a girl could want.

Candra had grown up in Jamaica, raised by a cold woman who'd lied to her, living in the servants' quarters on an estate. Even now that Candra and Rosamund had come to the States with the Drayers, Candra had only a tiny basement bedroom beneath their comfortable, elegant white house here in Crawford Corners.

But not anymore, Candra reminded herself.

Meg had already had her turn.

Now it was time for Candra to move into this beautiful home, to drive Meg's gleaming black Honda and attend Meg's exclusive private school.

And it was time for Candra to get to know their mother.

Giselle McKenna Hudson.

Candra turned toward the largest photograph in the center of the mantel, but something else caught her eye on the way.

She paused to look at the framed snapshot of a bearded middle-aged man. He must be Meg's stepfather, Lester Hudson. There was something about him . . . something that made Candra narrow her gaze at the picture and ponder those humorless eyes of his. She was positive that she didn't like him—but it was more than that. It was a feeling. . . .

She waited for more to come to her, but nothing did. Shrugging, she decided to forget Lester.

For now.

Finally, for the first time, she looked at the picture she had avoided since she'd walked into the room. The one of a beautiful green-eyed blonde.

Her mother.

Candra's breath caught in her throat when she looked directly into that clear, sunny gaze.

It was as if Giselle were looking right at her.

Laughing at her.

Abruptly, Candra grabbed the picture and raised it above her head, holding it poised, ready to let go and watch it smash violently on the brick hearth.

Then, with trembling hands, she lowered it, looked through tear-filled eyes into her mother's carefree face, and whispered raggedly, "How *could* you have done it? How could you have left me there and never looked back?"

All through biology lab, Mirabelle Moreau had been feeling uneasy. Something was wrong. She *knew* it, and she knew it had to do with Meg McKenna.

Right now, Meg was supposed to be at Dalila's apartment in Spring City, meeting her identical twin sister, Candra, for the very first time. She had been excited about it, and Mirabelle hadn't wanted to dampen her enthusiasm by warning her again that Candra might not be the type of person Meg was expecting.

She had tried to tell her, but Meg didn't want to hear it.

And she didn't want to hear, either, that Mirabelle had sensed something threatening hovering over Meg from the moment she had been introduced to her.

Mirabelle had asked her cousin Zoe about Meg.

"Meg? She's been one of my best friends," Zoe had said. "She's really cool—everyone likes her."

That had been a few weeks ago. Just the other day, Zoe had confided in Mirabelle that she was getting fed up with Meg, who was becoming, according to Zoe, "Really spacey and out of it. She's no fun anymore, and she just dumped her boyfriend for no reason."

Zoe had gone on to say that Meg had cheated on Shea and then denied it, even though a lot of the kids who went to Adamson-Swift high school with them had seen her at a party with another guy.

Mirabelle, of course, suspected that it hadn't been Meg at all. It had obviously been Candra, who seemed to have been drifting around Crawford Corners being mistaken for Meg.

Mirabelle had other suspicions, too. But she had kept those to herself, had tried to ignore the growing feeling that Meg was in some kind of danger. It had been nagging her for a while now, and today, her anxiety was stronger than ever.

She had to call and make sure Meg was all right.

As she hurried across the campus quad toward her dorm, Billington Hall, she tugged her long, light brown hair from beneath the straps of her book bag and tucked the sides behind her ears again.

Hopefully, Char wouldn't already be on the phone. Her roommate spent hours talking to her family back in Wyoming.

"Aren't you homesick?" she was always asking Mirabelle.

"Sure I am," she would say. After all, her parents and brother were thousands of miles away in New Orleans, and this was the first time she had ever been away from home. Char would expect her to miss them.

She couldn't tell her roommate the truth—that sometimes in the wee hours of the morning, after Char was breathing rhythmically, Mirabelle would leave Wainwright College.

That she would wing along the astral plane to the French Quarter, where the nightlife was in full swing. On a familiar, relatively quiet side street, she would drift into the shadowy house where she had grown up, and she would check in on her slumbering family, who, of course, were unaware of her nocturnal visits.

And there was no need to tell Char, either.

If her roommate ever woke up while Mirabelle was gone, she would never know. After all, Mirabelle's physical body would still be lying in the twin bed across from Char's, looking for all the world like she was simply in a deep sleep.

The phone rang, shattering the silent house, and Candra froze.

She had been going through the desk drawer in the upstairs rose-patterned wallpapered bedroom she'd discovered was Meg's.

Now she stared at the telephone on top of the desk, wondering frantically what to do.

It rang again.

Pick it up! she ordered herself. *You might as well—after all, you're Meg now.*

Chewing her bottom lip nervously, she reached for the receiver just as it started a third ring.

"Hello?"

"Meg? Is that you?"

Uh-oh.

"Yes," she said simply, and waited.

"What a relief," the female voice said in what Candra recognized as a heavy southern accent. "I was so worried about you."

"I'm fine," Candra said in the flat Connecticut Yankee dialect she'd gotten down pat over the last few weeks.

Her thoughts raced. Who was this person? Why had she been worried about Meg? What did she know?

She fought back the panicky feeling that rose in her stomach.

Relax. No one is going to figure anything out.

"Well? How did it go? Did you meet her?" the voice drawled.

Okay, so whoever this is knows Meg was going to meet me. That doesn't mean anything. Calm down.

Dalila Parker had told Candra that Meg had visited her apartment with a friend over the weekend. This had to be the friend.

Candra wondered, with a sinking feeling, who else knew that Meg had discovered a twin sister she had been planning to meet this afternoon.

"Yes, I met her," she said carefully.

"And?"

"Uh, I can't talk right now," she said impulsively.

"Why n—oh, I get it. Carrie's around, huh?"

"Yeah," Candra agreed.

Who was Carrie?

"All right, why don't we get together later?"

"I can't," Candra said. "Not tonight."

"Why not? I'm dying to know what happened, Meg."

"I know, but . . . I promised my mother I'd do some things for her."

There was a moment of silence. Then the girl said, "I thought your mother and Lester were in Fiji until next week."

It took a moment for the impact of her words to hit Candra.

They were in Fiji? But that meant she wouldn't be able to meet her mother. And, more urgently, it meant she'd backed herself into a corner with this nosy person on the phone.

Candra squeezed her eyes shut tightly and thought wildly.

"Of course they are," she said, fighting to sound casual. "But she left me a list of errands and stuff like that."

"Okay," the voice said dubiously. "Why don't you give me a call tomorrow, then?"

"I will."

"Good. See you, Meg."

"See you," she said, and hung up feeling half-worried that the girl was suspicious, half-relieved that she had called her Meg.

This wasn't going to be nearly as easy as she'd expected, this pretending to be her twin sister.

But there was no turning back now.

Mirabelle sat with her hand still on the phone in its cradle, a bemused expression filling her light green eyes.

When she'd first heard Meg's voice, she'd been so relieved to find her safe at home that she hadn't paid much attention to the nagging doubt that was still in the back of her mind.

But then she'd started to notice that Meg sounded edgy. This wasn't the first time she had reacted evasively to Mirabelle's questions. Mirabelle knew Meg well enough now to realize that she was a private person who didn't take kindly to prying questions.

Still, today Meg's voice had seemed different somehow. Almost . . . worried.

Mirabelle thought again about the aura of danger she'd sensed around Meg that first day. Was Meg aware of it now, too? Had something happened during the meeting with her twin—something that had left her frightened? Was that why she didn't want to talk about it?

And that bit about running errands for her mother was an excuse—Mirabelle was sure of it.

What was going on with her?

There *was* a way to find out. . . .

It wouldn't be hard for Mirabelle to astral project herself into Meg's house to spy on her.

She would feel guilty about it, of course. Cecile had taught her to be careful not to abuse her abilities—not to pry where she didn't belong.

But it was for Meg's own good, she reminded herself firmly.

Even so, Mirabelle couldn't do it right now. Char would be back from the dining hall any second now, and she would panic if she found Mirabelle in bed, asleep at six-thirty in the evening—so sound asleep she couldn't be awakened.

No, it would have to wait.

Candra paced Meg's bedroom, fully aware that she had just had a close call.

The girl on the telephone hadn't bought her flimsy excuse about running errands. And if one person was suspicious, soon others would be, too.

Candra would have to find out who the girl was, and she'd have to get her out of the way before she ruined the plan.

It shouldn't be hard to do. But it would have to wait. There were other things on Candra's agenda. More important things.

She reached for the phone again and dialed the number of the Lawson School in New Haven.

When it was answered, she asked for Landon Keller.

"Just a moment, please," said the prim voice on the other end of the line.

While she was on hold, Candra mentally went over the story she was going to tell Landon. Would he buy it? Would he cooperate?

Something told her he would.

Candra had seen to it. She had filled the red felt bag with charms and cast a spell to draw Landon to her. Sooner or later, he would be hers.

And he would never suspect it wasn't of his own free will.

"Hello?" his deep voice now said in her ear.

"Landon?"

"Yes . . ."

"It's me. Candra."

"Candra! How's it going?"

"Shhh . . . Craig Drayer isn't around there, is he?"

"No. He's in restricted detention for starting that fight, remember? Why?"

"Listen, Landon, you have to trust me. You can't let Craig, or any-one else, know you've talked to me."

"Why not? What's wrong?"

She took a deep breath. "I'm going to tell you a secret, Landon, and you have to swear you'll keep it."

"What is it?"

"Promise me you won't tell *anyone*."

There was a pause. "Are you in some kind of trouble?"

"Kind of. Do you promise?"

"Yeah, I promise."

"It's my grandmother . . ."

"What about her? Did something happen to her?"

"No. But she lied to me, Landon. She's not my grandmother after all. I'm not who I thought I was." At least that much was true. Now for the rest. She forced distress into her voice, as though she were an emo-tional wreck. "I have no idea *who* I am, Landon. She adopted me ille-gally. And when my grandmother found out that I'd discovered the truth, she was furious with me. She threatened me."

"What do you mean, she threatened you?"

"I can't tell you much about this, Landon. Not right now. But you have to trust me, and you can't tell *anyone* that you've heard from me. Especially not Craig. He'll probably be finding out any minute now that I left."

"Left? You mean you ran away?"

"Yes."

"Candra . . ." Landon trailed off. "I don't know what to say. Where are you now?"

"I can't tell you. But I need to see you, Landon."

"Come on, Candra, where are you? I'll come and—"

"No, I'll come to you," Candra interrupted. "In a day or two. I really need a friend, Landon," she finished in a desolate tone.

"I'm here for you, Candra."

"I knew you would be."

"Look," he said huskily, after a moment, "why don't you just go back home and talk to your grandmother? She won't—"

"No! You don't understand, Landon. You don't know what she'll do to me. You don't know how she punishes me every time I do the slight-est thing wrong."

"Yeah, but this is—"

"Landon, you promised. Please—I'm so scared. You can't say any-thing to *anyone*. You're the only person I can trust." She closed her eyes and silently repeated the spell she had cast on him, willing him to do as she asked.

"Okay, Candra," he said quietly after a long moment. "I won't tell anyone you called."

"Good. I have to go now," she said hurriedly. "I'll call you again soon."

"Make sure you do," Landon told her. "And Candra?"

"Yes?"

He hesitated. "I'm glad you called. I miss you."

"I miss you too," she said softly, as her heart fluttered joyously.

She hung up the phone and, wearing a satisfied smile, murmured, "Soon you'll be all mine, Landon Keller. Forever."

Mirabelle hurried across the dark, chilly campus, headed to the library to study.

Anything was better than being in the room while Char wept into the phone and told her mother repeatedly how much she missed her, and that she didn't know why she'd decided to come east to college.

She often said the same thing to Mirabelle, who reminded Char that Wainwright had given her a full scholarship—that was why she was here. Char was a talented artist, and Wainwright had one of the best art departments in the country. Besides, the private New England school was the next best thing to Ivy League.

And Char's parents, who were ranchers, could barely have afforded to send her to community college back in Wyoming. They must have been grateful for the scholarship, and Mirabelle thought Char should be, too, instead of acting like she'd been sentenced to four years in a hard labor camp in some third world country.

Mirabelle was glad to be at Wainwright, even though her first choice had been Tulane University, right in New Orleans. Her high school boyfriend, Alex, was going there, and they had planned to be together. But last spring, right before graduation, he had dumped her abruptly and cruelly.

You'd think Mirabelle, for all her clairvoyant powers, would have seen it coming. But she had been blissfully unaware, and the breakup had hit her like a cement block dropped from a skyscraper.

Later, she'd asked Cecile, who had taught her how to use her "powers," why she hadn't somehow sensed that Alex was going to leave her.

The maid had given her a small, wistful smile and said, "Despite your special gift, you're only human, Mirabelle. And when it comes to *les affaires de couer*, your human heart can put blinders on your supernatural intuition."

Great, Mirabelle had thought. *Just great. That's when I need my intuition more than any other time.*

After the breakup, Mirabelle had wanted nothing more than to get as far away from Alex and her memories of their relationship as possible. She had already applied to Wainwright, because her mother insisted. Jeanette Woodward Moreau had grown up in Connecticut, and Wainwright was her alma mater.

Besides, as Jeanette was always reminding Mirabelle, her sister—Mirabelle's aunt, Tara Cunningham—lived only a few miles from the campus. Wouldn't it be nice to get to know Cousin Zoe better? And of course, if Mirabelle couldn't get home for holidays, Aunt Tara and Uncle Greg would be glad to have her.

So here she was, in Spring City, Connecticut, a few thousand miles from home.

Too far away to drive there for visits very often. And Mirabelle never flew anywhere since, before she was in tune with her powers, Cecile had warned her never to get on a plane.

"I see danger for you if you fly, Mirabelle," the woman had said darkly.

At the time, Mirabelle had tried to convince herself that it was a bunch of hogwash. Cecile was always claiming to be a witch. But later, Mirabelle had discovered that it was true about Cecile—and that wasn't all. Mirabelle's own ancestor, her father's creole great-grandmother Nanette Moreau, had been a voodoo priestess back in the nineteenth century.

Cecile had taught Mirabelle to harness the powers she had inherited from Nanette, and to listen to her own premonitions. And eventually, she had realized Cecile's warning about flying was legitimate, because she gradually began to see ominous shadows surrounding herself whenever she imagined getting on a plane.

And she never had flown since. It hadn't been easy making convincing excuses about why she couldn't join her parents whenever they embarked on a vacation to Europe or Hawaii. When the time had come for her to come to the northeast for college, she'd arranged to catch a ride with the friend of a friend of a friend, Tony, who had turned out to be a real jerk.

But anything was better than getting on a plane.

Finally—she had arrived at the library, which was a major hike across the quad from the dorm. The facility was housed in a modern white concrete building that wasn't in harmony with the rest of the campus, which was mostly red brick and ivy-covered.

Mirabelle made her way through the book stacks to a carrel in the corner and set her book bag on the floor. She sat down, leaving her jacket on. She was wearing a sweater and a turtleneck, too, but she was still shivering from the crisp evening air. How was she going to survive winter in the northeast if she was already freezing in September?

"Hey, Mirabelle," a low voice said behind her as she was taking a pen and notebook out of her bag.

She looked up to see Ben Schacter standing there, a black nylon book bag slung over his shoulder. His longish dark hair brushed the collar of his hunter green corduroy barn jacket, and he had one thumb hooked in the front pocket of his snug, faded jeans.

"Hey, Ben," she said lightly. She liked the way he said her name. In his Long Island accent, it sounded like *Mehr-a-belle*.

"What's up?" he asked, swinging his book bag down and resting it on the floor against his leg.

"Not much. How's it going?"

He shrugged. "I just finished studying for the Logic test we're having tomorrow." Ben sat behind her in Intro to Logic.

"I was about to start."

"Good luck. I studied for hours and I don't feel like I know anything. I hate that class." He shook his head, then added, "Hey, Mirabelle, what's with your phone?"

"What do you mean?"

"I tried to call you a few times on Saturday and yesterday."

Caught off guard, she said, "Uh, you did?"

Why would Ben Schacter be calling her?

"Yeah. But the line was busy every time."

Mirabelle rolled her eyes. "That figures. My roommate's always crying on the phone with her family."

"Crying?"

"She's really homesick."

"Oh, geez. She should have my family. She'd be thrilled to be away, just like I am." He shook his head. "Well, listen, I wanted to ask what you're doing tomorrow night."

"Nothing . . . why?" she asked, casually tapping the pen she was holding against the edge of the desk, as though she didn't have a care in the world.

"Let's go out."

She hesitated. She liked Ben. She was attracted to him, too. His dark good looks and easygoing, flirtatious manner reminded her of Alex.

Which was why she should stay away.

"Actually, Ben, I can't," she said carefully. "I have a paper due at the end of the week, and I need to use tomorrow night to work on it."

He looked surprised, then nodded. "No big deal. I'll catch you another time." If he was bothered by her response, he wasn't showing it.

"Sure," Mirabelle said, telling herself she'd done the right thing, even as she was wishing she could take it back and tell him she'd go out with him after all.

But if she couldn't rely on her powers to guide her when it came to guys, she would just have to stay away from them. No way was she going to risk having her heart trampled again.

"I've got to get going," Ben said, buttoning his jacket. "I'm working in the campus center tonight, moving chairs to get ready for tomorrow's AIDs symposium."

Mirabelle nodded. She knew he was here on scholarship, and that he participated in the school's work-study program to make extra money.

He seemed so different from Alex, whose father was a wealthy import-export dealer. Alex had never worked a day in his life.

But that doesn't mean anything, Mirabelle reminded herself. *That doesn't mean Ben isn't capable of being a jerk when it comes to stuff like girls and dating.*

"See you tomorrow in class," he said, waving and slinging his book bag over his shoulder.

She waved back, then turned toward the carrel as he walked away. After a moment, she snuck a peek, and saw that he was glancing back at her, too. She felt her face growing hot as she quickly looked away.

Boy, did you blow it, she told herself. *You want to go out with him. You know you do.*

She'd had only one date since coming to college—last Friday night, she'd gone to dinner and a party with Bill, a tall blond fraternity guy whose last name now slipped her mind. It had been fun, but he wasn't her type. Which was probably why she'd said yes. No chance of falling for Bill.

Ben, on the other hand, was definitely her type.

And, thanks to her skittish heart, she'd just turned him down.

She was so rattled by what had just happened that for a while, she forgot everything else—even forgot to be concerned about Meg.

* * *

Candra was sitting in the living room, looking over the class schedule that was taped to the inside cover of a notebook she'd found in Meg's book bag, when the doorbell rang.

Startled, she wondered who it could be. Not that it mattered. She wasn't going to answer it. Let whoever it was decide there was no one home.

The only problem was, it was dark out now, and when she'd come back downstairs, she'd left the entrance hall light on, and she'd turned on several lamps here in the living room, too.

Apparently, whoever was at the door realized there was someone around, because they rang the doorbell again, then knocked.

Candra willed the person to go away. She was exhausted from everything she had been through today, and she wasn't in the mood to put on her Meg act just yet.

But then she heard the front door opening, and a masculine voice called, "Meg?"

And she remembered that she hadn't locked the door behind her when she'd come in earlier.

There was nothing to do but toss the notebook aside, hurriedly stand up, and call, in her practiced American accent, "In here."

A moment later, someone appeared in the archway between the hall and the living room.

The first thing that struck Candra was that he was really good-looking—almost as good-looking as Landon, though in a different way. This guy had dark hair, too; but his was cut conservatively short, and there was a slight cowlick over his forehead. He had clear eyes that were the color of the Caribbean sea, a strong jawline, and a nose that was slightly too large for his face—just large enough to make his otherwise perfect features seem human.

His shoulders, beneath the rich brown leather jacket he had on, appeared to be broad. He was wearing perfectly pressed khaki pants, and the expensive-looking burgundy loafers Candra had seen on Landon and on other kids around Crawford Corners, the ones who went to Adamson-Swift, the private school. Like them, everything about this boy spelled money.

"Meg, why didn't you come to the door?" he asked, frowning—not in anger, Candra realized, but in concern. She sensed that he was nervous about being here. Why?

"I didn't hear you at first," she said, careful to keep her voice steady and casual.

"I rang the bell twice, and I knocked, too."

She shrugged. "I was concentrating on something," she said, and gestured behind her at the notebook she'd tossed aside.

"Studying?"

"Yeah." She said it with a flat *a*, the way Americans did, and had to stop herself from tacking on the *mon* that Jamaicans used constantly.

No, Meg would never say *yeah, mon*.

Don't slip up, Candra commanded herself. *Think before you speak.*

The guy took a few steps closer to her. He looked as though he wanted to touch her, but was afraid to. Who was he? What was his relationship to Meg?

He seemed to be peering into her face. "Did you go to one of those tanning places or something?"

"No." She fought back a flood of panic, made her voice casual as she asked, "Why?"

"I don't know, your face just looks a little different. Like you've been out in the sun or something."

"Oh, that . . . I'm wearing this different makeup. I uh, accidentally bought a darker shade than I usually wear."

"I thought you didn't like makeup."

"I don't, normally, but . . ." She trailed off and shrugged, wishing he would just drop it.

Suddenly, behind him, a gray cat appeared in the doorway. Startled by the movement, Candra gave a little gasp.

"Oh," said the boy, "she ran up onto the steps when I got here. I let her in."

"Thanks."

Candra and the cat eyed each other. She wondered what its name was. Crouching, she made coaxing noises and held out her hand.

The cat's unblinking yellow eyes remained locked on hers, almost as if it knew. . . .

"Why's she acting so weird?" the boy asked.

"What do you mean?"

"How come she's not jumping all over you and purring like she always does?"

Candra shrugged and stood up. "I guess she's mad at me because I forgot to feed her this afternoon," she improvised, unnerved by the way the cat was still watching her.

"So where were you?" he asked, after hesitating.

"What do you mean?"

"This afternoon. Remember? This morning you said you had to go someplace, and that you'd tell me all about it tonight. You also said you'd explain what's been going on with you lately."

"I know I said that, but . . ." What could she say? What did he know?

"Meg, you do want to get back together, don't you?"

Just as she'd suspected—he was Meg's boyfriend.

And he wasn't bad, she thought, sizing him up. But he didn't have Landon's . . . what was it? Sex appeal?

There was something a little too wholesome about this guy, for Candra's taste. She found herself almost amused, suddenly, by the perfect crease in his pants and the way his leather jacket looked brand new, though it probably wasn't. He lacked Landon's casual, devil-may-care appeal.

"You haven't changed your mind about us, have you?" he was asking.

"Of course I haven't changed my mind," Candra said quickly, wondering why they had broken up in the first place.

"Then why won't you—"

She acted on impulse, covering the few steps that separated them and throwing herself against him, capturing his lips in hers.

He seemed startled but responded instantly, pulling her close and returning the kiss hungrily. Surprised, Candra opened her mouth against his, and her tongue collided with his. He moaned, and so did she, aroused despite the knowledge that this was wrong, that he thought she was someone else . . .

She moved her hands under his jacket, running her fingertips over his muscular arms and chest, then slipping them beneath the untucked long-sleeved polo shirt he was wearing. He gasped when her fingers came in contact with his warm skin, and his whole body seemed to stiffen the moment she reached down and swiftly unfastened the button of his khakis.

"Meg! What are you doing?" he asked hoarsely, wrenching his lips from hers and looking down at her. His aqua eyes were wide and questioning.

She froze with her fingers grasping the zipper tab, about to tug it downward. "What do you mean?"

"I mean, what the heck are you doing?" He pulled back, and her fingers fell away, her arm dropping helplessly to her side.

She watched as he quickly buttoned his fly again and pulled his shirt back down.

What was going on here? Why did he seem so surprised? He *was* Meg's boyfriend, wasn't he?

Why was he looking at her with a mixture of surprise—and yes, suspicion?

She fought the urge to let a smile slip across her lips. She certainly had him rattled.

"What happened, Meg?" he asked after a moment. "Forget who you were with? It's me, Shea—remember? Not the prep you *claim* you didn't cheat on me with that night out at Moseby. Obviously, *he* likes it when you try to undress him."

Her amusement faded. She just stared at him, unable to speak. Her thoughts were spinning. He was referring to the night *she* had been out at Moseby, the waterfront park on the edge of town—not Meg. She had been there with Craig, and Landon, and Landon's cousin Jack, at a party given by some of the seniors at Adamson-Swift.

The pieces fell easily into place in Candra's mind. She had been mistaken for Meg at the party. This—what was his name? Shea?—had heard about it, and assumed Meg had been two-timing him.

Despite herself, Candra felt a prickle of satisfaction, knowing she had unwittingly gotten Meg into trouble with her boyfriend. But she couldn't stand here and gloat—she had to say something.

"I'm sorry about that night," she said simply, avoiding Shea's piercing gaze.

His jaw dropped. "What's that supposed to mean?"

"It doesn't mean anything, except what I said. That I'm sorry."

"Then you're admitting it. You really did cheat on me."

She paused for only the slightest moment before nodding.

"Why did you swear you didn't, just this afternoon at school?" he asked, shaking his head. His aqua eyes pinned her, and she didn't let herself flinch at the pain reflected in them. "Why did you lie about being at that party? You were there, weren't you? I was right all along, and so was everyone else. And I was feeling so guilty for not trusting you, Meg. You *made* me feel guilty."

She shrugged.

He studied her for a long time, saying nothing, just pinning her under that hurt, puzzled gaze. It was as though he wanted her to take it back, to say that she hadn't betrayed him. And when she didn't, his expression darkened to anger.

"That's it, then," he said, abruptly stepping away from her, toward the hall. He almost tripped over the cat, who gave an angry *mew* and darted away. "I'm out of here."

Candra felt the merest flicker of guilt before she said, "Fine with me. And don't come back."

Shea slammed the door so hard behind him that the whole house shook.

For a moment, Candra just stood there, listening until she heard a car engine start and roar down the street.

Then her lips curved upward, and she whispered, with mock regret, "Gee, sorry, Meg. I think I just screwed things up with your boyfriend."

Then, still smiling, she went back to memorizing Meg's school schedule.

Mirabelle lay in her bed in the dorm room, trying desperately to concentrate.

A few feet away, Char was breathing evenly and rhythmically. She had been asleep for hours now, and had stirred only slightly when Mirabelle turned off the light and slipped into bed just past midnight.

Frustrated, Mirabelle focused again on separating her astral body from her physical one. She knew from experience that it took intense concentration to split the two, and to then will her consciousness into the astral body. But she had done it before, many times.

Of course, it had taken months of trying before she'd made the first breakthrough. That had been several years ago. She had been lying awake in her girlhood bedroom, practicing the exercises Cecile had taught her—beginning by imagining the physical index finger of her right hand as being merged with an astral index finger, and working her way up to an awareness of her body and its astral double as a whole.

And then it had happened—*boing!*—her astral body had gotten up, leaving her physical body behind in the bed. She had seen an image of herself moving away, and she had used every ounce of spiritual strength to will her consciousness into that other Mirabelle. It had worked—she was instantly *there*, across the room.

She had looked for the silver cord Cecile had told her about, the one that connected her astral body to her physical body. And she had seen it, shimmering in the moonlight, a sort of elastic lifeline that was capable of extending indefinitely. Cecile had warned her that if the cord was ever severed while she was projecting, she would die instantly. But somehow, she hadn't been afraid.

The next thing she knew, she had been moving through the walls of her room, out into the night, gliding along the physical plane to Alex's house. She had drifted through the walls of his bedroom and seen him lying there, asleep, with a slight smile on his face.

Then she had found herself hurling back along the physical plane, being slammed back into her body so violently that she was ill for several days afterward.

It had taken her some time to get up her courage to try and project herself again. And some time after that to have another breakthrough. Now, after a few years of practice, she was able to project whenever she felt like it, and she could ease herself back into her physical body so that she wouldn't get sick from the impact.

But tonight, it just wasn't working. Try as she might, she couldn't seem to leave her physical body.

And she knew why. A part of her mind refused to focus entirely on the business at hand. That part was still preoccupied with Ben Schacter, for some reason—too stirred by tonight's encounter with him to be entirely diverted.

She still hadn't been able to shake the feeling that Meg was troubled, but apparently, her thoughts of Ben were too intrusive, distracting her. She kept wishing she had said yes when he'd asked her out, kept wondering if he'd ever ask again.

She wasn't going to be able to project herself and check up on Meg tonight, and that was that.

The rose-bordered bedroom was dark, except for the candles that flickered on top of the wide, flat bureau. Cleared of trinkets, perfume bottles, and picture frames, it made a perfect altar.

Candra stood before it, holding the crossbone amulet above her head in both hands, her eyes squeezed shut as she concentrated.

Then she began to chant softly,

> *Forces of evil, contained in this charm*
> *stay with me now and protect me from harm*
> *and when you are needed, heed my plea*
> *to wound the one who wounded me.*

She lowered the crossbones and put them on the altar to finish the ritual. They had to be consecrated by the elements.

Earth—she sprinkled them with salt.

Water—she splashed holy water on them.

Fire—she passed the bones through the candle flame.

Air—she passed them through the incense.

Then she put the charm back into the left side of her bra. She had been wearing it there, over her heart, for several days.

Ever since she'd realized what she had to do.

Seventeen

Candra paused and took a deep breath before hurrying up the steps of the Adamson-Swift school.

Just act as though you belong here, she told herself. *No one will suspect that you don't.*

She had just parked Meg's black Honda in the parking lot among the other shiny, expensive cars. She was wearing Meg's navy and green plaid school uniform that allowed her to blend into the throng of students around her.

Could any of them sense that she was terrified? That she felt completely out of her element?

Of course not. As far as they were concerned, she was Meg McKenna.

The realization was comforting enough to set her feet in motion again.

She slipped through the heavy double doors that were propped open, and paused as her eyes grew accustomed to the dim corridors after the bright September sunlight. Which way should she go, left or right? She was pretty sure she wasn't supposed to go upstairs—according to the class schedule she'd found taped inside of Meg's notebook, her homeroom was in room A-11. That seemed like it should be on the first floor.

She hesitated, waiting for her senses to tell her which direction to take.

Left came to her after a moment, and she turned abruptly, crashing into someone who was just brushing past her. The girl, who was fair and pretty, with a smooth blond pageboy, turned around and said, "Oops, excuse m—hey, Meg, what's up?"

Candra shrugged. "Not much," she said, clutching her books against her accelerating heart. *Calm down*, she ordered herself. *If you don't relax, someone's going to get suspicious.*

But the girl seemed to be focusing intently on her, for some reason. Candra was about to move on when she said, "Meg, can I ask you something?"

"Shoot," she said, using the American slang word she'd picked up from Craig and Jane Drayer.

The girl blinked.

Uh-oh. Obviously Meg didn't normally say *shoot.*

Or maybe Candra had been mistaken about its meaning. . . .

"Meg," the girl said, catching a strand of her blond hair and twirling it around her index finger, "*what* is the deal with you and Shea? I mean, are you guys on, or off, or what?"

A question Candra could answer—that was a relief. "We're off," she said promptly. "Definitely off."

"You're kidding. I mean, yesterday afternoon, I heard that you guys were breaking up. Then Shea told Kyle Bennett at practice that you guys were fine. And then, late last night, Maura Nealey called me and said that she'd just seen Shea driving around out at Moseby with Andy Dorner, and when she asked him about you guys, he got all irritated and said it was over."

You guys. Candra added the phrase to her mental directory of American slang.

"Well, it is over," she told the blonde, whoever she was. "He came over to my house, and we broke up." *And that's the truth*, she thought with a satisfied little smirk.

"Wow. And I always thought you guys were *it.* I mean, everyone did. Did you really cheat on him?"

Candra hesitated, then decided, *why not?* "Yeah," she said crisply. "I did."

"I can't believe it! With *who?* Everyone's saying it was some preppie from out of town."

Candra just shrugged and gave the girl a mysterious little smile.

The girl jabbed her arm with a manicured hand. "Meg! Come on, tell me. I *am* still your best friend . . . aren't I?" Her tone was suddenly laced with doubt.

Best friend? Why not? This was actually fun, now that Candra was getting used to it. "Of course you are," she assured the blonde.

"Good. That's a relief. Because the way you've been acting lately, I was starting to wonder. So was Chasey. Hey, by the way, when you see her in homeroom, will you give her these?" The girl dug in her leather bag and pulled out a pair of delicate diamond drop earrings. She dropped them into Candra's hand.

"What are these?" Candra asked, staring down at the noticeably expensive gems.

"They're her mother's, the ones that old man Tiller gave her on their wedding day. These things are worth a fortune, but Chasey's mom never even wears them. She snuck them out so I could wear them for that photo shoot yesterday. They looked perfect with my outfit."

"What photo shoot?"

"*Duh*, Meg," the blonde said, rolling her eyes. "I got my senior portrait done, remember?"

"Oh, yeah . . . I guess I forgot for a minute."

"Well, don't *forget* to give those to Chasey. I was supposed to drop them off at her house last night, but I never got around to it."

"I won't forget," Candra said, pocketing the earrings.

"Hey, Zoe," called someone down the hall.

The blonde glanced up. "Yeah?"

"Get over here and tell Andy that we're having a quiz in Math today," said one of the guys who was clustered around a drinking fountain. "He doesn't believe me."

"Geez, Andy, where *were* you all last week?" called the girl. "See you, Meg, I've got to go convince that lughead that he'd better start studying."

"See you," Candra said, mentally entering the new data—Zoe: best friend.

Then she turned to her left and hurried down the hall. Sure enough, her instincts had been right on target. The classrooms began with A-1, and in no time, Candra had worked her way up to A-11 and slipped in the door.

The teacher, she knew from Meg's schedule, was someone named Mr. Pfeiffer. Was that him, the man with the slicked-back hair and glasses who stood glowering in the doorway?

Probably.

Candra could feel his eyes on her as she hesitated in front of the room and looked around.

It hit her that there was probably a certain seat she was supposed to take. Most of them were already filled with students who sat whispering quietly to each other, or studying. She eyed the empty chairs.

Which one was Meg's?

She had no idea.

She turned around. Luckily, the teacher was no longer watching her. He was yelling at some kid in the hall.

Candra swiftly covered the few feet between her and the teacher's desk, and saw a clipboard there. Right on top was something that looked like a seating chart. She was about to peer at it when someone said, "Hey, Meg, what are you doing?"

She looked up to see a pretty redhead—a familiar redhead, actually.

Candra had encountered the girl twice before—once on the street, when the girl had mistaken her for Meg, and once the night of that party at Moseby, when she'd glimpsed the girl emerging from the woods with some guy.

"I was just . . . nothing," Candra said, moving away from the desk.

"You're not still mad at me, are you?"

Candra started to say, *about what?* but caught herself. Instead, she shrugged and said, "I guess not."

The girl broke into a relieved grin. "Good. I didn't mean to bug you with all that stuff people were saying about you. I mean, I didn't believe any of them, Meg—you know that, right?"

"I know."

"And I didn't mean to pry into the thing with Shea, but I just couldn't believe it when I heard you guys had broken up."

Candra nodded. Clearly, her twin sister's love life was the object of close scrutiny by the students of Adamson-Swift. And it wasn't going to be easy for Candra to fade into the woodwork with all this attention focused on Meg.

"So did you really?"

"Did I really what?"

"Did you and Shea really break up?"

Exasperated, Candra gave the redhead a look. Then she said briefly, "Yeah."

"You're kidding. I mean, are you all right, Meg?"

"I'm fine."

The girl put a reassuring hand on her arm, then said, "Come on, we'd better get into our seats—here comes Pfeiffer."

Candra let herself be steered to an empty desk across the aisle from the one the redhead took. At least this was one seating chart problem solved, she thought, sinking into the chair as the bell rang.

After the Pledge of Allegiance, which Candra had made a point to learn during the past few weeks at Crawford Corners Public High School, the teacher took attendance in a gruff, military style. Candra remembered to say "here" when "Megan McKenna" was called.

And she learned that the girl across from her was Chasey Norman. As she filed the name away mentally, her fingers closed around the diamond earrings in her pocket. She should probably hand them across the aisle right now . . .

But the teacher looked like the type who would get bent out of shape over something like that.

Candra absently stroked the delicate gold settings and the small, hard precious stones that were cool beneath her fingertips.

What if she didn't give them back to Chasey just yet? What if she hung on to them for a little while? Maybe they could be a good luck charm for her.

After all, just touching the diamonds made her feel a sense of wealth and power.

Which was all she'd ever wanted.

The instant the bell rang, she stood abruptly, feeling almost as though she had to flee before Chasey figured out she had the earrings.

She realized, too late, that no one else in the room was standing. Maybe that hadn't been the bell after all.

She quickly plopped back into her seat, but the teacher's cold eyes were pinned on her, and she knew he was going to single her out.

"In a hurry, Miss McKenna?" he practically purred.

She shook her head, wondering what the problem was. That *must* have been the bell. Out in the hall, she could hear people chattering and locker doors slamming. But in this classroom, there was silence and no one moved. They all seemed to be staring at Candra.

"Perhaps you've forgotten how we do things in my homeroom, Megan," the teacher went on. "Perhaps you've forgotten that we do not make a mad exodus toward the door as soon as the bell rings, like so many programmed rats."

Programmed rats?

"No, we wait until we are dismissed, row by row. Don't we, class?" he asked, looking around at the others, who nodded on command, as though they were afraid not to.

"Because of Miss McKenna's *forgetfulness*, she will be the last to leave today. Row one, stand and file out, please. And when I get to your row, Miss McKenna, you will remain seated."

Candra watched as the rest of the students were dismissed, row by row, practically marching to the door like soldiers. She remained behind when her row left, and when it was Chasey's turn to leave, she turned and gave Candra a sympathetic look over her shoulder before slipping out into the hall.

When the room was empty, the teacher closed the door, sat at his desk, steepled his fingers beneath his chin, and rested his steely, ice gray eyes on Candra.

She wondered what his problem was. Was he trying to make her late for her next class? Trying to humiliate her? Trying to show her who was boss?

I'll show you who's boss, she thought, and straightened in her seat. She returned his gaze darkly, fixing him with her narrowed eyes.

You can play mind games with the rest of the spineless fools, but not with me, she told him silently.

Was it her imagination, or did the teacher suddenly seem uneasy?

Candra continued to stare at him, focusing every ounce of her negative energy on him, utterly absorbed in the objective of making him uncomfortable . . . of teaching this teacher not to mess with her.

After a moment, she could see him trying to maintain his composure, trying to keep his hands neatly propped beneath his chin.

But from where she sat, his legs beneath the desk were visible, and a telltale jitter had started vibrating his right knee.

Satisfied, Candra stood and picked up Meg's notebook and her purse. Wearing a tiny smile, she walked casually up the aisle, still watching the man behind the desk, who didn't move, didn't speak.

She paused right in front of him, gave a little wave, and said sweetly, "See you later, Mr. Pfeiffer."

Then she walked out of the room.

"Hey, Mirabelle."

She glanced up from the textbook she had been frantically scanning in hopes of cramming hours' worth of studying into the three minutes before Logic class would start.

Ben Schacter was sliding into his usual seat, wearing his usual faded jeans and looking appealingly windblown.

"Hi, Ben," Mirabelle said, trying to sound offhand. "How'd it go last night?"

"What?"

"Moving the chairs," she said, closing the book and sandwiching her hand between the pages to keep her place. "Didn't you have to move chairs or something?"

"Oh, right. I did. It was fine. How'd it go with you at the library? Get much studying done?"

She glanced down at the book. "Not exactly." She wasn't about to tell him *why* she hadn't been able to study—not the part about being distracted by him, and not the part about being distracted by Meg. "That's what I'm trying to do now—study, I mean."

He looked dubiously at the clock above the door. "You don't have much time."

"I know." She sighed, feeling frustrated—and overtired. Her shoulder blades ached, and her eyelids felt scratchy from the lack of sleep. "I hate this class. Maybe I should just drop it."

"It's that bad?"

"I just can't seem to *get* this Logic stuff. I guess I'm not very logical," she said, and smiled feebly.

"I can help you if you want," Ben offered matter-of-factly.

"You don't have to—"

"Look, Mirabelle, it's no big deal. This is the one class that *does* make sense to me. I guess I'm the *logical* type, huh?"

She smiled. "Guess so."

"So we can work together on the next section," Ben said.

"Oh, Ben, y'all don't have to do that."

"It's no problem."

"But I know you're really busy with your work program and everything else, and—" She caught the hurt look in his eyes and broke off.

"Okay, never mind, then," he said, shrugging. "I wasn't proposing to you, you know? I was honestly trying to help you with this class."

She felt like an idiot. Her face was growing hot. "I know you didn't mean—I mean, I know you just wanted to help. It's not that I thought . . ." She took a deep breath. "This is so stupid, Ben. Of course I'd love you to help me. I'm not really in the mood to fail this class."

He hesitated, then grinned his usual casual grin, and she felt relieved.

"Cool," he said simply. "We'll hook up one day this week at the library and I'll go over this stuff with you. I don't work *all* the time, you know."

She smiled weakly. "I know."

So now she was going to be spending a lot of time alone with Ben Schacter.

But not in a romantic way. Romance had nothing to do with it.

He's going to help you understand this crazy class, and that's all, she reminded herself. *So don't go getting any wild ideas about him.*

But it was too late.

The wild ideas were already flitting through her mind.

The first thing Candra heard when she walked in the front door after school was the bass beat of rap music coming from the floor above. Obviously, someone was home.

Clenching her jaw, she closed the door behind her as quietly as she could, hoping she wouldn't alert whoever was upstairs to her presence. It had been an exhausting day of make-believe, and right now, she wasn't in the mood to be Meg anymore.

She had taken two steps toward the stairway, planning to sneak up to her—to *Meg's*—room, when a voice stopped her in her tracks.

"There you are, Meg. I've been wondering what you've been up to."

Candra glanced toward the living room and saw a motherly, middle-aged woman standing there. The first thing that Candra noticed about her was that her fingernails were long and polished red, as though she were ready for a fancy night on the town, and yet she was holding a bottle of spray cleaner in one hand, a roll of paper towels in the other.

She had on black stretch pants that hugged her short, chubby legs, and a semiflattering black and red tunic top. Thick wire-framed glasses made her watery blue eyes look enormous. Her hair was the same soft gray that used to color the sky over Ocho Rios before an afternoon storm.

"Hi," Candra said cautiously, then added, "I've just, um, been busy with school and everything."

"I figured. You, I don't worry about. But that one up there . . ." The woman jerked her head in the direction of the throbbing music above. "Your sister's another story."

Your sister. Obviously, the pint-sized blonde Candra had seen in the photos above the mantel.

"Why? What's wrong with her?" she asked the woman quietly, as though the girl could somehow overhear her above the music.

"What's wrong with Carrie?" The woman shook her head, wearing a disgusted expression. "I'll tell you what's wrong with her. She waltzes in here, bold as you please, tracking mud all over the kitchen floor, which I had just washed, thank you very much. And when I tell her to take off her shoes, do you know what she says to me?"

"What?" Candra asked after a moment, realizing she was expected to reply.

"She says, 'Get out of my face, Sophie.' *That's* what she says to me. I've worked for your mother for over ten years, Meg, and I don't like to say a word against Giselle, God bless her, but do you know what I think?"

"What?"

"I think that child is spoiled rotten, that's what I think. And your mother isn't the only one who's doing it. That stepfather of yours is just as much to blame, even more. What are they going to say when their dear sweet little Carrie winds up on the street, or worse? From the wild look in her eyes today, I'd swear she's already on drugs. I caught her smoking a cigarette in her room a little while ago when I went up to tell her to turn that so-called music down. And you know what that means."

Candra shook her head, filing it all away mentally.

"It means nothing good, that's what it means," the woman—obviously the housekeeper—Sophie?—shook her head indignantly. "You, you're always sweet and respectful toward me. But that one, she's just . . . I ask you, Meg, do I deserve this?"

"No," Candra said serenely, "you don't."

"You're right. I don't. But what are you going to do," Sophie said, shaking her head and sighing just as the telephone started to ring.

Before Candra could react, the ring was cut short as the music was simultaneously turned down.

She looked at Sophie.

"Guess your sister's expecting a call, the way she snatched that up," the woman commented, then headed back toward the living room. "I'm going to finish doing the countertops, and then I'll be going. My son needs me to baby-sit tonight, so I have to be out of here by four."

"Okay. See you," Candra said, and headed slowly up the stairs.

At the top, she paused in the long L-shaped hallway and listened for a moment. The music was coming from behind the closed door Candra had tried to open yesterday. It had been locked then, the room beyond silent. Now, obviously, Carrie Hudson was in there, blasting rap songs, talking on the phone, and . . . doing drugs?

Candra smiled to herself, shook her head, and headed for Meg's room, with its fireplace, dusty mauve carpeting, crocheted lace bedding, and rose-and-vine wallpaper border.

She closed the door behind her, then turned the knob that locked it. She couldn't wait to get out of this restricting school uniform. She lifted it over her head as she strolled across the room to the closet, then let the plaid jumper drop to the floor in a heap before turning her attention to the rows of clothes in the walk-in closet.

The music started blasting again down the hall as she thumbed through the outfits on hangers.

Look at this gorgeous white linen suit with a designer label . . . and the creamy yellow cotton sweater with the designer label . . . and the black silk cocktail dress . . .

Candra pulled the dress out and held it against herself, checking her reflection in the cheval mirror across the room. Then she thought, why not?

Swiftly, she pulled the dress over her head and felt the soft fabric swish gracefully around her legs. Checking the mirror again, she decided she looked great in the dress. With one hand, she piled her hair on top of her head and held it there. It would look nice this way. But now her ears were revealed, and she needed . . .

Her gaze moved to the uniform that lay crumpled in front of the closet. She needed those earrings. She'd almost forgotten all about them.

Candra hurried over and reached into the pocket, feeling around for the delicate diamond drops. They must be in the other pocket, because this one was empty.

She quickly checked the other pocket.

Empty, too.

Her heart suddenly racing, Candra reached back into the first pocket. They had to be here. They *had* to be here. If they weren't . . .

There. Candra's fingers closed around something small and hard and she drew it out. It was one of Chasey's mother's earrings. She must not have dug far enough in the first time she'd looked.

Sighing in relief, she looked down at the rich gold setting and twinkling, perfect gem. Then she held it to her ear and looked up into the mirror.

Perfect. These earrings would be perfect with this dress. She imagined herself wearing this dress, with her hair swept up in an elegant twist and the diamonds twinkling at her ears, dancing in Landon's arms.

Wearing a dreamy smile, she reached into the pocket to fish out the other earring so she could see what it felt like to actually wear them.

But after a moment, the frown returned to her face.

It wasn't here!

How could it not be here?

Had she put one earring in the right pocket, and the other one in the left? She distinctly recalled putting them both together, but maybe she was wrong. Maybe somehow . . .

Candra searched the other pocket.

Nothing.

Frustrated, she dropped to her knees and started looking for the missing earring on the carpet. It must have dropped out when she'd thrown the uniform on the floor.

But after a half hour of searching, and back-tracking down the stairs and out into Meg's car, she realized the truth.

The priceless diamond earring was missing.

"Hello, is Meg there?" Mirabelle asked into the receiver, noticing the throbbing beat of rap music in the background.

"Who's this?" the voice on the other end of the line asked.

Mirabelle knew this must be Meg's younger half-sister, Carrie. Her tone sounded petulant and impatient.

"It's a friend of hers. Mirabelle."

"Who?"

"Mirabelle."

"Oh, well, she's not home right now," the voice said, and Mirabelle sensed without a doubt that the girl was lying.

Frowning, she asked, "Can you tell me where she is?"

"I have no idea. You'll have to call back. Bye." There was a click.

"You little brat," Mirabelle whispered, shaking her head.

"Who's a little brat?" Char asked from her bed, looking up from the sheet of stationery she was scribbling on. When she wasn't burning up the long distance lines, she was writing letters to her friends and family back home. It was a wonder she wasn't flunking out of school already.

"Just my friend's kid sister," Mirabelle said, hanging up the phone and picking up her jacket. "I'm going out for a while. If anyone calls, be sure to take a message."

You mean if Ben calls, she told herself as she headed toward the door. *And you shouldn't care one way or another. He's going to tutor you in Logic, and that's it.*

"Hey, Mirabelle?" Char called after her.

"Yeah?" She paused with her hand on the knob.

"Is everything all right?"

Surprised, Mirabelle looked back at her roommate. Char was usually so wrapped up in her own homesick misery that she paid little attention to anything or anyone else. Now her apple-cheeked, freckled face was wearing a concerned expression, and her wide brown eyes were focused on Mirabelle.

"I'm fine, Char," she said. "Why do you ask?"

"You just seem a little worried or distracted or something. Is something wrong with your friend?"

"I hope not," Mirabelle said, turning the knob and walking out into the hall.

God, I hope not.

Candra was on her way up the stairs to her room again, wracking her brain about what might have happened to the other earring, when Carrie's door was suddenly flung open. The blonde Candra had seen on the street and in the photo on the mantel came flying out into the hall, pulling on a leather jacket.

When she saw Candra, she rolled her eyes. "Don't start in on me," was the first thing she said, stopping short at the top of the stairs.

"About what?" Candra asked, still climbing. She was trying not to let the knowledge that this person was her blood relative—her half-sister—throw her off.

Stay calm. She won't notice a thing.

The girl was petite, pale and pretty, her features and coloring the opposite of Meg's and Candra's. She was wearing faded, ripped jeans and far too much makeup.

"Didn't Sophie go running right to you when you walked in the door? She said she was going to 'report me.' " The girl looked mostly amused, but there was a faint flicker of worry in her eyes.

"Yeah, she reported you," Candra said.

"And?"

"And what?"

"Don't you have anything to say?" Carrie asked, watching as she arrived on the top step.

Candra realized just how truly tiny this girl was. The top of her head was well below Candra's shoulder, making her seem almost childlike.

And suddenly, crazily, Candra found herself wanting to like this stranger who was her sister.

"What do you want me to say, Carrie?"

The girl looked surprised. "Oh, please. You always have plenty to say, Meg. I mean, aren't you going to remind me that you're the oldest and in charge when Mom and Dad aren't around? Aren't you going to try and stop me from going out?"

Candra shrugged. "Who cares what you do? Go ahead. Go out."

Carrie's eyes widened, but she maintained her snotty tone. "I plan to." She tossed her head and started down the stairs.

Candra stood at the top of the landing, watching her.

At the bottom, Carrie turned around and called back up, "Oh, by the way, two people called for you."

"Why didn't you let me know?"

"Because I was waiting for an important call and I didn't want you tying up the line all night."

Again, Carrie seemed to be waiting for a rebuttal.

Again, Candra shrugged. "So who called?" she asked after a moment.

"Some girl named Mirabelle. What's up with her accent?"

"What do you mean?"

"That southern drawl. I mean, get real." Carrie shook her head.

Southern drawl. That would be the same girl who called yesterday. Who was she, and what did she know?

"And Grandma called for you, too," Carrie said, heading toward the door. "She said for you to call her back as soon as you can. She wants to talk to you about your inheritance."

Inheritance?

"What about it?" she asked Carrie, trying to keep her voice even.

It was Carrie's turn to shrug. "*You* figure it out. I mean, you turn eighteen this Saturday. Isn't that when she's supposed to hand over the big bucks?"

Candra's heart did a flip. She murmured a vague response as Carrie headed out the door.

As soon as it had closed behind her sister, she let a smile crawl over her features.

The big bucks?

It was too good to be true.

On the other hand, hadn't she cast a money-drawing spell? Obviously, it was working.

Suddenly, the missing diamond earring lost all of its urgency.

Mirabelle checked the discreet street sign at the corner and saw that this was Meadowview Terrace. It was about time. She'd gotten off the bus in downtown Crawford Corners over a half hour ago. She hadn't realized that Meg lived so far out of town.

Her feet ached, still clad in the black pointy flats she'd worn to class and hadn't thought to change.

The street was quiet and dusk had fallen. It was dinner-time now, and except for an occasional car passing and pulling into a driveway farther up the street, Mirabelle saw no one.

She followed the winding road past sprawling but comfortable-looking homes set way back on large, treed lots. As she went, she checked the numbers on the mailboxes. Nineteen, twenty-one . . . she was getting closer.

And the higher the addresses went, the more aware Mirabelle became of a sense of uneasiness. Meg was in trouble. She just knew it. And she had the feeling that her friend was far away, somehow . . . even though she'd thought that Carrie had been lying about her sister not being home.

Had Meg left since she'd called? It was possible. The bus trip over from the college campus in Spring City had been a plodding one; it had taken nearly an hour. Between that, and the time it had taken for Mirabelle to hike out here, Meg could have taken off somewhere.

Mirabelle frowned and checked another mailbox.

Thirty-one.

Only a few more houses to go.

A dog started to bark somewhere nearby, but the sound ended abruptly with a yelp.

Mirabelle was half wondering what had happened to the animal when she spotted it.

Forty-one Meadowview Terrace.

It was a large, neat brick Colonial set about fifty yards back from the street. The manicured lawn was lush and dotted with occasional brightly colored leaves that had already started to drift down from the trees that covered the lot. There was a circular drive in front of the house, and on it was parked a black Honda Accord that Mirabelle recognized as belonging to Meg.

So she was home.

Mirabelle picked up her pace.

She had almost reached the twin brick columns posted on either side of the driveway when, for some reason, she was compelled to turn and look up at the stand of lilac trees off to the left, on the front lawn.

And there, even in the murky light, she saw something move slightly in the dark green branches.

No . . . not something.

Someone.

Candra had to get ahold of Meg's grandmother, but how was she going to manage that? For all she knew, the woman lived in California.

Still, she called information and asked for any McKennas listed locally.

"What is the first name, ma'am?" the operator asked.

"I have no idea." She had tried to come up with something mentally, even a first initial, but had drawn a blank.

"I need a first name."

"Can't you just tell me if anyone named McKenna lives in Crawford Corners?"

"I have a dozen people listed here by that name, ma'am."

"Oh." Candra shrugged. "Never mind," she muttered, and hung up.

Even if she did get all of the local McKennas' numbers, what was she going to do? Call each one and ask if they had a granddaughter named Meg? And if she found the right one, how was she going to explain the question she'd just asked?

She stood in the middle of Meg's room, pondering.

She had already checked the address book she'd found in Meg's desk drawer. Nothing under McKenna. Of course not. Meg had to know her own grandmother's number and address by heart.

There had to be some way of finding the number, though. Maybe she could check an old phone bill. She could use her powers of concentration to see if any of the numbers on it jumped out at her.

Where would the Hudsons keep old phone bills?

Candra went out into the hallway and started opening doors until she found a medium-sized study. It was furnished in heavy, dark furniture, and the walls were painted a masculine hunter green. Obviously, this room belonged to Lester Hudson.

The desk was clear except for an old-fashioned black telephone and several framed snapshots, most of them of Giselle and Carrie. The one shot that included Meg was at least seven years old, and not flattering of her. Candra felt a flicker of sympathy for her twin, but quickly brushed it away.

Why should she care that Meg had to live with a stepfather who didn't care about her? She'd had their mother, and everything money could buy. Everything Candra had done without.

The only other thing on the desk, under a golf-ball-shaped paperweight, was a sheaf of papers that were apparently business-related: flow-charts and memos and graphs.

The desk drawers were locked.

Why? Did old Lester have something to hide?

Candra looked around. Her eyes fell on another framed photo, this one a posed portrait of Lester and Giselle. She stared into Meg's stepfather's face and sensed something she'd missed the first time she'd seen his picture yesterday.

He wasn't sincere.

There was something *off* about him, something that told her he wasn't exactly what he appeared to be—which was, a boring, paunchy businessman.

Candra tried the top drawer on the tall wooden filing cabinet between the two windows. It was locked, too, and so were all the others.

What did Lester Hudson have to hide?

She would find out, she promised herself.

But not now. Right now, the main objective was to find Meg's grandmother's phone number and call her back.

But what if she couldn't find it?

Well, she supposed the woman would call *her* back eventually. But who knew when that would be? And who knew if Candra would be home when she finally did call? Or, even if she was, if that brat Carrie would give her the phone?

Meg's half sister's voice echoed through Candra's head again. *You turn eighteen this Saturday. Isn't that when she's supposed to hand over the big bucks?*

Candra *had* to find out what this was all about. A huge sum of money would be the answer to everything. Money, power—they were all she'd ever wanted, and one thing led to the other.

She stared at the heavy black phone on Lester's desk and whispered, "Come on—can't you tell me the number somehow?"

Then it dawned on her.

This phone couldn't—it was too old.

But with any luck . . .

Candra raced downstairs.

The telephone in the Hudsons' den was a cordless, high-tech, expensive model, just as she had expected. It was the kind of phone that could be programmed with frequently called numbers.

And right on top of the list jotted on the base, in swirly handwriting that had to belong to Giselle, was the word "Mom" beside the numeral.

Candra had no doubt that "Mom" was the grandmother who had called about the inheritance.

Could it be this easy?

She lifted the receiver and examined the rows of buttons until she found one labeled "Mem." That stood for "memory," she knew, having used the Drayers' telephone on numerous occasions. Now all she had to do was push the *one*, and wait while a rapid series of tones signaled that the number was being dialed.

After what seemed like an eternity, it was ringing.

And then a fragile-sounding voice said, "Hello?"

"Grandma?" Candra asked cautiously.

"Is that you, Meg?"

A pleased smile curved over her lips. "Yes," she told the old woman, "it's me."

Mirabelle stood frozen at the foot of the driveway, watching the figure that blended into the shadows among the lilac boughs.

A man.

It was the outline of a man. He was tall, and dressed in dark clothing, and *he* looked dark from where she was standing.

She stared and he remained motionless, and somehow she knew that he had sensed her presence.

She wanted to run, but something drew her to stay, to wait.

Finally, after an endless silence during which Mirabelle hardly dared to breathe, the man moved.

In one fluid motion, he stepped out of the sheltering branches and drew a finger to his lips, beckoning Mirabelle to be quiet.

She couldn't have made a sound if she'd wanted to. She was riveted by what she saw.

Black . . . he was black from head to toe: clothing, shoes, skin, hair. He was an imposing figure, well over six feet tall, with broad shoulders and strong arms that were left bare by his tee shirt. His skin had the smooth darkness of a ripe plum, and she saw, as he took several steps closer, his bulging biceps and his strong, proud neck.

His eyes were fastened on hers, and though he wasn't close enough for her to tell, she knew that they were the same inky shade as the rest of him.

And piercing.

She could feel them boring into her, and she again thought of running, as fast and as far as she could.

But somehow, she was unable to budge. It was as though nails had been driven through the soles of her too-tight shoes, pinning her to the blacktop, helpless to do anything but watch as the shadow man advanced again.

Finally, he was standing only a few feet in front of her, and she saw that he was about her age . . . or was he?

He looked barely twenty, but she was aware of an aura that told her this man was wise beyond his years.

She didn't know what she was expecting, but what he did next caught her completely off guard.

He smiled.

Even white teeth flashed in his midnight face, and she heard a low chuckle.

And then . . .

"Mirabelle," he said softly, and it was as though his deep, rich voice were physically caressing each syllable.

He knows who I am! How does he know? Who is he?

When she was able to make a sound, it was a quiet little gasp.

He smiled again, chuckled again. "You *are* Mirabelle, aren't you?"

She nodded, some distant part of her mind warning that she should be afraid, that she should get away now ... *While you still have the chance.*

But another voice, an increasingly stronger voice, said, *You can trust him.*

"How did you know?" she finally asked.

"Meg told me."

"Meg ... ? Who are you? How do you know Meg?"

His smiled faded. "I can't tell you."

"Can't tell me what? Who you are, or how you know her?"

"Both. At least, not now. Not yet," he said, glancing up at the house just as a figure passed in front of a lace-covered window.

From here, through the sheer, filmy curtain, Mirabelle could just make out familiar long, dark hair and a willowy figure.

Meg.

"But I will tell you eventually," the man told her in his resonant voice that bore the hint of an accent that she couldn't place. "Just as you will tell me ..."

"What?" she asked in a near whisper. "What will I tell you?"

He glanced in the direction of the figure silhouetted against the yellow lamplight. "Everything I want to know."

"What did you say, Grandma?" Candra asked, distracted. She had been so excited to make the connection with the woman that she'd been unable to stand still. So she'd paced around the den with the cordless phone, then walked into the living room, where she glanced toward the window ...

And felt it.

The disconcerting sensation that some kind of negative energy hovered just beyond the porch light.

"I just asked whether you'd heard anything from your mother," repeated the voice in her ear.

Candra forced her attention back on the conversation.

"From my mother? Not today," she said truthfully, and quickly changed the subject. "Carrie said you wanted to talk to me about ... something?"

"About your inheritance that Grandpa left in trust. Do you remember what he explained to you before he ..." The woman cleared her throat, and Candra realized that she was having a difficult time saying whatever it was that she was trying to say.

"Before ..." Candra prodded, one eye on the window, still wondering if it was just her imagination, or—

"Before he died," Meg's grandmother said in a choked voice, then seemed to collect herself. "He loved you so much, Meg, and he wanted you to have this money as soon as possible. He knew . . . well, he's provided for Carrie, too, of course, but he knew that you've had a rough time of it, with Lester and all, and he wanted you to have . . . freedom, I suppose."

Candra had never met the man, but he was her grandfather, too, and suddenly, she found herself moved. He and Meg must have been very close. And instead of feeling jealous over the realization, she felt . . . relieved.

Don't, she immediately scolded herself. *Meg had everything. She had money, and this house, and a family.*

But an image of Carrie's pinched, petulant little face floated into • her head.

And of Lester, creepy Lester, who clearly worshipped his own daughter but didn't spare any feeling for Meg.

And of Meg herself, whose eyes had seemed haunted by something—loneliness?—when Candra had watched her from the shadows last week.

But you had Mom, Candra told her sister vehemently, squeezing her eyes shut briefly. *Mom didn't want me.*

"Meg, I hate to say this, because you know I love your mother dearly," the woman on the other end of the line was saying. "But I also know my daughter inside and out. And Giselle has never been very . . . ah, responsible, when it comes to money."

"No, she hasn't," Candra agreed, though this was news to her.

"And Lester—well, it's none of his business. That's why I'd like to take care of the transfer before they come home on Saturday."

"The transfer?"

"Grandpa left the money in his bank in the city. If you can take Friday off from school and take the train in with me first thing in the morning, Meg, you can be present for the transaction. We'll have a nice lunch to celebrate your birthday, of course, and then we'll bring the check back up here so that you can deposit it into your account here before the office closes Friday afternoon."

"That sounds good," Candra said, feeling a little breathless. "Um, Grandma . . . how much is it?"

There was a pause, and Candra realized she shouldn't have asked. Maybe it sounded callous, or maybe Meg already knew the amount. But she just couldn't help it. She *had* to find out.

"I thought you knew," the woman said, then quickly added, "but then, I guess those days when Harry was so ill, and then when he—

when he died . . . looking back, they're a blur for me. They must be for you, too."

"Yes, they are," she said softly, trying to sound as grief-stricken as Meg's grandmother did.

And for a moment, her jittery excitement even dissipated as she thought about the impact this man's death must have had on his widow, and on his granddaughter.

But you're his granddaughter, too, she reminded herself. *And he didn't leave you anything. So this money should rightfully be partly yours.*

Then she heard the voice on the other end of the line murmur an amount that left her so startled she couldn't even speak for a moment.

"Um, Grandma, what did you say?" she asked when she found her voice. "I didn't hear you."

"One million dollars," the woman said more clearly.

"That's what I thought," Candra said, struggling to keep the jubilation from her voice.

Instantly, she forgot the uneasy feeling she'd been fighting. She moved away from the window, sank onto the couch and repeated, "One million dollars."

She thought of all the years of poverty in Jamaica, of the way the spoiled, wealthy Drayer children had treated her, of the shabby clothes she'd had to wear and the basement room she'd slept in.

"Thank you," she whispered, half to the dead man she had never known, and half to the gods who had heeded the money-drawing spell she had cast.

Mirabelle watched the silhouette of Meg move away from the window, then turned to the dark man beside her.

"Why are you watching her? What's going on with her? Please tell me. I've been so worried . . ."

He reached out and laid a long finger against her lips. At his touch, she felt a chill zap through her.

"Shhh," he said, locking her eyes with his bottomless ones.

He was frightening and strange, and she didn't know what he was doing out here in the shadows; but for some reason, she trusted him.

"Mirabelle," he said softly, "how much do you know? What has Meg told you?"

She only shrugged. Suddenly, she felt incredibly drained.

He was watching her closely. "Go home now," he said after a moment.

She frowned, wanting to protest. But all she said was, "Yes, I'm going to."

"I'll be seeing you again," he said.

Then he turned and walked away, moving swiftly and silently toward the trees at the side of the property.

Mirabelle stood watching him, wondering who he was, and what he was up to.

Should she stop him? Or call for help?

No. She shouldn't . . .

And she couldn't.

Because she was too overcome by a sudden, brain-numbing exhaustion.

She turned and automatically started walking back down Meadowview Terrace, heading for the bus stop in town.

Eighteen

Candra was getting the hang of being Meg at school. Today, she had remained seated until the homeroom teacher had dismissed her row, and noticed that he kept sliding furtive, nervous glances in her direction.

And she had chattered casually in an American accent with Chasey Norman, who hadn't asked about the earrings yet.

That was a problem Candra had decided to ignore for the time being. Diamond earrings were probably a dime a dozen to these rich girls, anyway.

Later in the morning, in Government class, she found herself sitting a seat away from Shea, Meg's boyfriend—make that ex-boyfriend.

He carefully ignored her, and she heard the kid behind him asking where he'd been yesterday.

"I was home with a stomach bug," Shea told him, and Candra heard the tension in his voice.

"Stomach bug? That's not what *I* heard."

"What'd you hear?"

"Just that you were too upset about breaking up with Meg to come to school."

The kid was a jerk, Candra thought, hating him for Shea's sake.

She felt his eyes on her and pretended to be very interested in the textbook she'd opened blindly in front of her on the desk.

She heard Shea whisper, "Shut up, you jerk," and the kid snickered.

And in front of her, she could hear two girls whispering about it. They kept sneaking glances over their shoulders at her and at Shea, and then giggling.

She caught the words, "Chasey said that Meg said . . ." and decided she was glad she wasn't Meg, glad she wouldn't have to deal with life at Adamson-Swift for much longer.

All she had to do was hold out until Friday.

And then . . .

Freedom, here I come, she thought gleefully as the bell rang and class began.

* * *

"Mirabelle!" called a voice behind her as she hurried toward Gaspar Hall.

She turned around. The quad was crowded with students, and at first she couldn't figure out who had shouted her name.

Then she saw Ben Schacter hurrying to catch up. He was dressed in faded, worn jeans, a thick navy blue plaid flannel shirt, and clunky work boots, and had his ever-present black book bag slung casually over his shoulder. He walked jauntily, as though he hadn't a care in the world.

"Ben," she said when he got closer. "How are y'all doing?"

He grinned. "Fine. Listen, I've got some free time later. Let's go over the new stuff for Logic so you'll be prepared for class tomorrow."

She hesitated. She'd forgotten all about Logic, and even all about Ben.

Ever since that bizarre encounter with the man who'd been lurking outside Meg's house last night, she had been able to think of little else. The whole walk back to the bus stop, the entire trip home, and even getting ready for bed were fuzzy and vague in her mind, as though she hadn't really been *there*.

Mentally, ever since she'd encountered the stranger, she'd been . . . somewhere else.

Thinking about him, wondering who he was, and why she had felt so drawn to him. Why she hadn't questioned him more, especially since he was obviously spying on Meg.

Who was he?

Why hadn't she called Meg to warn her? Or called the police to report him?

"Mirabelle . . . earth to Mirabelle," Ben intoned, waving a hand in front of her face. "Are you all right?"

She shook her head to clear it and focused on Ben. "Yeah, I'm . . . I'm fine. Just thinking about something else, I guess. Sorry."

He shrugged and said, in his easygoing way, "No big deal. So what time do you want to get together? I get done in the campus center at six."

Had she agreed to get together? She wasn't sure. But, because it was easier to go along with it at this stage than to back out, she nodded and said, "Six is fine."

"Okay. I'll meet you at your room, because your dorm's right near the center anyway."

"Fine." She checked her watch. "Well, I've got to get going. I have class."

"Yeah, me, too." He reached out and caught a reddish pink leaf that was drifting down from the tree they were standing beneath. "Here," he said, handing it to her. "Look at this. You don't have autumn foliage down in New Orleans, huh?"

She shook her head and examined the leaf, then tucked it into her notebook. "No, this is my first fall in New England," she said, and for the first time today, she noticed how glorious the campus had become.

When had this happened?

It was as though, overnight, someone had splashed gold and red and copper paint on everything. Now the midday sun filtered down through the leaves, turning the world into a dazzling Impressionist tableau.

Mirabelle looked at Ben, feeling as though she were noticing him for the first time since he'd caught up with her, and grinned. "Thanks, Ben," she said, reaching out and giving his arm a squeeze.

"For what?"

"For the leaf," she said lightly, patting her notebook.

And for snapping me back to reality.

Candra rushed home after classes and changed out of Meg's school uniform, leaving it draped across the queen-sized bed. Then she carefully but quickly started getting dressed in the outfit she'd selected last night from Meg's closet.

Slim-fitting black trousers.

A snug charcoal cashmere sweater that hugged her curves.

High-heeled soft leather boots.

A string of pearls she'd found in the jewelry box on Meg's dresser and couldn't resist.

She stepped back and studied her image in the cheval mirror, realizing that okay, maybe the pearls, which were classic and elegant, didn't really go with the boots, which were thick-heeled and trendy.

But on the other hand, how often did she get to wear real jewelry?

She nudged the thought of the missing diamond earring out of her mind and continued to check her reflection.

She'd brushed her long black hair until it shone, hanging soft and silky straight down her back. And her face was skillfully made up so that she looked at least five years older, in her opinion.

"Look out, Landon Keller, because here I come," she whispered into the mirror, then squirted on some Chanel perfume before grabbing Meg's black leather jacket, purse, and car keys.

At the bottom of the stairs, she bumped into Sophie, who was just walking through the foyer carrying a pile of newspapers.

"Meg, I didn't even hear you come in," the housekeeper said, looking startled. "I must have been out back."

"You must have been."

"Where are you going, all dressed up like that?"

"I have a date," she said, smiling more to herself than at Sophie.

"How *is* Shea? He hasn't been around with you after school lately."

"No, he hasn't. He's fine."

No need to go into any more detail than that. Let Sophie think she was going out with Shea. Why arouse suspicion?

"I don't suppose you've heard from Carrie?" the housekeeper asked, her lips tightening and the warmth dribbling out of her eyes.

"No . . . why?"

"Did she come home last night?"

Candra considered the question and realized that Carrie hadn't come home. Not unless she'd crept in at dawn, because Candra had lain awake most of the night, too excited about the million dollars to sleep. She'd finally drifted into oblivion just as the first light was filtering in the window. When the alarm had gone off a few hours later and she'd gotten up, there had been no sign of Carrie, not that she'd thought about it until now.

But why should she tell Sophie that?

True, Candra was no champion of her mother's younger daughter.

But on the other hand, the housekeeper was a little too nosy for her own good.

"Of course Carrie came home last night," she informed the woman. "She and I watched television together until bedtime."

The woman's eyes narrowed doubtfully; then she shrugged. "Well, good," she muttered. "I thought for sure that girl was out gallivanting God knows where with God knows who."

"Nope," Candra said flippantly. "Not this time." She jangled the keys in her hand.

"Go ahead, Meg," Sophie said. "Don't keep your date waiting. He's a nice boy."

Landon Keller's face flitted before Candra, and his muscular build, and she fought back a shiver of anticipation.

"Yes," she agreed a little giddily, "he sure is a nice boy, Sophie."

* * *

At five minutes past six, there was a knock on Mirabelle's door.

She turned away from the mirror, where she'd been brushing her long brown hair for the zillionth time and debating whether to put on some mascara so that her light green eyes would stand out more. Not that this was a date or anything.

"That's Ben," she told Char, who lay on her bed leafing through a thick photo album.

"Mmm," was all Char said as Mirabelle walked toward the door.

Her roommate was obviously lost in the hometown memories captured beneath the plastic sheets of the album.

She probably won't even notice I'm gone, Mirabelle thought, grabbing her book bag from a chair and opening the door.

"Hi," Ben said cheerfully.

"Hi, Ben."

"What's up?"

"Not much." *Except that I've been so jittery about seeing you tonight that I haven't been able to concentrate on anything else—not my moping roommate, not my schoolwork, and not Meg.*

"Are you ready to go?"

"I guess." She lingered in the doorway and looked down at the worn jeans and cream-colored sweater she was wearing. "Is it cold out?"

"You'll think so."

"What's that supposed to mean?"

"You're from the South. Thin blood. Put a jacket on."

Mirabelle found herself pleased at the casually commanding way he said it. Almost like he was her boyfriend—which he wasn't.

Still, she let him hold her bag and help her on with the jean jacket she grabbed from the chair near the door.

Then, as she pulled the door shut behind her, she called over her shoulder, "See you later, Char."

"Mmm hmm."

She rolled her eyes and started down the hall with Ben beside her.

"That's Char, the homesick cowgirl, huh?" he asked.

"That's her. I keep going back and forth between feeling sorry for her and wanting to knock some sense into her. She should be thrilled at the opportunity to come to a school like Wainwright on full scholarship."

"She's a long way from home, though."

"Who isn't?"

"That's true." Ben held the door at the end of the hall open for her, and they started down the stairs to the first floor. "What made you come all the way up to Connecticut for college? Louisiana has some excellent schools."

"I know."

"So why'd you leave?"

"I had to get away," Mirabelle said simply.

"From who?"

She glanced up at Ben as they emerged into the dorm lobby. "Why do you ask that?"

"What do you mean?"

"Why not ask, 'from *what*'?"

Ben shrugged. "I just have a feeling there's a *who* somewhere in your past."

"Oh."

They stepped out into the chilly autumn night.

"Well?" Ben asked.

"Well, what?"

"Is there a 'who'?"

"Yup," Mirabelle found herself saying. "But it's over. He's out."

"Good," Ben said quietly. He stopped walking.

So did Mirabelle. She looked at him curiously.

"If he's out," Ben told her, leaning down toward her, "then maybe I can be in."

And he lowered his mouth over hers before she realized what was happening . . . and that she wanted it to happen. She wanted to be kissed by Ben Schacter, had been fantasizing about it since they'd met.

And it was even better in reality. His lips were warm and firm and soft, and as he pressed them against hers for a long, sweet moment, Mirabelle forgot that they were standing on the sidewalk in front of Billington Hall, forgot that anyone could see them, and forgot that she had vowed not to get involved with Ben.

When he ended the kiss and lifted his head she wanted to protest, to reach up and bury her hands in his hair and pull his face toward hers again.

Her heart was pounding, and she couldn't seem to tear her eyes away from his.

For a long time, they stood there looking at each other.

Then Ben said, "Come on," and grabbed her hand.

"But the library's that way," Mirabelle said, as he tugged her in the opposite direction. She tried not to feel flustered by the contact of his warm fingers laced cozily between hers. "Where are we going?"

"It's after six. Aren't you hungry? I thought we'd grab some burgers at Radish's."

"Oh." Mirabelle hoped he didn't sense the stab of disappointment that shot through her.

What are you, crazy? she scolded herself. *You were hoping he was going to take you to his dorm. And what did you want to happen there? Something that can't happen with Ben, so forget it.*

"Would you rather go someplace else?" Ben asked.

"No, Radish's is fine," she said. The little diner was within walking distance, just a few blocks from campus. It was popular for its thick burgers, mountains of greasy curly fries, bargain prices, and jovial owner.

"You don't seem that enthused, Mirabelle."

"I am, but it's just—" *It's just that I was hoping you were going to take me back to your room so we could be alone together.* "I thought we were going to study."

"We are," Ben assured her. "But that doesn't mean we can't eat while we're doing it, right?"

"I guess not."

They walked toward the main campus gate, and Ben continued holding her hand.

I should pull my fingers away, Mirabelle kept telling herself, but she couldn't seem to do it. Ben's grasp was too reassuring, too . . . exciting. She fought the urge to move closer to him so that the whole length of her arm would be against his. She tried not to imagine what his bare arm would look like. Was it smooth-skinned and muscular? How about his chest? And his shoulders?

Well, you'll never know, Mirabelle reminded herself as they arrived at the diner. *So don't get all hot and bothered by him.*

The place was crowded, and all they could find were two stools at the counter. Mirabelle told herself she should be glad that they couldn't share the cozy privacy of a booth, where she would have to sit facing Ben, looking into his face.

There wasn't anything very intimate about sitting side by side with a view of the deep fryers and pie case.

They were waited on by the owner himself, Carl Radish, nick-named "Red," perhaps because of his last name, but more likely because of his flaming curly hair.

"What can I get you?" he asked, slapping two menus and two glasses of water in front of them.

Ben looked at Mirabelle. "Do you know what you want, or do you need to look at the menu?"

"I'll have a burger and curly fries. And a Coke," she decided without hesitation.

"What do you want on the burger? The works?"

"Except onion," Mirabelle said quickly, and told herself it wasn't because she thought Ben might kiss her again, or anything.

"Same here, exactly," Ben told Red.

"No onion—first date, huh?" Red asked with a grin as he picked up the menus again.

"It's that obvious, huh?" Ben asked, returning the grin.

"You bet. Married couples, they come in and order extra onion, you know? But not kids who have big plans for later." He winked and turned back toward the grill.

"You know what I think?" Ben asked, spinning toward Mirabelle on his swivel stool.

"What?" she asked, afraid of what he was going to say. *You'd better set him straight now*, she told herself. *Tell him this isn't a date.*

"I think Red only has two menus in this place. No one ever even reads them, either. They all just order burgers and curly fries. See?" He gestured around them.

Sure enough, everyone Mirabelle spotted was eating the same thing. She smiled. "You're probably right. For all we know, there *is* nothing else on the menu."

"You know what? Someday, I'm going to take you out for a *real* dinner," Ben said in a low voice. "Someplace with tablecloths and candlelight and lobster. Do you like lobster?"

"Uh huh, but Ben . . ."

"Yeah?"

She was about to tell him that it wasn't going to happen—that they couldn't go out to dinner together, because she couldn't get involved with him. And that this wasn't a date.

But before she could say it, Red materialized again, slapped two Cokes in front of them, and announced, "We're out of tomato. If you want to wait for it, I just sent one of the girls down the street to the grocery store. Otherwise, you can have everything on your burgers except tomato."

"But not onion," Ben reminded him, and Red grinned.

"Right, no onion. So what'll it be?"

"We'll wait for the tomato, right, Mirabelle?" Ben asked, picking up his book bag and unzipping it. "We have a lot of studying to do, so we'll be here awhile anyway."

She nodded, and Red touched his thumb to his forefinger in a *gotcha* gesture, then turned away.

Ben pulled his Logic textbook and a notebook out of his bag, set them on the counter, and looked at Mirabelle. "Ready?"

"Sure," she said, and took out her own book and notes.

And as Ben started going over the assignment with her, she reminded herself that this was the only reason they were here together—so that he could help her. That was all.

But it wasn't easy to concentrate when, every time his hand brushed against hers as he showed her something on the page, she found herself feeling all tingly.

The Lawson School was just as Candra had imagined it would be. Like Adamson-Swift, it was located on a tree-lined country road, and it was surrounded by a low stone wall.

Candra steered Meg's car through the gates and pulled up in front of a two-story brick building, parking in a spot marked "Visitor."

She checked her reflection in the rearview mirror before she got out, and was pleased by what she saw. Pearls and cashmere suited her, she decided, and opened the car door.

As she walked across the front drive to the wide double doors of the building, she heard a whistle. She glanced up and saw three boys, all of them in navy pants, white shirts, and ties, eying her from the sidewalk that led to another brick building that must be a dorm.

Candra smiled, more to herself than at them, and kept walking.

She pushed open the doors and, with Meg's boots tapping pleasantly across the polished wooden floor, made her way toward a desk where a woman sat waiting and looking expectant.

"Hi," Candra said, coming to a halt and looking the woman in the eye. "I'm here to see Landon Keller."

The woman pursed her lips and said, "And you are . . ."

"A friend."

"He didn't leave word that he was expecting anyone."

"He must have forgotten," Candra said.

Sensing that the woman was about to give her a hard time, Candra fixed her with a level gaze, pinning the woman's small brown eyes through her bottle-thick glasses.

And waited.

It took only a moment before the woman cleared her throat, picked up the telephone, and said, "I'll see if he's in his room. Your name is?"

"Candra Bowen," she said, and glanced around the entry hall while the woman dialed.

The ceiling was high, and the walls were lined with ornately framed portraits of formidable-looking, stern-faced men.

Candra stepped toward the painting closest to her and glanced at the brass plaque below. It read, *Calvin Morris IV, Class of 1911, Chairman of the Board, Morris Aviation.* Everything about the man spoke of elegance and money, from his neatly trimmed mustache to the gold watch chain hanging from the pocket of a coat that was probably made of silk.

Candra thought of the million dollars that was waiting for her. She promised herself that someday, her portrait would hang someplace in a gilt frame, too, with a plaque underneath that read, *Candra Bowen . . .*

No, make that *Candra Keller*, she thought, and smiled. She liked the sound of it.

"Miss?" the woman at the desk interrupted her thoughts.

"Yes?"

"Mr. Keller will meet you in front of the building."

"Thank you," Candra said primly, and strolled toward the door as though her heart weren't beating wildly at the thought of seeing Landon again.

Outside in the crisp early evening air, she took a deep breath and let it out slowly.

She pictured his face. Would he be surprised to see her? Of course he would. Glad to see her? If the spell worked its magic, he'd be more than glad.

Only a minute or two passed before she spotted him out of the corner of her eye, hurrying toward her. It was dusk now, but even though she couldn't see his face, she recognized his broad, six-foot-tall frame and his confident walk. He wore jeans and a dark-colored sweater.

She turned toward him, fastened her eyes on him, and chanted silently to herself, focusing every ounce of energy on the spell.

Then, as he drew closer, she caught sight of his expression, and she smiled.

He was definitely glad to see her.

"Candra!" he called, nearly breaking into a run to swiftly cover the last few yards between them. He pulled her into his strong arms, and she was exhilarated. For a moment, as she rested her head on his shoulder, she could think of nothing but how much she had missed him and how right this was—how right they were, together.

Then he pulled back slightly, and she lifted her head to look up into his eyes, those familiar, oddly colored eyes that weren't green, weren't blue, weren't gray.

"What are you doing here, Candra?"

"Visiting you," she said simply.

"But it's not like you happened to be in the neighborhood . . . how did you get here?"

"I drove."

"You drove *what?*"

"A friend loaned me her car," she lied smoothly. "I've been staying with her, and I told her all about you."

"Who is she?"

"Just . . . a friend."

He smiled slightly and murmured something that sounded like, "Mysterious."

"What?"

"You. You're mysterious. I can't tell whether it's deliberate or not, but it drives me crazy."

She raised an eyebrow. "Good crazy, or bad crazy?"

"Good. Definitely good." He bent his head and captured her mouth beneath his.

Candra lost herself in his kiss, fueled by the hunger she sensed in him. He tangled his hands in her hair, and she pressed herself against him, desperate for more, desperate to belong to him . . .

No.

Desperate for him to belong to her.

She pulled back and tore her lips from his. "Landon?"

He responded with a low groan and reached for her again.

She held back. "Landon, not here. Can we go to your room?"

"No. Jack's there."

"Well, then, can we go someplace else? Someplace where we can be alone together?"

He checked his watch. "Curfew's in ten minutes. I can't leave."

"But I drove all this way to see you . . ."

"Candra, I know, but they don't fool around here. I'd be given weeks of detention if they caught me—and they most likely would. I can't risk that."

"Not even for me?"

He stared into her eyes for a long moment. She willed him to say what she needed him to say, to feel what she needed him to feel. She concentrated with all her powers on controlling Landon Keller.

"I'd do anything for you," he said finally. "You know that."

It had worked. She fought to keep from smiling. *I didn't know that before, but I do now.*

He'd just told her everything she needed to know.

"Come on," he said, catching her fingers in his hand. "Let's go."

"What about curfew?"

"What about it?"

"I can't let you get into trouble." *Not yet.*

He frowned. "I thought you just said—"

"I got carried away. I was wrong. You shouldn't risk getting detention. Then how would we see each other?"

He pulled her closer to him, so close she could feel his heart throbbing through his sweater. "Maybe I wouldn't get caught," he murmured close to her ear.

"Maybe not," she agreed. "But if you did, it would ruin everything."

"What would it ruin?"

"That's my secret, for now," she told him, and placed a finger over his lips when she sensed that he was going to protest. "After all, you said I'm mysterious—you said you liked that. So I'll just keep it up."

He broke into a grin. "You just do that, Candra." He bent toward her again. This time, his kiss was sweeter, less urgent, and she sighed when he finally lifted his lips from hers and brushed them across her neck, burying his face in the hollow above her collarbone.

Her legs were wobbly, and there was a fluttery little sensation in the pit of her stomach. She wanted him to scoop her into his arms and carry her off someplace, someplace where they could be alone and where she could forget everything but how Landon made her feel . . .

But even as she longed to push everything else aside, reality rushed at her, filling her with uneasiness.

Meg . . . the charade . . . the money . . .

The money.

One million dollars.

Enough wealth to give her everything she'd always wanted. Power . . . respect . . . possessions . . . security . . .

And Landon Keller.

"You have to go now," she whispered into his ear, reluctantly stepping back and pushing him away.

He checked his watch. "You're right. What are you going to do?"

"Drive back to Crawford Corners."

"Is that where your friend lives? The one you're staying with?" he prodded when she looked at him blankly.

"Oh . . . yes." This was dangerous. She was so distracted by the sensations he had aroused that she'd almost forgotten what she'd told him. She couldn't slip up—couldn't make him suspicious.

"Well, can you give me a number where I can reach you?" he asked.

"No," she said quickly. "I'll call you."

"Why can't I—"

"Don't worry, Landon. I'll be in touch in a day or two. I promise."

"But how will I—"

He was interrupted again, this time by a bell that suddenly started ringing from the tower nearby.

"That's it . . . curfew," Landon said, and gave her a quick peck on the cheek. "I have to go."

"Go."

She waved and watched as he sprinted back toward the brick dormitory.

As soon as he'd disappeared inside, she headed for the car. She slid behind the wheel, then sat there for a long time, thinking about Landon, before she started the engine.

He was crazy about her. He'd said he would do anything for her.

The spell she'd cast on him was working.

Just as the money-drawing spell had worked.

Why did she suddenly feel an unfamiliar, hollow little ache in her chest . . . in the vicinity of her heart?

She was going to have everything she'd always wanted.

Except . . .

Stop that. You'll have everything, she told herself fiercely.

Everything that matters.

Mirabelle and Ben were among the last customers to leave Radish's before the diner closed at ten o'clock.

As they headed down the dark street toward campus, Ben said, "So what did you think? Was it a success?"

"I think I get it at last," she told him.

"Get what?"

"The Logic stuff. Isn't that what you meant?"

"Not exactly."

"Oh."

They were both silent for a moment.

Then Ben said, "I meant tonight, as in you and me. Together. Was it a success?"

Mirabelle hesitated. "It was supposed to be just studying, Ben—remember?" But hadn't she known, really, that it was more than that from the start? To drown out the nagging little voice in her mind, she spoke more insistently. "You were just supposed to help me with my Logic . . ."

"And I did help you with your Logic," he said reasonably.

"Right. And I—thank you."

"You're welcome. Now that that's settled, what about the rest of it?"

"What 'rest of it'?" *But you know damn well, and you're not fooling him one bit. He actually sounds like he's enjoying this little discussion!*

"That kiss back in front of the dorm, for one thing."

She felt her face grow hot, embarrassed by how bluntly he'd brought it up. She didn't know what to say.

"Listen, Mirabelle . . ." He stopped walking, forcing her to stop, too, and look at him. "I like you. You seem to like me. I'm attracted to you. You seem to be attracted to me. This other person, the one you left back in Louisiana, can't be holding you back—you said that's over. So what's the problem?"

"I just . . ." She took a deep breath. "I don't want to get involved with you, Ben."

There. You said it.

Liar.

"Why not? I'm not your type?"

He was exactly her type. Smart, sharp, confident, with dark good looks . . .

Just like Alex.

That was the problem.

But she didn't want to get into all that. And suddenly, she resented being put on the spot.

"No," she said shortly, "you're not my type."

She expected him to look hurt, to retreat.

Instead, hc tilted his head, studied her carefully, and said, "Could have fooled me."

"Ben—" She stopped short and stared over his shoulder.

"What?" he asked expectantly.

"I just . . . I thought I saw someone I know . . ."

He frowned and looked around. The street was deserted. "Out here? Now? There's no one around."

"Guess not," she murmured.

But her heart was suddenly pounding like crazy.

Because she was sure she'd seen it—seen *him.*

The enigmatic dark-skinned man who had been in front of Meg's house last night.

She'd glimpsed him there, just a moment ago, a few yards behind Ben, in the shadows by a clump of bushes.

And now he was gone.

At least, she couldn't see him.

But she sensed him still, somewhere nearby, watching her.

"Come on, Ben," she said uneasily. "Let's go." She started walking toward campus, away from the man she had wanted to trust just last night—the man who suddenly seemed sinister.

Why was he lurking again?

What was he doing following her?

Maybe he wasn't. Maybe he just happened to be—

Don't be an idiot. This is no coincidence.

Why hadn't she sensed that he was nearby? She should have been in tune, should have realized that someone was lurking. What was wrong with her powers?

Ben.

He was the reason she was losing touch with her intuition. Her feelings for him were a distraction—one she couldn't afford. This wasn't a game. Something dangerous was going on—and not just with Meg.

Mirabelle was involved now, too.

"Hey, are you all right, Mirabelle?" Ben asked, keeping stride with her. "You don't have to run away from me."

"I'm not. And I'm *fine*."

To his credit, Ben didn't push her. And if he noticed she kept looking over her shoulder, he didn't mention it. He didn't say anything at all, just walked along beside her all the way back to the dorm.

At the door, she said a distracted good night, cut Ben off in midsentence as he tried to say something else, then hurried past the R.A. at the desk. She rushed up the stairs, down the hall, and pushed open the door to her room.

It was dark, but she could see that Char was there, in her bed, already asleep.

Mirabelle closed the door quietly.

Then, for the first time since she'd arrived at Wainwright, she locked it behind her.

Nineteen

It was almost midnight when Candra slipped into the house.

She was exhausted.

She had made a detour on the way home. First, she'd stopped at a convenience store and bought a flashlight. Then she'd driven into a densely wooded state park several miles off the highway. There, she'd left the car and hiked along a trail through the dark woods until she reached a suitable spot for what she was planning. It was a peaceful, secluded clearing where the ground wasn't too rock-strewn for digging. She'd filed the location away mentally, making sure she knew just how to get back to it.

Then she'd hiked back to the car and finished the long drive back to Crawford Corners.

The house was dark, and for a moment she assumed no one was home. Then, as she started up the stairs, she heard the unmistakable beat of rap music coming from Carrie's room. It wasn't blasting like it had been before, but the bass was loud enough to be distracting.

And she needed to be able to concentrate.

With a sigh, she walked down the hall and paused for a moment, her hand poised to knock on Carrie's door.

Then she heard Carrie's voice, sounding more high-pitched than usual, saying, "Hey, Eddie, don't hog it all! Leave some for me!"

She heard the unintelligible rumble of a low-pitched masculine voice, then a few moments of silence before Carrie erupted into a fit of giggles that sounded vaguely hysterical.

Candra hesitated.

Obviously, Carrie had a guy in there with her, and from the sounds of things, they were up to something—most likely drugs.

Should she interrupt anyway?

No, she decided, and turned away from the door. She wasn't in the mood to confront anyone at this hour, especially after the long drive back from New Haven, and everything she'd had to think about.

She was halfway to her room when the music on Carrie's stereo suddenly increased several notches in volume.

A jolt of anger shot through Candra.

She whirled and marched back to the door down the hall. She rapped angrily on it before she could change her mind again.

For a moment, there was no response—just the sound of hurried whispers and scrambling behind the door. Candra raised her fist to pound again just as the door was thrown open and Carrie stood in front of her.

She was a mess. Her blond hair was stringy and unkempt. Her light green eyes were bloodshot, the pupils dilated. Her baggy jeans and flannel shirt were in disarray, and she reeked of booze.

"Hi, Meg," she said with a sloppy half wave. "What's up?"

"What are you doing?" Candra looked over Carrie's shoulder. The room was a mess—clothes and books strewn everywhere, the bed unmade. There was no evidence of another person, but Candra knew that he was there, somewhere . . .

She scanned the room briefly, and her gaze rested on a door that she instinctively knew led to the closet.

"Nothin'," Carrie told her. "What are *you* doin'?" Her own question seemed to strike her as hilarious, and she went off on a fit of wild laughter.

"I'm going to bed," Candra informed her icily. "And I'd appreciate it if you'd turn off the stereo. It's too late for all this noise." Despite her irritation, Candra was pleased to note that she sounded like a bossy older sister.

And apparently, Meg *was* a bossy older sister, because Carrie rolled her eyes and slurred, "God, you're always such a priss, Meg."

"I mean it." Candra turned around and started down the hall again. Then she stopped and fired her parting shot. "Oh, and Carrie? Get Eddie out of your closet and out of this house, or I'll tell Mom."

She allowed herself a glimpse of the surprised expression on Carrie's face, then marched on down to Meg's room.

The door was half open, which was odd because she could have sworn she'd left it shut.

As she turned on the light switch and stepped inside, she heard a startled *meow*. Something black and furry leapt off the bed.

Meg's cat.

The creature stood in the center of the floor, staring at Candra with unblinking feline eyes. Then its tail stood straight up and it hissed at her.

Amused, Candra said, "Oh yeah? And what are you going to do about it? You're just an animal. Get out."

As if it had understood, the cat arched its back, then streaked past her into the hallway.

Candra shrugged. So far, Meg's cat was the only one who'd caught on to her charade. Not a bad track record.

She closed the door behind her, started toward the closet, and then stopped. Her eyes narrowed into a frown, and she looked warily around the room.

Nothing was disturbed, except for a wrinkled indentation where the cat had been lying on the bed.

But still, Candra sensed that someone had been here.

And it hadn't been Sophie, or Carrie.

She was certain of that, because whoever it was had left vibes behind.

Dark, disturbing vibes.

Mirabelle rolled onto her back again and closed her eyes.

You have to concentrate. You have to focus on projecting yourself to Meg.

But she had been trying for over an hour now, and she simply couldn't.

Damn Ben Schacter! she thought fiercely. *Damn him for forcing his way into my life!*

It wasn't just Ben who was distracting her, and she knew it.

But blaming it on Ben was a lot less disturbing than thinking about the other distraction.

She found herself listening intently as she lay in the dark, conscious of every footstep in the dorm corridor, of every creak the old building made, of the chilly night wind blowing beyond her window.

She kept wondering if the dark stranger was still out there somewhere, kept trying to tune her powers in to him, kept coming up with nothing. *Nothing.*

Who was he?

What was his connection to Meg?

Mirabelle had considered trying to call her when she'd gotten back to her room, but had decided against it. It wasn't just that she didn't want to wake Char, or that it was late to be phoning someone.

No, Mirabelle had hesitated for some reason she couldn't put her finger on.

It would be better, she had decided instinctively, to see Meg first— to check in on her.

But that just wasn't happening, no matter how hard she tried.

Feeling utterly frustrated and helpless, she finally admitted to herself that this was futile.

She just couldn't focus on astral projection, couldn't find the intense level of relaxation and concentration she would need to lift herself out of her body tonight.

She flipped back onto her side and bunched the edge of the blanket beneath her chin.

Tomorrow, she promised herself, as weariness seeped into her body and brain. *Tomorrow, I'll get to the bottom of this. . . .*

It had been a while since Carrie had turned the stereo off and let Eddie, whoever he was, out the front door.

Now the house was silent.

Candra, wearing one of Meg's long white linen and lace nightgowns, carefully opened the bedroom door and peered out into the hallway. It was dark, and there was no light or music coming from Carrie's room.

Satisfied that she could begin, she closed the door and locked it.

Again, she thought of the presence she'd sensed when she'd first come into the room. The dark vibes were with her still, but no matter how she'd tried to concentrate, she hadn't been able to conjure an image of the person who had invaded this room.

If it had been a person at all.

But there was nothing more Candra could do about it now.

She walked over to the dresser.

After clearing her mind and taking several deep breaths, she lit the candles she'd arranged there, turned off the bedside lamp, and raised her arms above her head. With her eyes closed, she willed the tension out of her body and focused her energy on the crossbone amulet that lay before her on the makeshift altar.

After a contemplative pause, she began to chant,

> *Forces of evil, of thee I do ask,*
> *assistance in planning this grim mortal task*
> *The time has come to drive from this earth*
> *She who has stolen what was mine at birth.*

For a long time, Candra stood silent and motionless.

Then she slowly lowered her arms and reached for the charm that lay on the altar. The bones felt brittle and eerily alive, and she felt herself start to shudder against her will.

Stop that! she commanded, horrified.

You have to be strong. You know what has to be done.

And now she had taken the necessary step to set her ultimate plan into motion.

There was no turning back.

Candra leaned forward and blew out the candles, plunging the room into darkness.

She felt her way over to Meg's antique carved oak four-poster bed and slipped between the crisp, starched cotton sheets. She pulled the weighty goose down comforter over her and rested her head on Meg's plump feather pillows that were tucked into imported, hand-embroidered, lace-edged cases.

She closed her eyes . . .

And thought of Meg, who was fully clothed and lying unconscious on the wooden bureau in Dalila Parker's apartment.

Candra tried to ignore the pin-prick of guilt that jabbed into her.

Restlessly, she turned onto her side and reminded herself of everything that had belonged to Meg for nearly eighteen years—of everything she herself had never had.

She waited for the familiar venom to seep into her brain, waited to be consumed by the usual intense fury at her twin sister.

It didn't happen.

What she felt was . . .

Sympathy.

And a flicker of something else, something she didn't want to feel, something she had thought she *couldn't* feel.

She simply refused to acknowledge it.

She clenched her teeth so hard her jaw ached, struggling against the emotion that threatened to spill into her full consciousness.

No! I will not give in to this. I will not let it weaken me . . .

Candra managed to steer the mental invasion away, and after a long time, exhausted from the effort, she relaxed enough to drift off to sleep.

But there, in her dreams, she found that she was a little girl again.

A little girl who felt lonely and abandoned.

A little girl who longed for the mommy who had deserted her, but even more powerfully, longed for someone else . . .

Someone she had never known—yet somehow, always known—existed . . .

The other half of herself . . .

Her sister.

In her dream, the little girl became a young woman, and she stood in front of a mirror. The reflection was distorted at first, as though the glass was warped.

But then gradually it cleared, and Candra could see her own face staring back at her.

She smiled, and the mouth in the mirror smiled.

She reached out, and the hand in the mirror reached out.

But just when she was about to touch those outstretched fingers, the mirror shattered.

Noooooo! the dream Candra screamed, then sank to the ground among the shards of jagged, broken glass. Huddled there, she wept inconsolably, feeling as though her heart had shattered, too.

When she woke in the still, dark moments just before dawn, Candra found that she'd soaked both of Meg's pillows with real, bitter tears.

"Mirabelle! What are you doing here?" Tara Cunningham asked, opening the door wearing her floral silk bathrobe. She looked over Mirabelle's shoulder at the taxi that was just pulling away from the house. "Is everything all right?"

"Everything's fine, Aunt Tara," she said quickly. "I just need to . . . is Zoe here?"

"She's upstairs getting ready for school. Are you *sure* everything's all right?"

"I'm sure." She smiled and slipped past her aunt. "I need to talk to Zoe."

She hurried up the polished, curving staircase and down the hall to her cousin's room. The door was half-open, and Mirabelle poked her head in. "Zoe?"

The radio was playing and the bed was unmade, but there was no sign of Zoe. Mirabelle stepped inside and saw that the adjoining bathroom door was closed. Then she heard the shower running and Zoe's off-key voice singing.

She plopped down on the window seat to wait.

Maybe coming over here had been a mistake. It had been an impulsive act, an idea that had popped into Mirabelle's head the instant she woke up about an hour earlier. She had set it in motion before she could think it through, knowing she had to move fast if she wanted to catch Zoe before she left for school.

Now as she wondered how much to tell her cousin, she heard the water stop running. Two seconds later, the bathroom door opened, and Zoe, with one towel wrapped around her body and another turban-style around her head, emerged.

She gave a little shriek, then stared and said, "Oh, it's only you. What are you doing here, Mirabelle?"

"Hi, Zoe."

"Hi. What are you doing here?" her cousin repeated.

Mirabelle took a deep breath. "I need to talk to you. About Meg."

"Meg McKenna? What about her?"

"I was just wondering if you've talked to her or spent much time with her these past few days."

"Nope." Zoe removed the towel from her head and started rubbing her wet blond hair with it. "Meg's been in another world."

"What do you mean by that?"

"She and her boyfriend broke up Monday night, and both of them are basically out of it. Shea's moping around school. And Meg hasn't discussed it with me or Chasey."

"Have you tried to talk to her?"

"Kind of, but her attitude is like, leave me alone. She's really spacey. In fact, last night on the phone, Chasey asked me about these earrings I had borrowed from her last week, and I'd given them to Meg to give back to her. I guess she totally forgot, which isn't like Meg. She's usually Miss Conscientious."

"Is she?" Mirabelle murmured. She was wondering if she could have been wrong about something out-of-the-ordinary going on with Meg. After all, breaking up with a boyfriend the same week you met your twin sister for the first time had to be stressful. Why shouldn't Meg be on edge and distant?

"Yeah, and not only that, but she hasn't said one word to Shea. Not one word! I thought for sure she'd be all over him, trying to get back together again. I mean, just a few days ago, she was totally in love with Shea. But everyone says she's the one who dumped him, and that she cheated on him. Personally, I can't picture Meg doing something like that, but . . ." Zoe shrugged and tossed the wet towel onto the floor. She looked closely at Mirabelle and asked, "Why do you care, anyway?"

"I'm just worried about her. I talked to her Monday and she seemed upset, and I thought maybe I could help, but . . ."

Zoe gave a little laugh. "You're really a bleeding heart type, aren't you, Mirabelle?"

"I really am," she agreed, relieved that her cousin seemed to accept such a simple motive for her interest in Meg. "So anyway, can I ride with you to school and catch Meg before she goes to class?"

Zoe looked mildly surprised. "Are you serious?"

"Yeah."

Luckily, Zoe was the kind of girl who took things in stride. She shrugged and said, "Okay," then reached for a comb. "I'll be ready in about twenty minutes. Why don't you wait downstairs with Mom? I'm sure she'll be thrilled to see you. She keeps saying she wishes you'd come over more."

"She does?" Mirabelle realized she hadn't been here to visit her aunt since she'd moved into the dorms a few weeks ago. She'd been too preoccupied with other things.

An image of Ben flashed into her mind, and she promptly shut it out. He was history.

She stood and headed for the door. "Do whatever you have to do," she told Zoe, "I'll wait downstairs."

This is the last day, Candra told herself as she walked up the wide stone steps of the Adamson-Swift school. *At this time tomorrow, I'll be on the train to New York with . . . Grandma.*

She couldn't help wondering what it was going to be like to meet the older woman who was, after all, her true grandmother.

Unlike Rosamund.

Candra hadn't thought much about Rosamund these past few days. She hadn't let herself. But now, unbidden images entered her mind.

She thought of the time when she had been bitten by a snake back in Jamaica, in the garden behind the Drayer house. It had been Rosamund who sucked the venom out of her leg, who had bandaged the wound, and who had stayed by Candra's bed that night, watching over her.

So? What does that prove? Candra thought coldly. *What was she going to do, let you die?*

And it wasn't like Rosamund had ever shown her any real warmth, or hugged or kissed her even once. It wasn't like Rosamund hadn't lied, all Candra's life, about who she really was.

But Candra thought of how frightened the woman had been on the flight to New York from Jamaica last month. She remembered feeling sorry for her, trying to comfort her. She remembered *caring* about Rosamund, and it hadn't been that long ago.

But that was before you knew the truth—before you found out that she's nothing to you. Not your grandmother. Not your flesh and blood. Nothing but a liar.

"Meg!"

Candra jumped as someone grabbed her arm. She spun around to see Chasey standing behind her in the hallway, enveloped in a cloud of expensive perfume as usual.

"God, didn't you hear me calling you for the last twenty minutes?"

Candra blinked and echoed, "Twenty minutes?"

"Okay, not twenty minutes, but I've been shouting your name, trying to catch up to you, and you've totally ignored me. I mean, what's up? Are you in a fog or something?"

"I guess I am." And that was the truth, for a change.

"Well, listen, I wanted to ask you about the earrings."

Candra snapped out of her stupor as if someone had slipped an ice cube down her back. Then, just as swiftly, she recovered and put the blank expression back on her face. She looked at Chasey. "Earrings? What earrings?"

"Duh, Meg! The ones I loaned Zoe for her senior portrait? The diamonds? The ones she gave you to give back to me?"

Candra shrugged. "She never gave me any earrings to give back to you."

Chasey's jaw dropped. "She did so!"

"No, she didn't," Candra said calmly. "I would have remembered something like that."

"Not the way you've been acting lately, Meg. You're really out of it—you have been ever since you and Shea broke up. It's like you're someone else."

Warning bells jangled faintly in Candra's brain. Was Chasey actually suspicious? Did she know, somehow?

Don't be ridiculous. She can't possibly have any idea that you're not Meg.

Still, Candra had better watch her step.

"Listen, Chasey," she said in as reasonable a voice as possible, "I'm really sorry if there's been some mix-up, but believe me, Zoe never gave me a pair of diamond earrings to give you. I may be bummed about breaking up with Shea, but I wouldn't forget something like this."

Chasey looked doubtful, but Candra could see that she was starting to waver in her conviction.

"You know," Candra continued, lowering her voice confidentially, "I don't want to accuse Zoe of anything, but you know how she is."

She was taking a chance there, because of course *she* had no idea how Zoe was. But weren't most American girls a little . . . flighty? She could imply that without coming right out and saying it, and let Chasey's brain do the rest.

"What do you mean?" Chasey asked.

"You know," Candra said. "What if she accidentally lost one of the earrings or something?"

Chasey's blue eyes widened. "What do you mean?" she asked again.

Candra shrugged. "Figure it out," she said, and started walking again.

Chasey fell into step beside her. "You think Zoe's lying to me?"

Candra didn't answer.

"If she's lying to me . . ." Chasey shook her head. "I'll see you in homeroom, Meg—I'm going to go find Zoe."

"See you." Candra kept a satisfied smile from creeping across her lips.

She'd taken a few more steps down the hallway when she became aware of . . .

Someone.

Someone whose energy was tapping directly into Candra's consciousness.

It took her a few moments to figure out who it was. She looked around the crowded school corridor and scanned the faces of the students passing by. No, none of them was sending off any kind of awareness.

Candra kept walking, slowly, and felt the presence grow stronger.

Then she spotted her.

A girl leaned against the wall outside Mr. Pfeiffer's classroom, and her gaze met Candra's immediately.

Candra stopped.

Who was she? The girl had long light brown hair, parted in the middle. It framed a face that was unenhanced by makeup, and yet was strikingly pretty. Her light green eyes had a startling intensity, and they bored unblinkingly into Candra's.

She had never seen this girl before—she was certain of that. And yet, there was something about her . . .

Candra felt an immediate connection to her.

In one casual yet deliberate movement, the girl pushed herself away from the wall she'd been leaning against and moved toward Candra.

And as she approached, Candra was struck by the fear that somehow, this girl knew who she really was—that she was going to give her away.

But when she stopped a few feet away, she said, "Meg?"

Relief coursed through Candra. This girl had some kind of psychic energy—there was no doubt about that. But she didn't know. Candra was safe—for now. She knew she had to be more careful than ever around this stranger.

"Hi," she said, trying not to sound tentative. She fixed the girl with a steady, confident gaze and waited.

"How are y'all? I've been worried."

The instant she heard that drawl, Candra realized why she'd felt a connection to the girl. She was the one who had called that first night Candra had been at Meg's house. The one who had known that Meg was supposed to meet her twin on Monday afternoon.

Candra kept her face carefully expressionless. "Worried? Why were you worried?"

"I don't know. I guess my imagination got carried away."

"Well, I'm fine," Candra said, and then, for good measure, she added, "except for the fact that Shea and I broke up."

"I heard. That's too bad."

"Yeah, well . . ." Candra shrugged noncommittally.

"What happened?"

"It was just one of those things, I guess." She changed the subject to something safer—something that might give her a clue as to who, exactly, this girl was. "What have *you* been up to?"

She hesitated, then shrugged and said, "Same old thing." Then she leaned closer to Meg and said in a low voice, "What about Candra?"

The sound of her own name on this stranger's lips sent a jolt through her. She fought to maintain her composure, struggled to keep her voice level as she said, "What about her?"

"You told me on the phone the other night that you met her at Dalila's. How did it go? What was she like?"

"She was wonderful. The moment I saw her, it was as if I already knew her."

"Are you going to tell your mother?"

"I don't know. I don't know what we're going to do. But right now, it has to be a secret. No one knows . . ."

"Except Dalila."

"Except Dalila. And you."

"I'll keep it to myself." The girl's strange, light green eyes were unwavering. They were probing Candra's face, as though trying to unearth her secrets.

Candra shifted uncomfortably.

Then, out of the corner of her eye, she saw Mr. Pfeiffer approaching down the hall.

She was about to say she had to get inside the classroom when suddenly, the girl reached out. Her fingers closed over the creamy silk of the blouse Candra wore with the plaid school uniform.

"This is pretty," she said, grasping a fold of fabric right near the top button, which Candra had left unfastened.

"The blouse? Thanks." She fought the urge to roughly push the intruding hand away. Something told her the grasp was deliberate, that the girl was up to something.

She moved closer to Candra, and her suddenly sharp gaze travelled downward. "Where's your necklace?" she asked abruptly.

"What necklace?" Now Candra did jerk backward and brush the hand away. She narrowed her eyes at the girl and tried not to betray the trepidation that coursed through her.

"The jade baby ring you always wear."

An image flashed through Candra's mind. She saw it, the tiny jade ring on a delicate gold chain. She'd left it on the unconscious Meg's neck after realizing it was soldered there.

"I . . . lost it. The chain broke."

"When?"

"The other day." Candra fought to keep the anxiety out of her voice, fought not to reveal the overwhelming rage she felt toward this stranger.

"Miss McKenna! What are you doing loitering in the corridor? Do you know what time it is?"

Never had the obnoxious teacher's voice been so welcome. Meg turned toward Mr. Pfeiffer, who lifted a thumb and jerked it in the direction of the classroom just as the homeroom bell rang.

"I have to go," Candra told the girl, and hurried into the room. She slid into her seat and looked toward the door. Just before Mr. Pfeiffer closed it, she caught a glimpse of the stranger.

She was standing in the hallway, looking thoughtful.

Twenty

Mirabelle had only met Shea Alcott once, but she easily picked him out of the crowd of students in the hallway when the bell after homeroom rang.

Still, his appearance had changed considerably in the last few weeks. Not that he was any less handsome or well-dressed. But the boy Mirabelle had met at Zoe's party had radiated confidence. Now Shea's shoulders were slumped, and his dark head was bent as he walked along alone, clasping his books against his right thigh.

Mirabelle made her way up to him and tapped his shoulder. "Shea?"

He turned around and looked at her blankly. "Yeah?"

"I'm Mirabelle Moreau, Zoe's cousin. We met at her party a few weeks ago?"

"Oh, yeah, that's right. Nice to see you again," he said politely, then tilted his head at her and looked puzzled. "Don't you go to Wainwright?"

"Yeah, I do. I'm here because I need to talk to you."

"To *me?*"

"About Meg."

His expression closed, and he set his jaw stubbornly. "I don't want to talk about Meg."

"Shea, I know you guys broke up and everything. This isn't about that. It's . . . look, can we go someplace where we can talk privately?"

"I have a class to get to," he said, shaking his head and checking his watch. But Mirabelle had spotted the flicker of interest in his eyes when she'd mentioned Meg's name.

"Can't you skip it?"

"No way. I'd get a cut slip on my record."

Mirabelle paused. Clearly, Shea Alcott wasn't the type who broke rules. She took a step closer to him and said in a lower voice, "Listen, Shea, Meg is in trouble."

"What kind of trouble?"

"Serious trouble."

He shrugged, as though to show that he either didn't believe her or didn't care, but his expression revealed stark concern.

"Shea," Mirabelle said, "I'm supposed to be in class, too. But I was so concerned about Meg that I had to come over here because I knew you were the only other person who would be able to help her."

"Meg and I are through," he protested feebly. "She's the one who wanted it that way."

"I know that's what she might have said, but she didn't mean it. At least, I don't think she did."

"What kind of trouble is she in?"

"I told you. It's serious. And *dangerous*," she added, because she was nearly certain of that now. "Please, Shea, come with me and talk to me about her."

He hesitated only briefly before saying, "All right. I'll meet you right here by the stairs in a few minutes."

"Where are you going?"

"To tell my English teacher that I won't be there this period. I'll say I have to take care of something for tomorrow's assembly. I'm senior class president. She'll let me out. That way, I won't get a cut slip."

Mirabelle couldn't help smiling at his earnest tone. "Great—I'll be waiting," she told him, and watched him move swiftly down the hall.

While she waited, her thoughts went back to Meg. Her mood darkened instantly. If what she suspected was true . . .

But it was so farfetched, it couldn't be true.

Could it?

Candra moved mechanically toward Meg's first period class, her mind still on the encounter with the strange girl outside of homeroom. She was suspicious—that much was obvious. But she couldn't know anything for sure, could she?

She might. The girl wasn't like Zoe, or Chasey, or the others Candra had met. This one had some degree of power—nothing as potent as what Candra had sensed in Meg, or in Dalila Parker, but she had something.

She was trouble.

Candra would have to take care of her before she—

"Meg! How dare you!"

Candra turned at the sound of the angry voice and found herself face-to-face with a furious-looking Zoe.

Uh-oh, she thought.

"How dare I what?" she asked sedately.

"How dare you deny that I gave you those earrings . . . and then imply to Chasey that I had lost them!"

"What earrings?"

"You know damn well. You know I gave them to you on Tuesday before homeroom, and that you promised to give them to Chasey."

"You did not," Candra said, shaking her head. "You never gave me any earrings."

"I did too, you lying—"

"You . . . did . . . *not*," Candra said in a low, menacing tone, and fixed her with a powerful stare.

Zoe actually flinched, as though she had been stabbed. She took a step backward, and the angry, accusatory look vanished from her face.

"Never mind," she mumbled after a moment, before she turned and hurried away.

Candra watched her go, her eyes still narrowed.

The wrath that had bubbled up inside her didn't fade away. She felt energized.

The bell rang, signalling that she should be in her next class.

Candra ignored it.

Instead, she turned and started down the stairs toward the front door, reaching into Meg's bag for the car keys as she went.

"Where are we going?" Mirabelle asked as Shea backed his car out of the parking lot and headed down the winding lane that led away from Adamson-Swift.

"To this little doughnut place down the road. I figured we could talk in private there."

"Good idea."

As they rounded the sharp bend at the bottom of the drive, a car on the road ahead of them was just pulling out onto the highway. It was a black Honda.

Mirabelle leaned forward and squinted. "Hey, isn't that—"

"Meg," Shea said flatly. "What's she doing leaving school grounds during a class?"

"I don't know, but follow her."

"What if she sees us?"

"She won't," Mirabelle said with more certainty than she felt.

Shea pulled out onto the road, and they picked up speed, staying a safe distance behind the Honda.

The highway led toward town, winding through a rustic area that was dotted with a mixture of affluent estates and big clapboard farmhouses. Centuries-old low stone walls and ancient trees bordered the road on both sides.

"Man, what's with her driving?" Shea muttered after a few minutes.

"What do you mean?"

"Did you see how fast she took that curve? And the speed limit out here is only forty-five. She's doing over sixty. Meg's not usually like that."

"She's normally a cautious driver?"

"Yeah, she is. I don't want to get a ticket or anything," he added nervously, checking in the rearview mirror, then glancing at the speedometer.

Mirabelle focused on the driver in the car ahead. All that was visible from this distance was the outline of her head against the seat rest.

Are you who I think you are? Mirabelle wondered. *And if you are, where's Meg?*

They passed a white road sign, and Shea said, "We're getting into town now—the speed limit's down to thirty-five. She'd better slow down."

But she didn't. If anything, she speeded up.

"I can't keep up," Shea said in a strained voice. His hands on the steering wheel were white and clenched. "She's going over seventy now. This is dangerous."

Mirabelle bit her lip and shook her head. They were losing ground, but Shea was right. They were going far too fast, and they were on the fringes of the village now.

Suddenly, without using a turn signal, the Honda made a screeching right turn onto a side road.

"Whoa, what's she *doing?*" Shea asked. "Did you see that?"

"Yeah—follow her!"

They approached the spot. He slowed, signaled and made the turn, but now the Honda was nowhere in sight.

Mirabelle scanned the road ahead through the windshield. It was narrow and winding and led through a shadowy, woodsy area.

"Do you know where we are?" she asked Shea as the car bounced over the rutted pavement.

"Somewhere near the water. There's a whole network of roads back here—a lot of summer houses. I don't know the area well at all. Do you see her?"

"No."

"I think we lost her."

"I think that was her intention," Mirabelle said grimly. "She must have seen us behind her."

Shea shot her a sidewise glance, and she saw that his eyes were worried. "What's going on, Mirabelle?"

She hesitated, glancing at the road ahead one more time. The Honda was definitely gone.

And as far as she was concerned, her suspicions had been more than confirmed.

"Okay," she said to Shea with a heavy sigh. "Let's go have that talk."

Candra steered the car along the unpaved side road that was little more than a path, until she came to a dead end. There was nothing to do now but stop and wait.

And wonder how she was going to find her way out of here.

She'd just kept turning and going deeper and deeper into the nearly deserted neighborhood, navigating a maze of curving, tree-lined lanes that went from paved to gravel to plain old dirt.

Now she leaned back in the seat, slammed her hands on the top of the steering wheel, and cursed out loud.

Damn that girl—who was she?

Candra had sensed the presence in the car behind her as soon as she'd pulled out onto the highway in front of the school. She hadn't wanted to let on that she knew she was being followed, but she'd kept her eye on the car in the rearview mirror.

As soon as she'd realized that the driver was Meg's boyfriend, Shea, she'd felt a stab of panic. Her mind had raced as she drove along with them behind her.

Too many people were involved now. Too many people could get suspicious.

She felt as though everything was closing in on her. If she didn't make her escape soon, she was going to be trapped. Someone would figure things out and go to the police, and then what?

The money. Think about the money.

And Landon. You've almost got him. . . .

Everything's finally coming together.

You just have to hold on for one more day. Less than twenty-four hours.

The thought had calmed her enough that she could think clearly again and concentrate on driving. That was when she'd realized that the first thing she had to do was lose the car behind her.

It hadn't been hard. She had instinctively known that someone like

Shea wouldn't keep up and go over seventy in a thirty-five-mile-an-hour zone.

She'd lost them all right . . . for now.

But she had to keep them out of her hair until tomorrow.

The worst part was, dodging Shea and that nosy southern stranger had to be the least of her priorities. She had other things to take care of.

Starting with Meg.

And now she was more determined than ever not to let any crazy emotions get in the way. She had to concentrate on taking care of herself, and to hell with everyone else. If she didn't, everything she had worked for would be lost.

Candra sighed and set her mouth grimly. She knew what had to be done, and she couldn't put it off any longer.

POSSESSION

Dedicated to my nieces, Elizabeth and Caroline,
And to David and Nancy, with love

To my boys, Morgan and Brody,
And, again, to Mark

One

Elmont Avenue was the broad main drag in what had once been a colorful section of Spring City. Years ago, the neighborhood had been home to jazz bars, nightclubs, and restaurants that had drawn the wealthy New Yorkers who summered in Westchester County and Connecticut. Now many of those places had been turned into sleazy bars or X-rated video stores, and some of them were boarded up or falling down. Bums lay in doorways, and the occasional hooker paraded down the street or loitered on the corner. Shady characters congregated here and there, and shifty-eyed kids roamed around looking for trouble.

Amidst the seedy atmosphere there was a conclave of immigrants from the Caribbean region. Many of them worked for the wealthy families in nearby Crawford Corners or Greenwich.

As a result of their presence, new businesses had begun to crop up on the Elmont strip. Small fruit and vegetable markets sold plantains and papayas and mangos. Secondhand stores featured bright-colored clothing and beaded jewelry. And a few dimly lit occult shops sold herbs and incense and special powders, among other things.

It was in front of one of these shops that Candra Bowen parked her twin sister Meg's Honda. She stepped out, set the alarm, and looked around again to make sure Meg's boyfriend Shea's car wasn't lurking somewhere nearby. She hadn't seen it behind her as she drove here, though she felt vaguely aware of a lingering sense of danger.

Still, the car was nowhere to be seen. She must be imagining things.

Candra walked briskly toward the shop. She pushed the door open and was greeted by the sound of reggae music and a pungent, spicy aroma that instantly carried her back to Jamaica.

Caught off guard by an unexpected wave of homesickness, she hesitated in the doorway.

"Good mornin', my lady, can I help you today?" a voice said in a familiar, lilting dialect.

Candra turned and saw an enormous woman sitting in the corner, beside a counter. Her skin was so black that her eyes and teeth looked stark in contrast, and her round body was clad in a garish turquoise and orange caftan.

"Yeah, *mon,* I need to buy a few things." As soon as the words had left her lips, Candra realized she'd forgotten to use the American accent that had started to become second nature to her. Now her accent was as pronounced as the shopkeeper's Jamaican *patois.*

She shifted uncomfortably and looked hard at the woman, who didn't seem fazed.

She merely nodded, and, with a grunt, hoisted her enormous heft out of the chair. She lumbered over to stand behind the long glass counter that lined one wall of the shop. On a shelf behind the counter was a portable tape player and a stack of tapes. She reached up and turned down the volume, then turned back to Candra.

"And what items would you be needin' today, my lady?" the woman asked, motioning around. "I have everything here. Everything. You see?"

Candra stepped over and glanced at the objects that were arranged inside the counter on a tattered length of black velvet. There were pentacles, chalices, and ritual knives with carved handles. There were cords of different materials and colors, and bowls and incense burners. On a wide tray at one end was an arrangement of wands, some of them crystal, some made of wood or silver.

"You need something in this case, *mon?*" prodded the woman. "What do you need? Let me take something out and show you."

"No, nothing that's in there," Candra said, and turned around. "I need . . ."

She trailed off. Against the opposite wall was a wide network of shelves that were lined with stacks of vials and jars and candles and paper-wrapped packages.

That was more like it. She moved over and started to inspect the contents of the shelves.

"You browse, my lady," the woman said as the reggae song ended. "I'm going to change this cassette tape. Maybe we hear some Bob Marley, eh?"

Candra nodded, scanning a row of small jars. *There.* She reached up and selected one that contained a rust-colored powder. One ingredient down, two to go.

She moved over to a display of vials that held different oils. It didn't take her long to locate the one she needed.

Behind her, the reggae music had started on the tape player again, and the woman asked, "You finding what you want, *mon?*"

"Mmm hmm."

Now for the last item. Candra examined a neat stack of paper-wrapped parcels, each marked with the name of a different root. She found the one she needed and pulled it off the shelf, then walked back over to the woman.

She set the items on the counter and said, "That's it."

The woman nodded and turned to the cash register. As she rang in the last item, she looked up at Candra. "These three things together will cast a powerful spell, my lady."

Candra nodded. She met the woman's scrutiny with a level gaze of her own.

After a moment, the woman shook her head and muttered, "That's your business."

"That's right," Candra agreed, reaching for Meg's wallet. "How much do I owe you?"

Shea looked at his watch as the waitress walked away after taking his and Mirabelle's order.

"What's wrong?" Mirabelle asked, though she knew. Shea wasn't the type of boy who would take cutting school lightly. But she knew he was desperate to make sure Meg was all right. "You're going to miss another class?"

He nodded, then said, "It's okay. This is more important." He leaned forward, propped his elbow, rested his chin on his open hand, and looked at her. "Tell me what's going on."

Mirabelle took a deep breath. "I don't know where to start."

"The beginning is always a good place," Shea prompted.

So she started there. She told him how, the first time she had met Meg, at Zoe's party, she had sensed that Meg had powers.

"Powers?" Shea repeated incredulously. "What are you talking about?"

And so Mirabelle had to backtrack even further, and tell him about Cecile, her family's maid back in New Orleans, and her own voodoo powers. She could see the doubt building in Shea's expression as she talked, and finally, she broke off and said, "You don't believe me."

"You're right," he told her as the waitress came back to their booth with a tray. "I don't."

Mirabelle waited until the woman had set down a steaming cup of coffee in front of her and a foamy, whipped-cream-topped hot chocolate in front of Shea, then walked away again.

Then she said, "I know it's not something that seems plausible at first, Shea, but you've got to believe me."

"You're trying to tell me Meg McKenna—my *girlfriend*—is a witch?" he asked, and shook his head. "Impossible."

"That's not what I'm trying to tell you at all. You're missing the point. I'm saying that Meg has a certain—energy—that, should she choose to develop it, could allow her to have control over different aspects of her life, and other people's lives."

"Uh-huh, right." Shea sipped his cocoa.

Frustrated, Mirabelle dumped creamer into her coffee, stirred it, then set the spoon down and said, "Look, whether or not you believe this is beside the point. The real issue here is that Meg's gotten involved in something that's way over her head."

"What do you mean?"

Mirabelle told him everything she knew then—about the box Mirabelle had found in her grandmother's attic, and about the mystery surrounding her birth, and about Dalila Parker, the enigmatic woman who had mistaken her for someone else. Someone who looked just like Meg.

Shea listened and asked an occasional question. She could tell that though he found some of this surprising, he didn't seem to doubt any of it.

She concluded with how, on Monday afternoon, Meg had gone over to Dalila's apartment to meet the twin sister she had never known. And how, ever since then, she'd been distant and—well, different.

"You're right about that," Shea said. "We broke up Monday night. I went over to her house, just like I'd told her I would. We were going to get back together—we'd talked about it at school that afternoon, and she'd told me she would explain everything that night. I guess she was going to tell me all the stuff you just did."

"Probably."

"But she didn't. When I got there that night, she was acting really strange."

"Strange, how?"

"I don't know . . . not like herself. What do you think happened, Mirabelle?"

She hesitated. If she told him what she suspected, would he think she was out of her mind?

There was only one way to find out.

She sipped her coffee, put her cup down, and cleared her throat. "I think that the reason Meg's not acting like Meg is because she's *not*."

"She's not what?"

"Not *Meg*." Mirabelle looked Shea in the eye and said, "Meg's gone, Shea. The person you and I just saw driving her car was Candra."

Out on the avenue again, Candra tucked the small brown paper bag into Meg's leather purse and decided to walk the few blocks to Dalila Parker's apartment over Rivera's Newsstand.

As she moved down the sidewalk she attracted whistles and catcalls from men on the street, and honks from those who passed by in cars.

She couldn't help being pleased at the attention.

She was still wearing the plaid school uniform, but it was short enough to show off her long, lean legs. She swung her hair as she moved down the street, feeling momentarily carefree.

Then, as she waited to cross a busy side street, she felt a prickle of awareness coming over her again.

Startled, she looked around, half-expecting to see Shea's car behind her.

It wasn't there.

But the sensation grew steadily stronger.

Someone was nearby.

Who?

The light changed and Candra moved across the street. When she reached the opposite curb, she looked over her shoulder again, then scanned the sidewalk and street ahead. She didn't see anything out of the ordinary. Cars and buses moved along, and here and there, people loitered or walked or sat on steps, all of them strangers.

Puzzled, Candra picked up her pace.

Again, she glanced over her shoulder.

Behind her on the sidewalk she saw an older white woman dressed in shabby clothes and carrying shopping bags, and, farther back, a young-looking black man who was walking along with his head down.

She'd never seen either of them before.

And yet . . .

She couldn't shake the eerie feeling that she was being shadowed.

She crossed another street. This was the last block before Dalila's. She walked quickly, as though that would allow her to escape whatever, or whoever, was making her anxious.

But the feeling grew more intense.

She looked back again. The woman who'd been there was gone.

Now only the young black man remained. He wore black pants and a black coat, Candra noted vaguely. He was too far behind her for her to make out his features, but he raised his head, and Candra could feel him staring at her.

He's just some neighborhood guy—probably one of the ones who whistled at me before, she told herself.

But she wasn't reassured.

There was something about him—something that made her uneasy.

Candra turned her head again and kept walking, fighting back the sense of panic that was building inside her.

A few more steps, and she had reached Rivera's Newsstand. She stopped in front of the door that led to Dalila's apartment above, then looked over her shoulder one more time.

The man was gone.

But she knew that he was still nearby. He might not be watching her, but he was in tune with her on a deeper, *darker* level.

The realization made her tremble.

She hesitated, wondering what to do.

But what *could* she do? The man was a stranger. He'd done nothing but walk down the street.

Get hold of yourself, Candra, she thought, and took a deep breath, let it out slowly.

Could it be that all the stress she had been through lately was causing her mind to play tricks on her?

Was she imagining danger where there was none?

That had to be it, she concluded. Just her imagination.

It *had* to be.

Mirabelle looked at Shea as they walked out of the diner, leaving behind their unfinished beverages and a few dollars they'd tossed on the table to cover the bill.

"Are you all right?" she asked again.

"Fine," he repeated. "Really."

But he didn't look fine at all. His handsome face was pale and she could see his hands trembling as he fumbled in his pocket for the car keys.

He unlocked the passenger's side door and opened it for her, then went around to the other side and climbed in. As he put the keys into the ignition, Mirabelle reached out and touched his sleeve.

"Wait," she said. "Shea, I know you need to get back to class, but—"

"No," he interrupted. "I'm not going back to school today. I just . . . I can't."

"What about—I mean, won't you get into trouble?"

He shrugged.

Mirabelle hesitated, then said, "Look, Shea, I know you're pretty shocked right now. I feel the same way, believe me. But we've both got to get past that and concentrate on what's important."

"Meg," he said in a voice that was barely audible.

She nodded. "We've got to find her."

"We've got to go to the police."

"We can't," Mirabelle said immediately.

"Why not?"

"What would we tell them? That Meg is missing, even though she's not? That Meg isn't Meg, even though she looks just like her? They'll think we're nuts."

"Not if we explain the whole story."

"We can't. There's no proof of anything. And besides, we don't *know* the whole story. There's way more to this than you can imagine."

"What do you mean by that?"

"I mean, it's just like I told you before. Meg is mixed up in something very . . . dark. Something the police have no control over."

"Yeah, right. Meg's a witch."

Frustrated by his mocking tone, Mirabelle folded her arms and looked out the window.

After a moment of silence, Shea cleared his throat and said, "I'm sorry, Mirabelle. It's just that I have a hard time believing that my girl-friend, who is the most normal person in the world, has some kind of magical powers, or whatever."

She looked at him. "I told you, she wasn't even aware of them."

"I know what you told me." He sighed. "Aside from that, what are we talking about here?"

"Voodoo. Black Magic. Whatever you want to call it—that's what's happening, on some level. And we have to be extremely careful, Shea. This isn't something you handle lightly."

He was staring at her in disbelief. "Voodoo. Black magic," he echoed, then slapped the steering wheel and shook his head. "Mira-belle, no offense, but I don't buy it."

"Why not?"

"There's no such thing as magic."

"Maybe not in your world—at least, not that you know of. But where I come from, it's real, Shea, and you don't mess with it. You have to believe me when I tell you that Meg stumbled into something that's way over her head, and there's no easy way out."

"How do you know?"

She paused. She couldn't tell him about the strange, dark-skinned man she'd seen outside Meg's house, and again on the street near campus. It didn't necessarily mean anything—at least, it wouldn't to Shea. But the more Mirabelle thought about the man, the more certain she was that he was part of something powerful—and sinister.

"Mirabelle? How do you know all this?" Shea asked again.

"Intuition," she said simply.

She waited for him to scoff again.

But he didn't. He was just quiet for a long time.

Mirabelle looked out the window. Outside, the day that had started off sunny and unseasonably warm had become gray and chilly. When she got back to campus, she'd have to go back to her room for a jacket before going to class.

For some reason, she thought of Ben Schacter, then promptly tried to push the image of him out of her head.

It wouldn't budge.

She saw his face again, felt his reassuring grasp on her hand. . . .

With Ben, she had felt safe. She'd been removed from this whole crazy Meg thing in those fleeting moments they'd spent together. Ben was so solid, so levelheaded . . .

How would he react if he knew what Mirabelle was tangled up in? Would he think she was out of her mind? Or would he somehow be able to help?

Of course he couldn't help, she told herself. *Don't even think of dragging him into this. Don't even think of having anything to do with him, period. You already made up your mind to steer clear of guys like Ben. Remember what happened with Alex?*

Shea's voice startled her. "So if we don't go to the police," he said abruptly, "what do you suggest we do?"

It took a moment for Mirabelle to focus again. When she did, she realized that until now, she'd had no idea what they should do. All she knew was that they had to find out where Meg was.

But as she thought about it, she realized that there was one person who might be able to help.

"Dalila Parker," she said resolutely.

Shea blinked. *"What?"*

"Dalila Parker. She's the woman I told you about, the one who was supposed to introduce Meg to Candra."

"What about her? You think she knows where Meg is?"

Mirabelle hesitated. "I don't know. If she *does* . . . then I guess it would mean she's involved somehow. Although I doubt that. I didn't get that kind of feeling about her."

"You don't think she'd hurt Meg?"

"I don't think she would. But . . ." Mirabelle shook her head. She'd been so distracted lately, could she really trust her own perception of Dalila?

She sat up straight and looked at Shea.

"Mirabelle? Now what?"

"If you're not going back to school, let's go over there and see what we can find out," she said, motioning at the keys in the ignition. "Come on."

"Where is 'there'?"

"Elmont Avenue in Spring City."

"Elmont Avenue! Do you know what kind of neighborhood that is?"

"Yeah, it's pretty bad. But that's where Dalila lives. And it's not that big a deal—we'll be fine. Come on, Shea. Let's go." Suddenly, she felt an urgent need to get to Dalila's.

He shrugged and, looking reluctant, started the engine.

Don't worry, Meg, Mirabelle thought as Shea pulled out onto the highway. *We're going to find you and get you out of this mess. Just hang in there, wherever you are.*

Two

"Candra? What are you doing here, *mon*?" Dalila Parker asked in her thick Jamaican accent. She stood in the doorway of her apartment wearing a flowered housedress and an orange turban wrapped around her head. Vibrant beaded earrings dangled against her cheeks, and on both wrists she wore stacks of brightly colored bangles.

"How have you been, *mon*?" Candra asked, shedding her American accent once again.

She stepped past the woman into the familiar apartment. The splashy color scheme was a stark contrast, not just to the cloudy day outside, but to the seedy neighborhood itself, and to the dingy stairway that led up to Dalila's door. Crossing the threshold was like walking into a Caribbean beach scene.

Candra glanced at the tropical fabric that covered the couch and chairs, the jungle of plants, the aquarium filled with exotic fish, and the parakeets in their birdcages near the window. On the clean white walls were framed posters in coral and turquoise and yellow and purple, island-style art that depicted simply drawn stick people and animals.

"What do you want, *mon*?" Dalila asked again in her lilting *patois*.

Again, just as she had been earlier in the store, Candra was being swept by a wave of homesickness.

She forced it away.

It was bad enough that she'd been distracted by her wild imagination out on the street, when she'd convinced herself that that man was following her. She needed to gather her wits about her now.

She shot the woman a level look and forced her voice to sound businesslike. "I just wanted to see how things are going. You know, with . . ." She trailed off and gestured at the closed door that led to Dalila's bedroom.

Behind that door, she knew, Megan McKenna lay prone on the long dresser top, looking for all the world like she was merely asleep.

"It's fine, *mon*," Dalila said. "Why wouldn't it be?"

"Of course it's fine." Candra shrugged. Out of the corner of her eye, she spotted Dalila's cat, Erzulie, lying on a throw rug nearby.

Good, she thought. *This might work.*

"I also wanted to thank you, Dalila," she continued, reaching out and taking the woman's ebony-skinned hand in hers. She squeezed Dalila's fingers and injected a note of warmth into her tone. "I don't know what I would have done without you. You're the only one who's ever understood me. You cared enough about me to help me make my most precious dream come true, and I hope you know how much it means to me."

She raised her eyes and glanced at Dalila's face. The woman was studying her intently, and Candra could tell she wasn't entirely buying this sudden heap of gratitude.

No, Dalila was wary. And she should be.

But Candra was going to get past that.

"So? Did you meet your mother, like you wanted to?" Dalila asked, pulling her hand out of Candra's grasp.

"I'll tell you all about everything. Why don't we sit down and have a cup of tea?" Candra suggested.

Dalila tilted her head and shrugged. "Why not," she agreed. "I'll go put the water on. Come on into the kitchen with me."

"All right, but first I need to use your bathroom."

"Over there," Dalila said, jerking a thumb at a door on the opposite wall.

"Thanks." Candra made her way over. Inside the bathroom, she locked the door behind her and turned on the water in case Dalila was listening on the other side.

She unzipped her purse and, trying not to rattle the bag, took out the items she'd bought at the store down the street. She spread a tissue on the edge of the sink and swiftly sprinkled the powder and the herb into the center of it. She carefully folded the tissue, tucked it into her pocket, then opened the package containing the root. She removed a gnarled stalk half the length of a pencil and put that into her pocket, too.

Then she stashed the bag back in her purse, zipped it, and flushed the toilet. As she reached for the doorknob, she willed the room on the other side to be empty.

It was, except for the snoozing cat on the rug.

She could hear Dalila moving around in the kitchen.

Moving with combined stealth and speed, Candra slipped over to the door that led out to the hall. She opened it cautiously, just a crack. Then she approached Erzulie, who was still asleep a few feet away.

In one quick motion, she swooped down over the cat, picked her up, and deposited her in the hallway outside the door. She closed it with a quiet click, muffling the cat's startled *meow*.

Then she strolled into the kitchen, patting her pocket casually to make sure the tissue packet and the root were both still there.

"What kind of tea do you like?" Dalila asked, busy at the counter. She had taken two mugs out of the cupboard and was peering into a glass canister.

"What do you have?"

"Regular, camomile, rose hip . . ."

"Regular's fine."

"No problem, *mon*."

Candra watched as Dalila took out two tea bags and put one in each mug just as the kettle on the stove started rattling. Dalila quickly took it off the burner before the low-pitched whistle could build and poured steaming water into the cups.

"Have a seat," she said, gesturing at the small table in a corner of the tiny kitchen.

"Why don't we go into the living room?" Candra suggested quickly, then added, "My back is bothering me and I'll be more comfortable on the couch."

Dalila shrugged, picked up both mugs, and headed for the other room.

Candra followed, making a point of rubbing her shoulders as though they were aching. She settled back into the couch and said, "That feels good."

Dalila frowned. "What happened to your back, *mon*?"

"I don't know—I guess I pulled it out somehow." She watched as the woman set both mugs down on the coffee table in front of the couch. She was about to sit in a nearby chair when Candra looked around and said, "Where's Erzulie? Don't you have her anymore?"

"Of course I have her. She's right—" Dalila turned and started to gesture at the spot on the rug near the door where the cat had been snoozing. "She was right there. Where is she?"

"I haven't seen her." Candra leaned forward and pulled one of the mugs toward her. The other one was within easy reach. "I hope she didn't get out when you opened the door to let me in, Dalila."

"She does that sometimes, but I didn't think she—Erzulie, here kitty, kitty," the woman said, walking around the room and making kissing sounds. "Erzulie?"

"What was that?" Candra asked.

"What?" Dalila stopped and listened.

"I don't know, I just thought I heard a meowing sound coming from somewhere. Maybe out in the hall?"

Dalila frowned and crossed to the door.

Candra immediately reached into her pocket and withdrew the small tissue packet and the root.

As Dalila undid the locks and opened the door, Candra emptied the mixture of powder and herb into the mug that was farthest from her.

"Erzulie?" Dalila called stepping out into the hall. "Are you out here? Come on, kitty. . . ."

Candra swiftly stuck the root into the tea and stirred it around, chanting silently.

"There you are, you sneaky, naughty girl. What are you doing out here?" Dalila bent and scooped the cat into her arms, then closed and locked the door again and turned back to Candra. "I didn't even see her slip past me when I let you in," she said, shaking her head. "I must be getting old."

Candra tried to be casual about tucking the wet piece of root and crumpled tissue back into her pocket. "You're not getting old. I didn't see her do it either."

Dalila set the cat down and shook her head, coming back over to the chair. She sat down and reached for her mug of tea. "Now tell me about your mother."

"Well, actually, she isn't around. She and Meg's stepfather are out of the country."

"Out of the country? Where?" Dalila paused with the cup half-raised to her lips.

"In Fiji. On vacation. They won't be back for a few more days." She tried not to stare as the woman sipped her tea at last. To focus on something else, she averted her gaze and caught sight of Erzulie. The cat was a few feet away, sitting perfectly still. Her feline eyes were fixed intently on Candra, as if to say, *I know what you're up to.*

"Well," Dalila said, lowering the mug again, "If your mother's out of town, you're out of luck."

"What do you mean?"

"You only had one week to see her. In a few days, I take the spell off your twin in there."

"That's what I wanted to talk to you about."

"No, *mon.*"

"No, what?"

"No, I'm not going to extend the spell," Dalila said firmly. "We had a deal. It's a shame you didn't get to spend time with your mother, but that's not my fault. I can't be involved any longer than I agreed to be. I don't like this. I need to get your sister out of here."

"I didn't say she wouldn't be out of here." Candra sipped her own steaming tea and willed Dalila to drink more of hers.

As if spurred by the silent command, the woman raised her cup and downed some more. When she'd finished swallowing, she said, "What do you mean, *mon*? You want me to keep the spell on her and move her someplace else?"

A smile curved Candra's lips. "Exactly."

"No way, *mon*."

Drink some more tea, Dalila. Go ahead. Drink it down.

Candra said, "You don't even know what I want you to do."

Dalila seemed as though she was about to protest again, but instead she hesitated, then said, "Okay, what is it?"

Candra cleared her throat, leaned forward, and lowered her voice to a near-whisper. "I want you to take Meg out into the middle of nowhere, to the spot I picked out, and I want you to dig a hole, and I want you to put her in it. Do you understand what I'm saying?"

Dalila's eyes widened in dismay, but Candra noticed with satisfaction that they were beginning to look a little glassy. The spell was starting to work.

"You're talking about murder," Dalila protested, but her voice sounded almost flat. She set down her mug on the table.

Candra said nothing, just looked at her.

"I can't kill someone, Candra. I can't do that."

"Not even," Candra took a dainty sip of her own tea, "for a lot of money?"

"How much money?" Dalila asked, then in the next breath shook her head and said again, "No, *mon*. I can't kill someone."

"A hundred thousand dollars." Candra had planned to offer her more—as much as it took. But maybe it wouldn't take much. The woman was under a powerful spell.

"A hundred thousand dollars?" Dalila made a scoffing sound and picked up the mug again. "Where are you going to get that kind of money? You have nothing."

Candra tilted her head. "Don't be so sure, Dalila. I'm not Candra this week, remember? I'm Meg."

The woman stared at her.

"And as Meg," Candra continued, "I have everything Meg has. Everything I *should* have had all along. It's only right, Dalila. *It's my turn!*"

Her voice rose on the last three words and she clamped her mouth shut, struggling to remain calm.

"I see what you're saying, Candra," Dalila said. A tiny frown settled between her dark eyebrows. "But I can't do it."

"Why not? Think about the money. Think about *me,* Dalila. I've had nothing my whole life, because *she* stole it all from me." She jerked a hand in the direction of the closed bedroom door. "She had everything, the house, the clothes, the fancy school, the car—a family. She had a family. I had no one. She had our mother. As far as they were concerned, I didn't even exist!"

Candra stood up and her angry words blazed through the quiet room.

"You don't have to help me, Dalila. And I don't expect you to understand. But this past week, for the first time in my life, I've felt like I was *someone*. People have treated me differently. They've noticed me. They've respected me."

But it wasn't you, an inner voice intruded. *You were pretending to be someone else.*

She sank into the couch again and rubbed her temples. Suddenly, she was exhausted. She didn't want to try, any longer, to convince this woman to help her, and she didn't want to think about how miserable her life had been before she'd stepped into Meg's world.

She just wished everything would go away—Meg, Dalila, her mother . . .

And what about Landon Keller?

Just thinking about his all-American good looks, about the way he had kissed her, made Candra tingle.

And what about the money?

You know you don't want the money to go away. Landon either. You can have it all, and you will if you can just hold on a little longer. Don't give up on it now—not when you're so close . . .

She moved her hands from her face and looked up at Dalila.

The woman was sitting absolutely still, clutching her mug between her palms and staring off into space.

"Dalila?" Candra prodded.

As if she was coming out of a trance, Dalila blinked and focused on her. "Yeah, *mon,* I understand."

"What?"

"I understand what you're saying. I'll do it."

"Do what?"

"Whatever you say."

Candra felt a pinprick of guilt. *This isn't Dalila talking. It's the spell. She has no control over her own mind, her own actions, and she's sitting here agreeing to murder. Look what you've done.*

But Candra forced those thoughts away and focused on what was important.

"You'll help me?" she asked, just to be sure.

Dalila nodded. "Yeah, *mon.* For a hundred thousand dollars, I'll do it."

Power. What an exhilarating sense of power, knowing that her wish was this woman's command.

Money and magic—what a combination!

There's nothing you can't do, Candra told herself, feeling a delicious prickle of excitement. *There's nothing that can't be yours now.*

She fought the urge to hug herself in anticipation, instead folding her hands in her lap and focusing intently on Dalila's willing face.

"I'm glad you see things my way," she said smoothly. "Now here's you need to do . . ."

"Turn right! You can park right over there," Mirabelle said, pointing to a spot on a side street off of Elmont.

Shea automatically made the turn, but protested, "I can't leave the car on the street around here, Mirabelle. I mean . . . *look.*"

She glanced out the window and saw a group of scuzzy-looking teenage boys eyeing them from the steps of a run-down house nearby. "It'll be fine, Shea. It's broad daylight. No one's going to do anything."

"Yeah, right." Still, he pulled into the spot she'd indicated, between a twenty-year-old Buick that was missing its hubcaps and a rattletrap pickup truck with plastic sheeting fixed over the spot where the side window should have been. He put the car in Park and hesitated with his hand on the key, again looking nervously at the group of kids.

"Think of Meg," Mirabelle said, as a bum teetered along the sidewalk, sipping from a bottle in a paperbag.

"I *am* thinking of Meg. It makes me sick that she's been hanging around in this neighborhood, for God knows what reason. Do you know what kind of lowlifes there are around here? Do you know what they can do to innocent girls like Meg?"

Mirabelle just nodded. Now wasn't the time to remind him that Meg was apparently involved with people who were far more threatening than the vagrants and street kids on Elmont.

"Come on, Shea," she said, putting her hand on the door handle.

"Let's go. This shouldn't take long. We just have to find out if Dalila knows anything."

He nodded and got out of the car. He shot a wary look at the kids on the steps as he locked the doors.

"Don't *worry*," Mirabelle said, grabbing his arm and pulling him across the street. "It's only a car."

"I know. But if something happens to it, my dad'll have a fit. He'll want to know what the hell I was doing in this section of town. He'll probably think I'm on drugs—he's always asking me about that."

"Your dad thinks you're on drugs?"

Shea shrugged as they walked around the corner onto Elmont. "It's because he used to be pretty messed up himself, before he went through rehab—which was after he left me and my mom. Now he's a model husband and father to his new family. And he keeps telling me to stay out of trouble. As if I'd want to get *into* trouble, after growing up watching what drugs and booze did to him."

"Mmm hmm." Mirabelle had stopped entirely listening to Shea. She looked over her shoulder as they headed down Elmont, then scanned the sidewalk ahead. Something wasn't right. She was getting bad vibes.

"Mirabelle?"

"Yeah?" She darted a glance at Shea, then checked over her shoulder again.

"I said, is everything all right?"

"Yeah." She picked up her pace. "Come on, let's get to Dalila's. It's a block away."

"You seem like something's wrong."

"Nothing's wrong." *Not that I can see. But there's something, somewhere . . .*

The block before Rivera's Newsstand was long and lined with several porn video stores, a run-down mom and pop market, and a few occult shops. The shops, most of which didn't have signs, were identifiable by the odd assortments of items displayed in the windows. Back in New Orleans, Mirabelle had been no stranger to places like these. But here she hadn't yet ventured into one—there had been no need. Yet.

Now, as she passed the last occult shop before the corner, she felt an almost magnetic tug. She turned, looked in the window, and gasped.

"What?" Shea asked, touching her sleeve as she stopped on the sidewalk. "What happened?"

She blinked and peered at the storefront.

"Mirabelle?"

"I just . . . it's . . . it's nothing," she said faintly, staring.

"Then why are you looking at that store like that?" Shea followed her line of vision. "Is that a *skull* in the window?"

Mirabelle nodded vaguely.

"No wonder you're freaked out."

"It's not a real one," she said, trying to focus on what he was saying. "It's carved, you know, like—a decoration."

"Nice," Shea said, shaking his head.

"Yeah, well, come on." She started walking again. "Dalila lives right over that newsstand across the street."

As they stood waiting for the light to change, Mirabelle threw one last look over her shoulder. She half-expected to see him standing there on the sidewalk, staring at her.

But he wasn't there.

No, and she was sure she had only imagined seeing the familiar glittering black eyes of the dark-skinned man watching her from inside that store.

"Do you understand everything?" Candra asked Dalila one more time.

"Yeah, *mon.*" She nodded, and Candra tried not to be bothered by the detached look in her eyes or the mechanical sound of her voice.

"Good. And you're sure you can do it?"

Dalila lifted a shoulder, as if to say, *Why not?* "No problem, *mon,*" she said in an offhand manner. As the spell had taken a more solid hold on her over the past hour, she had been entirely agreeable, not at all fazed by the details of Candra's plan.

It was Candra who was having a hard time with it. Even as she laid it out neatly, step-by-step, for Dalila, she found herself balking mentally, emotionally. It was all she could do to keep from telling Dalila to forget it, that she'd changed her mind, that she couldn't do something so drastic—at least, not just yet.

But then she kept reminding herself that *she* didn't have to do anything. It was Dalila who would handle the whole thing.

All Candra had to do was give orders . . . then leave, and never look back.

Now she set down her mug—the tea had long since grown cold— and rose from the couch, shaking her long hair back from her face. "I'm going to go now," she told Dalila. "I have a few details to take care of. But I need you to make sure that you—"

She broke off and stood absolutely still, listening, suddenly wary.

"What is it?" Dalila asked after a minute, watching Candra from her chair. "Did you hear something?"

"No, it's not that, I just . . ."

I felt something.

It was an all-too-familiar, keen awareness of something—or someone—threatening.

Whatever—*whoever*—it was, they were nearby.

Her thoughts flew to the dark-skinned man she'd glimpsed on the street earlier.

But no, it wasn't him. She was certain of that.

This sensation was different than the chill that had overtaken her as she'd walked to Dalila's. That had been stark, irrational fear.

This was more like a vague anxiety, the same thing she had felt when she'd been driving away from the school earlier. . . .

Could Shea and that strange Southern girl have followed her here? Were they lurking somewhere nearby?

She discarded the possibility, even as she acknowledged that she seemed to be sensing their presence again. It was impossible. She hadn't seen them behind her. She was positive of that.

But then . . .

"Somebody's here," Dalila said, as a door suddenly creaked somewhere downstairs.

Candra heard footsteps—two pairs of them—coming up the stairs. And though she didn't hear their voices, she was instantly certain that her instincts had been right. It was Meg's boyfriend and that nosy girl—she was sure of it. They had found her somehow.

She fixed Dalila with a grim, warning gaze and held a finger to her lips, motioning for the woman to be quiet.

Dalila nodded. At her feet, Erzulie kept her suspicious feline eyes leveled at Candra, but she, too, seemed tuned in to the approaching visitors. Her back arched and her tail stood upright.

There was a knock on the apartment door.

Nobody moved.

Another knock.

After another long pause, Candra faintly heard a voice and strained her ears.

"She's here," said the Southern-accented whisper.

"How do you know?" That voice belonged to Shea Alcott, Candra knew.

"Shhh . . ." The girl murmured something else to him, but Candra couldn't catch it.

After a moment, the footsteps retreated down the stairs, and the door at the bottom opened to allow a brief interlude of street noise to float upward before it was slammed closed again.

Out on the street again, Shea said to Mirabelle, "What did you mean, she was in there? How did you know?"

"I just *felt* her," she said, distracted. She didn't like the vibrations she was getting around here. First, she'd thought she'd seen that guy watching her from the window of the occult store, and now she had the unsettling feeling that Dalila had been on the other side of the door, listening, not answering. Why?

"What do we do now?" asked Shea as they crossed the street again and started toward the car.

"We wait . . ."

"For what?"

"For me to come up with another idea."

He muttered something, and Mirabelle looked sharply at him.

"What did you say?"

"Nothing," he said, then added, "just that we should stop screwing around and go to the police."

"That's what I thought. We can't go to the police, Shea—I thought I explained all that to you."

"Look, Mirabelle, I know what you said, but I can't stop thinking that Meg might be in trouble somewhere, and we're just sitting here wasting time."

"We aren't wasting time! I have a plan already—just give me until tomorrow, and I promise things will be all right."

"Why until tomorrow? What's the plan?"

She couldn't tell him. She couldn't say that she was going to astral project herself tonight, no matter what. No distractions. No more delays. She had to do it. She had to find Meg, before it was too late . . .

Too late for what?

She had no idea why she felt as though time was running out, she only knew that she was beginning to feel a growing sense of urgency. Meg was in danger—she was as sure of that as she was that the girl driving the Honda this morning had been Candra.

"There's that skull again," Shea said, pointing as they passed the store again.

Mirabelle looked closely at the plate-glass window, but she knew she wasn't going to see what she'd seen before. The aura of darkness was gone. If the man had actually been there earlier, he was nowhere near her now. She would have sensed it.

She and Shea walked the remaining blocks in silence.

When they turned the corner onto the street where they'd left the car, Shea stopped in his tracks and cursed under his breath.

Startled, Mirabelle looked up at him, then followed his gaze to the car.

The driver's side window was smashed.

"Oh, Shea . . ." She didn't know what to say, only hurried to catch up with him as he stalked toward the car. There was no sign of the gang of kids who had been hanging around at the house nearby.

"The stereo's gone," he informed her flatly. "And the portable CD player. And my case of CDs."

"I'm really sorry."

She half-expected him to blame her—after all, she'd assured him that everything would be fine despite the seedy neighborhood. What had she said? *It's only a car.* She cringed at the memory of her impatience with his cautious attitude. She'd deserve it if he wanted to be angry now.

But Shea only nodded grimly and kicked a piece of glass with his foot.

"Y'all have to report this. I'll go call the police from the pay phone on the corner," Mirabelle offered.

He could have made a sarcastic comment about her willingness to go to the police now. But instead he nodded again and muttered, "Thanks."

As Mirabelle walked away, she glanced over her shoulder. She saw Shea leaning on the hood of the car, everything about him bleak and miserable.

Shaking her head, she hurried toward the pay phone.

"Who was that girl?" Candra demanded, turning to Dalila as soon as she was sure the visitors weren't going to come back.

"Mirabelle Moreau," the woman said, fiddling with a ring on her hand.

"Who?" Candra repeated, even though she thought she'd heard the name. The woman was mumbling, and it irritated her.

"That was Mirabelle Moreau. A friend of Meg's. She was here with Meg one day last week, *mon.* I don't know who the other person was—some guy."

"Meg's boyfriend, Shea," Candra told her. "I thought they'd followed me here, but if Mirabelle has been here before with Meg, maybe it's just a coincidence."

Dalila shrugged. "I don't like hiding, *mon*. They knew I was in here. I heard her say it. Do you think they know about . . ." She trailed off and jerked a hand in the direction of the bedroom door.

"No," Candra assured Dalila, though she wasn't at all sure Shea and Mirabelle weren't somehow aware of Meg's presence here.

"I don't like this," Dalila said again. "I tell you what, *mon*. I don't want to wait to get rid of her. Let me do it tonight, before—"

"No!" Candra said sharply. "Don't do it tonight. Wait, just like I told you."

"All right, *mon,* all right."

Candra ignored the little voice inside her brain that said Dalila was probably right—that it would be wiser to get rid of Meg as soon as possible. For some reason, she didn't want that.

I'm not ready, she told herself, before she realized again that *she* wasn't the one who had to do the deed.

Dalila would handle it.

So what wasn't Candra ready for? Annoyed with herself, she searched her mind for an answer.

She didn't like the one she found.

I'm not ready to let go of her just yet, she realized with a pang, and then shoved the thought away as urgently as it had come. "Don't do anything until I tell you," she warned Dalila again. "I mean it."

"I won't." The woman looked at her. "Are you sure this is what you want, *mon*? You're not going to change your mind?"

"Of course I'm sure," she said, scowling. "Just not yet, okay?"

"Okay, *mon,* no problem. Not yet."

Candra hardened her expression, the muscles in her face aching with the effort.

If only she could easily do the same thing to her heart.

Three

By the time Candra got home from Dalila's, the sky had darkened ominously and it was pouring out.

She parked her car as close to the door as she could, then dashed through the rain with her sweater over her head. It wasn't until she had opened the front door and stepped into the warm, quiet foyer that she realized Sophie was here. And the housekeeper was sure to notice the fact that she—well, Meg—was still supposed to be in school at this time of day.

Sure enough, she'd no sooner taken the sweater from over her head and shaken the moisture out of her hair than she heard footsteps coming in from the kitchen. "Meg? Is that you?"

"Hi, Sophie."

"What are you doing home? Are you all right?"

"I'm fine. I just . . . I forgot something I need for an afternoon class, so I ran home on my lunch hour."

"I hope you were careful driving. It looks nasty out there. I hate weather like this."

"I was careful." Candra started up the stairs.

"Meg?"

"Yeah?"

"I want you and Carrie to keep the doors locked at night until your parents get back from this trip."

Candra paused and turned around to look at the woman. "Of course we keep the doors locked," she said, though that wasn't necessarily the case. "Why? Is something wrong?"

"No, everything's fine," Sophie said, then wrung her dustcloth in her hands and added, "I just thought I saw someone hanging around here when I pulled up early this morning, that's all."

"What do you mean? Where?"

"Now, Meg, don't get all worried. I told you, I'm not even sure I saw it. Lord knows with these old eyes of mine, I can barely see to do my counted cross-stitch anymore."

"Sophie," Candra said in a low voice. *"What did you see?"*

For a moment the woman looked startled at her tone. She frowned and seemed about to admonish Candra. But instead she simply shrugged and said, "It looked like a man—a dark-skinned man, and I thought I saw him hiding in the bushes in front of the house as I pulled into the driveway. But when I looked again, I didn't see anyone. So it was probably just my imagination."

"Probably," Candra agreed, nodding. But her heart had started pounding, and she thought of the man she'd thought was following her on Elmont earlier. He'd been dark skinned.

"So anyway, I just wanted to warn you to keep the doors locked. You know how your mother likes to tell the whole town all about her business. Everyone in Crawford Corners probably knows she and Lester are away for the week, and that you and your sister are here alone overnight—not that you should worry," she tacked on hastily.

"I'm not worried," Candra assured her, and continued on up the stairs.

She walked down the hall to Meg's rose-bordered bedroom and closed the door behind her. Then, still standing in the same spot, she looked around carefully, making sure everything was as she'd left it this morning.

It was, and this time she didn't feel what she had when she'd come home late last night—that eerie sensation that someone had been here.

Last night it had been easy to chalk the feeling up to stress and her imagination. Now, given what had happened over on Elmont Avenue, and what Sophie had just told her, Candra wasn't so sure.

But if someone really had been here, who was it? And if the dark-skinned man on Elmont really had been following her, then again, who was he? Candra had never seen him before in her life—at least, she didn't think she had.

Don't make yourself crazy, she told herself, sitting down at Meg's desk and reaching for the phone.

You have other things to worry about. And now, thanks to that nosy housekeeper, you have only a few minutes before you have to leave again and pretend you're going back to school.

Which, of course, she wasn't about to do.

No, there was no way she was going to risk having to face Meg's friends Chasey Norman and Zoe Cunningham again, or that obnoxious teacher Mr. Pfeiffer, or Meg's boyfriend, Shea. No, she would just have to lay low until tomorrow, and then it would all be over.

She dialed the phone and then waited until a pleasant voice said, "Good afternoon, The Lawson School."

"Good afternoon. I need to speak to one of your students," she said briskly and in a flawless American accent. "His name is Landon Keller."

The voice on the other end started to protest, just as Candra had expected.

She narrowed her eyes and concentrated, focusing her energy on controlling the woman on the other end of the line. After a moment, she smoothly interrupted and said, "I understand your policy during class hours, but I'm afraid this is an emergency. I'm Landon's mother, and it really is urgent that I speak to him right away."

"Oh, I'm sorry, Mrs. Keller," came the swift response. "Can you hold for a moment, please?"

"Certainly."

But it took more than a moment. As Candra sat there clutching the phone to her hear, she listened to the rain thumping on the roof of the big old house, and to the sound of Sophie vacuuming somewhere downstairs. She tapped her fingers on the desk and, as she waited, wondered where she was going to go now that she had to leave the house again.

Back to school was out of the question, and she certainly couldn't go back to Dalila's now that Meg's boyfriend and that girl, Mirabelle, were sniffing around there. . . .

For some reason, she suddenly thought about Rosamund.

Why had *she* popped into Candra's head?

You hate her, remember? Don't even think of having anything to do with her ever again. She lied to you; she was a fraud.

But still, Candra found herself picturing the woman's familiar face and wondering how she was. How had she reacted when she'd found the note Candra had left, telling her she was going back to Jamaica and not to look for her or report her missing? Had she been at all upset? Did she miss Candra even slightly?

Of course not. She was a cold, uncaring person. She never showed you any warmth, never kissed you or hugged you or acted like family.

And why should she have? Candra asked herself bitterly. Rosamund *wasn't* family. And yet, she'd raised Candra and had led her to believe she was her grandmother.

And Candra had actually believed it.

That was part of what hurt so much. She had never suspected that Rosamund was lying to her. She had instinctively trusted the woman, had even, on some level, loved her.

After all, Rosamund was the only family Candra had ever known. They had spent every day of their lives together until Candra had left the Drayer household early this week and become Meg. It was only natural that she should wonder about Rosamund now.

But she wasn't going to do anything about it.

No, she certainly wasn't going to give it another thought. Not now, when she was on the verge of getting what she'd always wanted. Not when she was about to put all this behind her and start over.

There was a click in her ear, and then Landon's voice came on the line. He sounded worried. "Mom?"

She heard typing in the background and realized he was on the phone in the secretary's office. "Landon, don't give it away—it's me, Candra."

There was a pause, and then he said hesitantly, "Uh, is everything all right?"

"Yes, everything's fine. I was just calling to say that I'll pick you up tomorrow night outside the main gate of the school."

"Why?"

"Because I want us to be together, Landon. I have a surprise for you."

"All right, that will be fine," he said stiffly. "I'll see you then, Mom."

She smiled. "I'll see you then. And Landon?"

"Yes?"

"Be sure you pack a bag."

There was another startled pause, and then he said, "Okay, I will. Thanks. Bye."

"Good-bye."

She replaced the phone in the cradle and sighed. He hadn't given her any argument. She hadn't expected him to. He was under a powerful spell—just like Dalila was.

Landon would do whatever she asked.

Just as Dalila would do whatever she asked.

For the first time in her life, Candra was tasting power, real power.

She settled back in Meg's desk chair and waited for a feeling of satisfaction to come over her.

But all she felt was a sharp twinge of doubt.

And as hard as she tried, this time, she couldn't make it go away.

By the time the police were through writing up their report, Mirabelle realized that she would have to hurry if she was going to make it back to campus in time for Philosophy class.

She and Shea got back into the car wordlessly. He started the engine and pulled out onto the street.

It was raining out now, and Mirabelle knew he had to be getting soaked through the broken driver's side window, but he didn't mention it.

"Where to?" was all he said after he'd made a circle back around to Elmont Avenue.

"Would you mind dropping me on campus?"

"Wainwright? It's not far from here, is it?"

"Nope. Go up there to that next light and take a left, and that should put you back on the road that leads to I-95. Then all you have to do is stay on for two exits, and we'll be there." She tried to inject an upbeat note into her voice.

Shea only nodded and followed her instructions. The windshield wipers beat a glum rhythm in time with the rain on the car roof.

"Wow, this is lousy weather, huh?" Mirabelle said to break the silence as they waited for another light to turn.

"Yeah, and I guess it's only going to get worse," Shea said, flipping the defog lever to high. "That hurricane that hit the Caribbean and Florida the other day is supposed to be headed up the coast."

"A *hurricane*?"

"Yeah, only now it's just a tropical storm, supposedly. But we're supposed to get rain and high winds by tomorrow night."

"I hope we've found Meg by then," Mirabelle said without thinking. She glanced at Shea belatedly and saw his jaw tighten.

"We'll find her," he said firmly. "We have to. You said you have another plan, right?"

"Yeah, but . . ."

"What is it?"

"You're not going to believe it." Still, Mirabelle decided to bite the bullet and tell him about the astral projection. The worst he could do was laugh at her.

He didn't do that. Instead, he just listened carefully, tilted his head when she was finished, and said, "You know what, Mirabelle? I believe you."

"You do?"

He shrugged. "What choice do I have? Is it really any stranger than everything else that's happened?"

Mirabelle's lips curved in a tiny smile. There was more to Shea Alcott than she'd first suspected. He kept surprising her. She hoped Meg knew how lucky she was.

They reached the campus a few minutes later, and Mirabelle directed Shea to the building where her Philosophy class was held.

"Perfect timing," she said as he pulled up to the curb out front. "I thought I was going to be late."

"Don't you need your books or anything?"

"It's okay, I'll share with someone." She leaned across the seat and spontaneously gave him a tight squeeze. "You've been great, Shea. Don't worry, everything is going to be all right. I promise."

"Are you sure? Are you saying that because you can see the future?"

She hesitated, seeing in his eyes how much he needed to be reassured. But she couldn't give him false hope. "No," she said after a moment. "I'm saying it because it's what I need to believe—that Meg will be fine."

He nodded.

Mirabelle opened the door and stepped out into the rain, waving as Shea pulled away. She turned and had taken two steps toward the building when she saw him.

Ben.

He was standing a few feet in front of her holding an umbrella, merely watching her, and she knew from the look on his face that he had seen her get out of the car. She knew, too, what he was thinking.

"Hi, Ben, what's up?" she asked, trying to sound casual. She expected him to hold the umbrella out, to shelter her from the rain, but he didn't move it.

"Who was that?" he asked flatly.

"Who was who?"

"That guy you were hugging in the car."

"Oh, him." She stood there with rain pouring down over her, streaming through her hair and over her face. "Nobody you know."

He nodded, then without a word, turned and walked toward the building.

Mirabelle had no choice but to follow him to class.

There was nothing she could say. She couldn't tell Ben who Shea was, because that would mean telling him about Meg, and there was no way she was going to go into that with him.

It's better this way, she told herself as she slid into her seat and wrung the water from her hair.

You wanted Ben to leave you alone. That's exactly what he's going to do now. You'll be able to concentrate on Meg.

After all, Ben certainly wasn't distracting her now. He sat in front of her and kept his back turned. Mirabelle could feel the chill radiating from him.

For a moment, she again considered trying to explain. But what could she say? And what would it matter in the long run? She had no intention of getting involved with him again.

But still, she thought of last night, how he'd kissed her out in front of the dorm, and she couldn't help feeling wistful.

Candra drove slowly down Soundview Avenue toward the huge white house where the Drayers—and Rosamund—lived. She didn't know what she was doing here, only that the car had seemed to head in this direction of its own accord.

She checked the rearview mirror and saw that there was no one behind her. Good. She slowed as she approached the familiar house, unsure of what she expected—or wanted—to see there, but again unable to help herself.

She saw that Monica Drayer's black Mercedes was parked in the circular driveway. Jonas's Ranger Rover was missing, and so was Craig's BMW, which would be with him at The Lawson School.

As Candra passed the house, she couldn't help wondering what Rosamund was doing right this second. Probably down in the basement, folding laundry, or maybe dusting the upstairs bedrooms. She thought of how Rosamund had always worked with silent efficiency, her hands flying from task to task and her mouth set in concentration.

It was hard to believe she would never see the woman again.

The realization brought a sudden and unwelcome lump to Candra's throat.

She pressed her foot on the accelerator and left the big white house behind abruptly, not looking back.

You should be glad you're leaving her behind—her, and all the rest of it.

She thought of Crawford Corners High School, of Mrs. Birch, her kindly gray-haired homeroom teacher, of Kim Williams, the Jamaican girl who had tried to befriend her.

And she thought of how uncomfortable she'd been there from the very first day, of how she hadn't fit in—not that she'd tried. Funny— the kids at Crawford Corners had looked down on her even as Candra had secretly looked down on them, knowing that she was destined for something better.

Now here she was driving a sleek black car, wearing a private school uniform, living on Meadowview Terrace. . . .

As someone else.

So what? It's your birthright, she reminded herself, turning off Soundview without thinking. *You deserve this just as much as Meg ever did. More, because she's already had eighteen years of it. It's your turn now.*

Candra drove blindly, trying to convince herself that she was doing the right thing—that all of this was the right thing. Not just what she'd done so far, but what she planned to do.

But murder . . . how can that be the right thing? How can Meg deserve that?

"Stop it!" Candra said into the empty car, as though the sharp sound of her own voice could stop the thoughts from intruding and threatening to ruin everything.

There could be no turning back now.

And if the guilt was going to come, let it come later, when she could deal with it. Right now, it was all she could do to hang on until tomorrow.

The light ahead turned red and Candra made another turn at the corner, driving aimlessly along the leaf-strewn streets that were shiny and wet.

The rain had stopped, Candra noted vaguely, but the sky still looked ominously gray, as though it could open up again at any second.

Her thoughts wandered back to Meg, and then, because she didn't want to dwell on that, found their way to Rosamund again.

And more guilt.

What's wrong with you? You can't do this to yourself!

She clenched her jaw and turned another corner, then realized, with a start, where she was.

On the street that led to Crawford Corners High. And, she realized, looking at the dashboard clock, classes had just ended for the day. She saw a trickle of students on the sidewalks around the school.

There was nothing to do but keep going, past the yellow-brick building.

She found herself searching the faces of the kids she passed, looking for someone familiar. But they were all strangers. She hadn't been there long enough, really, to recognize many people, or, luckily, to *be* recognized. The last thing she would need now was for someone to spot her driving by.

She wondered what her grandmother—no, Rosamund—had told the school when she'd disappeared. That she'd run away? That was doubtful. Probably just that she'd gone back to Jamaica . . .

She slowed for another light that was just turning red, at the corner just past the school. A group of students waited to cross on the opposite sidewalk. Candra braked and glanced idly at them as they started across the street.

Her heart did an abrupt flip-flop in her chest.

Kim Williams.

As though she suddenly sensed Candra's presence, the girl turned her head and looked right at her through the windshield of the car. Her ebony eyes widened in recognition.

Candra? her mouth said silently, and she broke away from the group of kids and hurried to the driver's side window, tapping on the glass.

Reluctantly, Candra rolled it down. "Hi, Kim," she said.

"Hey, *mon.* What are you doing here? I thought you had left town."

"Oh, really?" She looked up at the light. *Come on, change, so I can get out of here.*

"Yeah, your grandmother told Mrs. Birch that you'd gone back to Jamaica."

Just as she'd thought. She nodded. "I am going back, I just haven't left yet."

"I wish I had known that, *mon.* Some guy was asking me about you the other day, but I told him you'd left the country."

A warning bell went off somewhere in the back of Candra's mind. "Some guy? Who was he?"

Kim shrugged. "He was young, about eighteen. And he was black—had a heavy Jamaican accent. And he was *very* good-looking."

"What did he ask you?"

"Only whether you—"

Kim was interrupted by an angry honk from the car behind Candra. The light had turned green.

"Pull over, *mon,* so we can talk—over there," Kim said, gesturing at a parking lot up ahead.

"No, I can't," Candra said automatically. "I have an appointment in a few minutes."

"Well then, give me a call tonight. I'll be home. Do you still have my number?"

"Yeah, I have it . . . bye." Candra pulled away, through the light, and looked in her rearview mirror.

Kim had run to the opposite curb and was standing there, watching her drive away.

You probably should have stopped and talked to her, Candra told herself, biting her bottom lip. But she hadn't been willing to risk the prying questions Kim would be sure to ask.

Still, she needed to know more about this person who had been asking about her. Again, she thought of the man she'd seen on Elmont this morning.

He had been in his late teens, she thought, remembering. And he'd been black, and he'd been hanging around a neighborhood that was full of Caribbean immigrants.

But Candra had never seen him before in her life.

So how could he have been asking about her, if he was the one?

And if he wasn't the one, who had it been?

The whole thing was a puzzle.

There was only one thing she knew for sure—something suspicious was going on, something that made her distinctly uneasy.

And for the first time in a long time, Candra felt helpless.

Four

The first thing Mirabelle did when she got back to the dorm was take a long, steamy shower. She felt chilled to the bone, and not just from getting soaked in the rain.

She kept thinking about how cold Ben had turned in a matter of seconds, how he'd walked out of Philosophy when class was over without giving her a backward glance.

It's just as well—she'd repeated that to herself so many times it was like a mantra. But she couldn't seem to forget about him.

And she had to, because she needed to concentrate on finding Meg. Astral projection was hard enough when you knew where you needed to go. This time, she would be striking out blindly, feeling her way along the astral plane until she found her friend, wherever she was.

She felt better after her shower. Wrapped in a warm terry-cloth robe, she made her way back along the corridor to her room. The dorm was quiet at this time of day—most people had gone to the dining hall for dinner.

Mirabelle realized now that she hadn't eaten a thing all day, and she felt hollow inside. But there was no time to go to dinner. Char would be leaving any second now, and she was counting on using the time while her roommate was gone.

When she opened the door to her room, she found Char sitting cross-legged on her bed, talking on the phone.

Make that crying into the phone. Again.

Mirabelle sighed inwardly and tried to ignore her roommate's tearful conversation as she got dressed in sweats and an old flannel shirt.

"I know, Mom, I'm trying," Char said, sniffling. "But it's just not working . . . I know, but—I am. . . ."

Mirabelle towel-dried her hair in the mirror above her bed, then sat down with a magazine to wait. She turned the pages idly and wished Char would get off the phone and go to dinner.

Finally, she heard her say, "All right, Mom, I will . . . I know, and I'm really going to try and do that . . . Okay, I love you, too. Good-bye."

There was a click, and Mirabelle looked up to see her roommate putting the receiver back into the cradle.

"That was my mother," Char said, meeting her gaze.

As if I didn't know. "How is she?" Mirabelle asked aloud.

"She's fine. But—" Char's voice broke.

"Char? You okay?" Mirabelle got up and walked over to her roommate, laying a hand on her shoulder.

"No," Char said, crying again. Suddenly, she looked and sounded like a lost little girl, and Mirabelle's heart wrenched. "I'm not okay at all. I'm miserable here, Mirabelle. I just want to go home."

Mirabelle patted her shoulder and tried to think of something reassuring to say.

Char's tears grew more bitter, and she buried her face in her hands. "I *hate* it here. I want to go home," she wailed again.

"Well, look, Char, you're going for Thanksgiving, right? That's not so far away."

"It's almost two whole months! That's *forever!*"

Wrong thing to say, Mirabelle realized. She hesitated, not wanting to do what she knew she should. She had other things to worry about; she couldn't spend the night hand-holding this girl who was still practically a stranger.

But as she listened to Char's sobbing, she knew she didn't have much choice. Finally, she patted the girl's shoulder again and said, "Listen, I know what will make you feel better."

"What?"

"A big burger from Radish's. And some french fries. They always make me feel better when I'm miserable. Come on, I'll treat you."

Char looked up, and her round, pitiful, tear-drenched face brightened a little. "Yeah?"

"Yeah. Come on, stop crying, before y'all end up with a big headache and swollen eyes."

Char actually smiled and sniffled. "I've had headaches and swollen eyes from crying ever since I got here."

Mirabelle grinned and nodded. Wasn't that the truth!

Char stood up and wiped her eyes on her sleeve. "Thanks, Mirabelle. Going to Radish's would be nice. Just let me run to the bathroom and wash my face, and then we can go." She grabbed a towel and dashed out of the room.

There goes your chance to try and find Meg, Mirabelle told herself. Now she'd have to wait until later—much later.

But what else could she have done? Poor Char really needed a friend right now.

Mirabelle just wished she'd suggested going someplace other than Radish's.

It had been the first thing to pop into her head, but going there would only remind her of Ben. Again.

Candra was in Meg's room, packing, when she heard a door slam downstairs.

She froze, instantly remembering Sophie's warning, and listened intently, then relaxed.

It was only Carrie—even after these few days, she already recognized the pounding footsteps on the stairs. She knew what Carrie was going to do, too—go into her room, slam the door, and blast rap music on the stereo.

Oh, well. This was the last night Candra would have to put up with her.

She turned back to Meg's closet and was reaching for a pair of burgundy Italian leather boots when she heard the bedroom door open suddenly behind her. Startled, she turned and saw Carrie framed in the doorway.

"Hey, what are you doing?" the girl demanded, her bloodshot green eyes going from Candra to the open suitcase on the bed.

Candra hesitated, then realized a denial would be ridiculous, since it was obvious what she was doing. "Packing," she said shortly, and turned back to the closet.

"Why? Where are you going?"

"I'm visiting someone overnight tomorrow."

"Who?"

"A friend."

"Which friend?"

"None of your business." Out of the corner of her eye, she saw Carrie walking over to the bed. Candra moved to stop her before she could look inside the suitcase, but it was too late.

"How come you need all this stuff for one night?" Carrie asked, as Candra zoomed in and closed the top of the bag beneath her nosy scrutiny.

"None of your business," Candra repeated.

Carrie shrugged. "Whatever."

Surprised, Candra looked up at her.

"I mean, I don't blame you if you're skipping town," Carrie told her, and Candra saw an amused smile forming on her lips.

"What do you mean by that?"

"Didn't you hear? It's all over school."

"*What's* all over school?" Candra realized her voice was starting to sound shrill, and she struggled to calm down.

"That you stole Chasey Norman's mother's diamond earrings."

"*Stole* her mother's—? I did not! That's ridiculous."

"Oh, yeah? Well Chasey and Zoe both think you did. And I heard that they're going to go to the police to file a report on you."

Candra's stomach turned over, but she fought to remain blase. For all she knew, Carrie was making this up.

"Why would they go to the police? That's the stupidest thing I ever heard. I haven't done anything."

"*Except* steal the earrings. And you know what's weird about that?" Carrie went on, casually folding her arms across her skinny body and looking Candra in the eye. "That you'd rip off your best friend the day before you get your million-dollar inheritance from Gram."

Carrie's suspicious, Candra realized, feeling a twinge of panic as she stared at the tiny blonde. *She's suspicious . . . but what is she thinking? She can't possibly know who I am . . . can she?*

She turned back to the closet and said evenly, "Would you please get out of my room now? I have a lot to do."

"I'll just bet you do."

Candra's hands shook. What was that supposed to mean?

She doesn't know. She can't know, she reassured herself. But as she felt Carrie's eyes probing into her back, she couldn't be entirely positive.

After a moment, she heard the girl walk out of the room, closing the door hard behind her. Seconds later, another door slammed down the hall, and rap music blasted from the stereo.

Candra let out a shaky breath.

Things were getting too weird, too fast.

All you have to do is hang in there until you meet Meg's grandmother for the trip to the city, she reminded herself.

But suddenly, tomorrow morning seemed a long way off.

The phone was ringing as Mirabelle and Char unlocked the door to their room.

"I'll get it!" Char bounced across the room and snatched up the receiver.

Mirabelle noticed that her roommate looked a hundred percent better than she had before. Dinner had actually been fun. They'd run into a bunch of other people from the dorm at the diner, and had spent a pleasant couple of hours laughing and talking over burgers and fries.

Mirabelle had found herself keeping an eye on the door, hoping that Ben wouldn't show up . . . or was she hoping that he would?

In any case, he hadn't, and she'd resolved to put him firmly out of her mind—again.

"Mirabelle?" Char said, holding out the telephone receiver. "It's for you. *A guy,*" she added in a stage whisper.

Ben, Mirabelle thought as she accepted the phone and sat on her bed.

What was she going to say to him?

You don't owe him any explanations, she reminded herself firmly.

"Hello?" she said curtly, as Char opened her closet across the room and took out a long flannel nightgown.

"Mirabelle?"

She frowned. "Who's this?"

"It's me . . . Shea."

"Oh, Shea—hi."

"I've been waiting for you to call, and finally I just couldn't stand it anymore. Sorry to—"

"No, it's okay. I just hadn't called because, um . . ." She eyed Char, who was humming to herself and pulling the nightgown over her head. "I haven't been able to find anything out yet."

"Oh." He sighed. "Well, I'll tell you one thing. You were right about Meg not being . . . Meg. I'm positive now that Candra's switched places with her."

"What do you mean?"

"Zoe just called me. She said Meg stole a pair of diamond earrings from Chasey Norman. Meg would never do a thing like that in a million years."

"No, she wouldn't," Mirabelle agreed. "What else did Zoe say?"

"That the earrings actually belonged to Chasey's mother, and that if Chasey told her, she knew they'd have to go to the police and report it."

Mirabelle shook her head. "That's not good."

"It sure isn't. What if they arrest Meg? I mean, Candra? It'll be a huge scandal around here, Mirabelle. Crawford Corners is a small town. People don't forget things like that. Meg's reputation will be shot. I think . . . I mean, I know you don't want to do it, but I think we should go to the police now. Before they go to Meg—I mean, Candra," he corrected again.

Mirabelle sighed. The last thing she wanted to do was go through this whole thing once more. "Go to the police, and tell them what?" she asked Shea, trying to be patient.

"That Meg is missing."

"But she isn't. They'll take one look at Candra and haul *us* off for psychiatric testing."

"Well, there must be some way to prove that she's an imposter."

"Shea, trust me. There isn't. Not yet. What we have to do is worry about finding Meg, before . . ." She hesitated, then decided to tell him the truth. "Before it's too late. She's in danger, Shea. I can feel it. Something really dark is closing in on her, wherever she is."

There was silence on the other end of the line.

"Just let me try this my way, Shea," Mirabelle said. "Give me until tomorrow. And if I haven't found Meg, then we'll talk about an alternative plan. Please, Shea."

"Okay," he said in a voice so soft she could barely hear him.

"I'll call you first thing in the morning. I promise."

"Okay. G'night." He hung up before she could say another word.

Slowly, she replaced the phone in its cradle.

"What was that all about?"

She looked up to see Char watching her curiously, and realized she'd forgotten all about her roommate. She must have overheard every word.

"Nothing," Mirabelle said shortly.

"But didn't you say something about the police? What's going on?"

She wanted to snap, *It's none of your business,* but caught herself. She wasn't in the mood to deal with Char's wounded feelings, especially after she'd spent the last few hours trying to cheer her up.

So she just shrugged and said, "A friend of mine is missing, that's all. That was her boyfriend. He's worried about her."

"But what was that about her being in danger, and something dark . . ."

"I just have a hunch she's in trouble, that's all."

That answer seemed to satisfy Char, who merely shrugged and said, "Oh. Hey, want to go watch TV in the lounge for a while? I heard that Nina and those guys rented *How to Lose a Guy in 10 Days.*"

"Again?"

Char shrugged. "They love that movie. So do I. Kate Hudson is so excellent in it. Come on, let's go."

"No thanks," Mirabelle said. "I've seen it a zillion times. But you go ahead." *Please. Get out of here so that I can do what I have to do.*

Char hesitated. "I don't know. I've seen it a zillion times, too. Maybe I'll just stay here and finish that letter to my mom and dad."

"Char, go on," Mirabelle urged, trying not to sound too forceful. "You'll have fun. I'm just really exhausted. I think I'll try to get some sleep." She yawned loudly.

"Okay," Char said after another moment, and pulled her fluffy pink bathrobe on. "But if anyone calls for me, will you come and get me?"

"Definitely," Mirabelle promised.

"Don't lock the door. I'm not bringing my key."

"Okay."

She watched as her roommate walked out the door. As soon as it had closed behind her, Mirabelle got undressed and threw a pair of pajamas on. Then she climbed into bed, turned off the light, squeezed her eyes closed, and began her relaxation exercises.

Candra waited until Carrie had left the house, apparently on her way to some party with Eddie. Then she slipped down the hall to Lester's study.

She hadn't forgotten what she'd sensed that first night she'd been here—that Meg's stepfather wasn't what he appeared to be.

This was her last chance to find out what was in those locked drawers and cabinets in his office. After tomorrow, she'd be gone.

So it shouldn't matter, she told herself, hesitating with her hand on the doorknob. *You're leaving all of this behind. Why would you care what Lester's up to?*

The truth was, she wasn't sure why, but she wanted to know. Maybe because the more time she spent in Meg's world, the more she felt like she actually *was* Meg. Or at least, the more she felt linked to her twin sister.

Not that any link could be strong enough to stop Candra from what she had to do, she reminded herself hastily.

But it couldn't hurt to do a little investigating, as long as she had a whole night to kill here, and nothing else to do.

She pushed the study door open and saw that everything was exactly the same as it had been the other night. The blinds were still drawn, the few items on the desktop were undisturbed, and the drawers were still locked.

Candra reached into her pocket and took out the bobby pin she'd found in Meg's bathroom. She sat in the desk chair and surveyed the row of drawers thoughtfully, rolling the bobby pin back and forth between her forefinger and thumb.

As she tried to concentrate, she began to feel a prickly sensation on the back of her neck, as though she was being watched. Though she knew it was ridiculous, she turned anyway and saw that only a window was behind her. It looked out over the backyard, and she was on the second story, so no one could possibly be peering in at her.

Still, she stared at the glass, feeling anxious.

The room and her own face were mirrored there, and she could vaguely make out the outline of tree branches beyond the reflection.

If she lowered the blinds, she could be certain no one could see her. But that was silly.

There's no one there, she told herself, shaking her head and turning back to the desk. She forced herself to ignore the irrational eerie feeling and to concentrate.

After a moment, she zeroed in on the bottom drawer and said aloud, "That's the one."

Whatever she was looking for would be in there—she sensed that. Now all she had to do was get it open.

She knelt on the plush forest green carpet and got to work.

It was working!

Mirabelle turned and looked over her shoulder. There, on the bed beneath her, was her body. The other Mirabelle was merely a physical shell, now that she had separated her astral body from it and willed her consciousness into it.

And there, shimmering in the dim light of the room, was the silver cord that connected her astral self to her other self. The cord would stretch indefinitely, allowing her to travel through the night to Meg's side, and then back again before anyone realized she'd been gone.

Turning away from the bed, Mirabelle again focused her concentration on Meg.

Within moments, she had left the dorm room behind, and was soaring rapidly along the astral plane in search of her friend.

Must find her . . . I must find her . . .

Fleeting images rushed past—houses that spilled yellow lamplight from their windows, city streets dotted with passing headlights, dark patches of woodland where small animals scampered in the undergrowth.

And then the blur of scenes became one vivid impression, and she was drifting through it, and recognition settled over her.

Elmont Avenue stretched before her, alive with neon signs and prowling hustlers and the mingling rhythms of rap and reggae music.

Mirabelle moved more slowly but with a growing sense of purpose toward Rivera's Newsstand. It had long since closed for the night, metal gates locked over the windows and door.

As Mirabelle floated toward Dalila's apartment, she realized somehow that the woman wasn't there, that she'd gone out for the evening.

And yet, the apartment wasn't empty.

Her senses seemed to grow sharper, intensifying everything around her. She could hear the ticking clock on the living room wall even before she entered the room, and beyond that, a dripping faucet in the kitchen and the quiet breathing of Erzulie, who was asleep on the floor.

As she moved toward the bedroom as though guided by some unseen force, she heard something else. A rhythmic sound.

A heartbeat.

It seemed to be beckoning her. Mirabelle drifted over to the closed door, and then through it.

And there, on the long, low, dresser beneath the window, was Meg.

At last, Candra heard a faint click and felt the lock give.

It had taken longer to pick this thing than she'd expected. As she'd worked, she'd tried to focus on the task instead of on the vague uneasiness that wouldn't seem to leave her. But she kept glancing over her shoulder at the window, expecting to see something suspicious.

You're just jittery because you're snooping, she told herself.

And she couldn't imagine what she might find in Lester's desk, or what she was even looking for. She only knew that some inexplicable force had drawn her here, and she didn't question it. Too many times in her life, intuition had been her guide. She didn't doubt that there was some reason it had led her here.

Now, as she slid the drawer carefully out toward her, she eagerly looked inside, half-expecting the answer to jump out at her immediately.

But all she saw was a neat row of labeled hanging files. Lester Hudson was obviously a meticulous, organized person. The labels were typed and each folder was precisely aligned with the one before.

She thumbed quickly through the clear plastic tabs and saw that there was nothing out of the ordinary—*Insurance, Mortgage, Taxes* . . .

This was ridiculous. She didn't even know what she was looking for. She should just forget the whole thing. But . . .

No. Keep searching. It's here, a voice whispered in the back of Candra's mind.

It was the same voice that had guided her to Meg, even before Candra had been aware that she had a sister somewhere.

And so she settled more comfortably in front of the drawer and went through the labeled file folders again, this time more carefully.

And five minutes later, as her fingers grazed a file whose label read simply, *Merriweather,* she knew, inexplicably, that she had stumbled upon whatever it was that had drawn her here.

She drew the folder out and leaned back against the wall. Just as she opened it on her lap, a sound from the doorway startled her.

She gasped and looked up, expecting to see . . .

What?

Lester Hudson standing there, pointing a finger and saying, *A-ha! I've caught you red-handed?*

"Oh, it's just you," she said, exhaling and shaking her head at Meg's cat, who trotted into the room.

The animal stopped in front of her and looked at her. Its fixed green eyes were unnerving, and Candra frowned and said, "Go on, get out of here."

The cat didn't flinch, didn't move.

After a moment, Candra shrugged and said, "Fine, then, stay. You're just a stupid animal anyway."

She went back to the folder. The first thing she saw was a pale pink invoice.

It was from Merriweather Investigation Services, located in Spring City, Connecticut, and it was addressed to Lester Hudson.

So Lester had hired a private detective agency. Why?

Obviously, to find something. But what?

Frowning, Candra glanced over the bill. It wasn't itemized, and there was nothing to see but the five-figure total and the red stamp that marked it Paid.

Beneath the bill was a sheet of yellow legal pad paper. On it, someone had scrawled a telephone number.

As soon as Candra saw the area code, her heart did a startled flip-flop.

809.

The area code was all too familiar.

Jamaica.

Whatever—or whoever—Lester sought had something to do with the island.

Beneath the yellow sheet was a white folder marked *Confidential Report.*

This was it, Candra realized. Somewhere in this report was the answer.

But as she reached for it, the front doorbell shattered the silence.

Mirabelle stared at Meg, who lay perfectly still on the dresser top, except for the barely visibly rise and fall of her chest. She was dressed in a pair of shabby jeans and a navy New York Yankees T-shirt, and her dark hair fanned out beneath her head. Around her neck was the familiar jade baby ring on its slender gold chain. Her eyes were closed, her lips slightly parted, and she looked as though she were sleeping.

But she wasn't.

She was under some spell, Mirabelle realized, moving closer. Just as she reached out to touch her, she heard something.

The sound was coming from the distance—from her dorm room miles away. It grew louder, more insistent, and Mirabelle turned away from Meg, looking back over the astral plane.

"Mirabelle!" someone shouted. "My God, come on, Mirabelle, wake up! Wake up!"

The voice was frantic, and it belonged to Ben.

Instantly, Mirabelle understood what had happened.

She had to get back there immediately.

As soon as she'd made the decision, she found herself hurtling back along the plane toward her physical body.

Even as she went, she was aware that it was happening too fast. The energy was too powerful . . .

It was dangerous to be jerked back into her body this way . . . she had to slow down, before . . .

Too late—it was too late.

Mirabelle saw a blurred image of her other self rushing up to meet her, and then there was nothing but blackness.

"Hi, Meg," Zoe said unsteadily, standing on the front porch with Chasey, who looked equally nervous.

Candra eyed the two of them, then nodded and said, "Hi."

They looked at each other, and Candra saw Zoe give Chasey a little nudge.

"We just, um, wanted to talk to you," Chasey said, not meeting Candra's gaze. "We thought it was better than—well, you know."

Candra shook her head. "Better than what?" Her mind was still on the report she'd found in the file upstairs. She had to get this confrontation with Meg's friends over with and get back to Lester's study before . . .

Before what?

You have all night, she reminded herself, even as her sense of urgency grew.

When Chasey didn't respond, Zoe took over. "We thought coming to see you was better than going to the police," she said, trying to sound matter-of-fact but not quite succeeding.

Candra made her voice sound alarmed. "The *police?*"

"We don't want to do that," Zoe said hastily. "After all, Meg, the three of us have been friends for a long time, and—look, can we come in?"

Candra shrugged and stepped back, holding the door open.

Zoe and Chasey walked into the foyer, then stopped and looked at each other, and then at her. They seemed to be waiting for something.

Candra realized she was supposed to play hostess. Glancing up the stairs, thinking again of the detective's report that lay waiting for her, she said, "Come on into the living room."

The two of them were obviously familiar with the house, because they led the way and flopped down on the floral print couch, side by side.

Candra perched on the edge of a Windsor chair across from them, and waited.

"Meg, I don't want to believe that you would do something like this," Chasey blurted.

"Something like what?"

"Stealing my mom's earrings. I mean, *why* would you do it?"

"I didn't—"

"We figured you didn't *steal* them," Zoe interrupted. "That's why we came over."

"Well, it's about time," Candra said, folding her arms across her chest.

There was a moment of silence. Candra glanced over her shoulder into the foyer. Had she just heard a sound coming from upstairs—like a creaking floorboard?

No, it must have been her imagination.

"You lost them, didn't you, Meg?" Chasey said.

"We figured that must have been what happened—you lost them and then panicked," Zoe chimed in quickly. "And if that's what happened, it's okay, just—admit it."

Suddenly, Candra resented both of these girls, with their expensive clothes and Connecticut accents and uncomplicated lives. How dare they come here and demand that she confess to them, as though she were some lowlife criminal and they were—

"What was that?" Chasey asked abruptly, looking toward the stairway in the next room.

"What was what?" Candra asked, following her gaze.

"I just thought I heard something coming from upstairs."

"So did I," Zoe agreed. "It sounded like a footstep."

"A footstep?"

"Aren't you alone?" Chasey asked. "Is Carrie here?"

"No, she's out." Candra tried to ignore a renewed twinge of trepidation. "There's no one here but me . . . and the cat," she suddenly remembered with relief. "It must have been the cat."

Of course that's it, Candra told herself. The animal had been in the study with her when she came downstairs. Thank goodness. For a second there, she had thought—

What?

Why did she keep catching herself having these irrational, paranoid thoughts?

"Well, anyway . . ." Zoe said, leaning forward and clasping her hands over her knees. "Did you lose the earrings, Meg?"

Reluctantly, Candra turned her attention back to the two girls on the couch. What was she supposed to say? If she continued to deny ever getting the earrings, they might go to the police. The last thing Candra wanted was to get them involved.

If she admitted she'd lost the earrings, she'd be off the hook—at least where the law was concerned. All she'd be guilty of was lying. Besides, who cared? As of tomorrow, she—and Megan McKenna—would vanish forever.

"You're right," she said abruptly, looking from Zoe to Chasey. "I lost one of them. I was really upset, and I didn't know what to do, so I . . . I lied. I'm really sorry, you guys."

She couldn't tell if they looked relieved or disappointed.

Chasey cleared her throat and said, "I'm really glad it wasn't . . . something else. You know, that you didn't . . ."

"Steal them?" Candra offered helpfully, suddenly feeling as though a weight had been lifted from her shoulders.

"Yeah," Chasey said.

"We knew you hadn't been yourself lately, Meg, with the breakup and everything," Zoe told her. "We kind of thought there had to be a reasonable explanation."

"I guess I just panicked when I couldn't find that earring," Candra said. "But don't worry, Chasey, I'll pay you back. Tell your mother I'll replace the one that was lost."

"I don't think you'll be able to do that," Chasey said. "They're one of a kind earrings. You'll probably have to buy her a whole new pair. It's going to cost a fortune."

"Oh, well," Candra said lightly with a shrug. "As of tomorrow, I'll *have* a fortune. It's my birthday, and my grandmother's giving me my inheritance."

"Oh, yeah, it's your birthday," Zoe said, slapping her forehead. "How could we have forgotten?"

"Don't worry about it," Candra told her.

"Well, we have to celebrate. We'll take you out tomorrow night, right?" Zoe said, looking at Chasey.

"Yeah," Chasey said, although Candra could tell she wasn't entirely enthusiastic.

"You guys don't have to do that."

"Don't be ridiculous. We always celebrate each other's birthdays." Zoe stood up. "We'll talk about the plans in school tomorrow."

"I won't be there," Candra told her, getting to her feet. "I'm going into the city with my grandmother."

"Well, then, we'll pick you up at eight. Okay?" Zoe offered.

"Fine," Candra said, smiling. She was thinking, *By that time, I'll be long gone.*

She led the two of them back into the foyer and opened the front door, anxious to get rid of them.

Finally, after a few minutes of small talk, they left, heading down to the shiny BMW parked behind Meg's car.

Candra waved and called good-bye, then closed and locked the door. "Good riddance," she muttered, and headed up the stairs again.

She quickly walked down the hall to Lester's study. The door was still ajar, just as she'd left it. The cat had left the room, she noticed as she walked back toward the desk.

She bent to retrieve the file, which she'd left on the floor where she'd been sitting.

It was empty.

Candra gasped, tossed it to the floor, and looked around, quickly scanning the desk, the chair, the tops of the file cabinets.

There was no sign of the pink invoice, the yellow legal paper, or the confidential report.

And she knew she'd left them in the folder, carefully tucking them inside before she went down to answer the door.

Panic built inside of her as she picked up the folder again. It was empty. No doubt about that.

She thought again of the creak she had thought she'd heard coming from upstairs, and of Zoe saying, "It sounded like a footstep."

Somehow, someone had gotten into this office and stolen the contents of the file.

But who?

And why?

And *how*?

"She's coming around! Mirabelle?"

It was Char's voice, traveling to her as though across a vast distance. Mirabelle tried to turn her head toward it, but it felt like it was weighed down by a boulder. Her eyelids, too, were heavy—too heavy to lift, though she struggled to do it.

"Mirabelle?" another voice said. "Come on, please? Open your eyes, Mirabelle."

That was Ben. And she realized, then, that it must be his fingers that were stroking her hand, which was lying across her stomach like another lead weight. Ben's touch was gentle and warm and so reassuring that she needed desperately to see him.

Focusing every drop of strength she could muster, she managed to raise her eyelids slightly, enough to see what was going on around her.

The first thing she noticed was Ben's face, above her, and the broad grin that spread over his features as his eyes collided with hers.

"She's awake," he said to someone over his shoulder, then turned back to her. "Mirabelle, stay with us now. Don't slip away again."

She tried desperately to find her voice, to reassure him that she wasn't going anywhere. But the effort was too draining, and she couldn't speak, couldn't even keep her eyes open again.

Before she allowed them to drift shut, she noticed that she wasn't in her bed in the dorm. The walls around her were stark white, not pale yellow, and the light in the ceiling beyond Ben's head had been the square, fluorescent kind.

"She's going out again," she heard Char say worriedly.

"Mirabelle," another voice said, "if you can hear me, open your eyes again."

Who was that? She had no idea.

She labored to raise her eyelids, to let them know she heard them, but it was impossible. Her strength was zapped.

The last thing she heard, before she drifted away again, was Ben saying, "Is she going to be all right, Doctor?"

Doctor, she realized groggily. *There's a doctor with me. I'll be just fine . . .*

And then, once again, there was nothing at all.

Five

At exactly seven o'clock on Friday morning, a gleaming silver Cadillac turned into the driveway of 41 Meadowview Terrace.

Candra had been standing in the foyer, peering out the window, waiting. She'd been up since five—well, actually, she'd been awake all night, but had forced herself to stay in bed until then. Now, as she slipped into Meg's dark blue Burberry raincoat and headed for the door, she felt the bone-numbing ache of exhaustion.

Maybe you can take a nap when you get back from the city, she told herself, picking up Meg's leather purse from the table near the door.

But she knew that a nap was out of the question. Even if she *did* have time for one, she couldn't imagine actually sleeping. Not in this house. Not after what had happened last night.

The fact that the contents of the Merriweather file had disappeared had left her so shaken she'd thought of little else in the hours since. It wasn't so much that she was frustrated at having it snatched out from under her . . .

No, it was more that she detected a growing aura of darkness around her. Whoever had taken the file was the same person whose presence she had sensed in her room that night, and on the street yesterday near Dalila's.

Was it the young black man she'd imagined was following her?

It didn't make any sense—she'd never seen him before in her life, so why would he have been following her? And what did he have to do with any of this, if he *had* been?

A horn tooted outside, and Candra sighed and unlocked the heavy front door. It was pouring, and a steady, chilly wind had blown in off the water sometime during the night. Now it pushed against the door as Candra struggled to pull it closed, and drove the rain against her as though it were being tossed from buckets as she ran down the steps and opened the passenger's door of the car.

It wasn't until she was actually climbing into the front seat that it struck her: she was about to meet her grandmother. Her *real* grandmother, unlike Rosamund.

Suddenly, her hands were trembling, and to calm herself, she concentrated momentarily on pulling the heavy car door shut against the gusting wind. Only when it had slammed abruptly, closing her into the plush maroon interior, did she turn to look at the stranger on the seat beside her.

"Meg," the woman said warmly, and reached for her. "Happy birthday, sweetheart."

Candra allowed herself to be folded into a hug that was surprisingly fragile. She closed her eyes, overcome with unexpected emotion, and breathed the scent of expensive, powdery perfume.

"Hi, Grandma," she nearly whispered when she managed to speak around the lump that had risen in her throat.

The woman released her and stroked her hair briefly. "You're soaked. It's so awful out there."

Candra nodded, not trusting her voice.

She studied her grandmother. She was built like Carrie, small and slender. Her hair was the same blond color as Carrie's, and as Giselle's had been in the photographs Candra had seen, and her eyes were an identical light green color. But this woman's expression lacked the saucy glint Candra had seen in every picture of Giselle.

If anything, her gaze was the opposite—introverted and worn and troubled.

And when she spoke again, Candra's heart plummeted.

"Meg," she said worriedly, "they're saying that hurricane might be headed in our direction. I don't think it's such a good idea to go into the city today."

"Hurricane?" Candra forced herself to say lightly, and laughed. "This is no hurricane, Grandma. Just a little rain. We'll be fine."

"But on the weather report last night, they said—"

"Those reports are never right," Candra interrupted. "Besides, I heard that the storm is most likely going to veer off course and go out into the ocean later today." That was actually true—she'd been listening to the radio reports on Meg's stereo as she was getting dressed. Well, it was *mostly* true—the meteorologist had said the unpredictable storm *might* veer off course—it was still too soon to tell.

The woman looked doubtful. "I don't know . . ."

"Come on, Grandma," Candra cajoled, trying not to come across as frantic as she felt.

You can't back out now! She screamed silently. Not when the million dollars was so close.

"It'll be fun to spend the day together," she added hopefully, "Just the two of us."

"We can always go Monday . . ." Her grandmother bit her thin lower lip, which was carefully lined with plum lipstick.

"But Monday isn't my birthday," Candra pointed out, making sure her voice came out sounding wistful.

That seemed to do the trick.

Though she still seemed reluctant, the woman nodded and said, "You're right. Today is your special day, and I did promise. Besides, we'll be home before the weather gets any worse."

"Of course we will."

"Well, then, we'd better get going before we're late for our train." Her grandmother shifted the car into drive and pulled out onto the street.

Candra settled back against the seat and smiled.

"Mirabelle?"

Again, the voice intruded on the dark, silent place where she was drifting.

"Mirabelle, it's me, Ben. Wake up, please?"

She felt the quiet urgency of his words drawing her slowly out of oblivion, and struggled to remember where she was, what was happening.

It came back to her in a rush, and her eyes snapped open.

"Hey—you're awake!"

She saw Ben standing over her, wearing a rumpled blue plaid shirt and looking startled. She blinked and glanced beyond him, again seeing the stark white walls and rectangular fluorescent lights she'd glimpsed before . . . was it last night?

"You're in the infirmary," Ben informed her, as if he sensed her confusion.

She frowned and searched for her voice. "How . . . ?" she managed to croak.

"Shhh, don't try to talk. I found you unconscious in your room. I stopped by to—well, to say I was sorry for jumping to conclusions when I saw you with that guy yesterday afternoon. I thought you were asleep when I saw you in bed, but when I tried to wake you up, you didn't respond. It was like you were . . ." He trailed off and shuddered.

Mirabelle remembered hearing him calling her when she was in Dalila's apartment, how his voice had jerked her astral body violently across the astral plane, back to her physical self.

Cecile had warned her that something like that could be deadly, if the sudden pressure on the silver cord caused it to sever.

Thank God that hadn't happened, Mirabelle realized now. She'd survived.

But the trauma had obviously left her in bad shape. She felt feeble and listless and sore all over, and it was all she could do to muster the strength to speak again.

"When . . . what . . . day . . . is . . . it?" she asked Ben, and found herself exhausted by the mere effort to communicate.

She felt a squeeze on her fingers and realized he was holding her hand, that he had been even before she'd come to. How long had he been here?

"It's Friday," he told her. "Friday morning."

Friday? Mirabelle fought to concentrate. That meant she had only been out overnight. Grateful that more time hadn't elapsed, Mirabelle suddenly thought of Meg.

Alarm shot through her as she recalled what she had seen in Dalila's apartment.

She had to get back to Meg, had to help her before it was too late.

I have to get out of here! she hollered at Ben.

When he didn't respond, she realized, with trepidation, that she hadn't made a sound. Her mouth seemed to be moving but nothing was coming out.

"Shhh," Ben soothed, and stroked the back of her hand. "Don't try to talk, Mirabelle. You need to rest now. Go back to sleep."

She attempted to speak again, but now her lips wouldn't even budge. She was utterly drained of what little physical energy she'd recovered, and mentally, she was fading fast.

To her horror, she felt her eyelids fluttering closed again.

She tried to fight the wave of drowsiness that was overtaking her.

It was futile.

No . . . she thought weakly, even as the darkness rushed in to claim her again.

Can't . . . must get to Meg before . . .

"Grand Central Station—last stop on this train. Grand Central Station," the conductor's voice boomed over the loudspeaker.

Candra, who was sitting beside her grandmother, in the window seat, watched eagerly through the rain-spattered glass as they pulled out of the black tunnel they'd entered somewhere up in Harlem.

She wasn't sure what she expected to greet her on this, her first real visit to Manhattan, but she couldn't help being disappointed. The train creaked and groaned and slowed to a painstaking halt beside a dingy-looking platform, its concrete columns and walls lit by bare yellow bulbs.

Candra glanced at the woman beside her, who offered a tight smile. "Here we are," she said, as around them, commuters gathered their belongings and headed for the doors.

Candra nodded. Her grandmother hadn't spoken much during the trip. She'd seemed nervous, and spent most of the time with her head back and her eyes closed, though she jumped and gave a little gasp every time they hit a bump or another train rushed past them.

Now Candra followed her out of the row and down the aisle, noting the bustle that was taking place around them. The people who rode the train into Manhattan from the Connecticut suburbs appeared to be a well-to-do and sophisticated bunch. No one seemed fazed by the grungy-looking platform or by the way they were forced to stand crowded together as they inched up the stairway toward the station itself.

Candra felt her grandmother clutch her arm as they joined the throng. "Stay with me," she said. "Don't get lost."

"I won't."

Within a few minutes, they were emerging into the main terminal, and Candra tried not to look around in awe. This was more like it! Grand Central Station was an impressive, cavernous structure that belied the shabbiness of the tracks below. Candra glanced from the rows of ticket windows and shops to the sweeping staircases to the trio of musicians who were entertaining a crowd of commuters at one end.

This is New York, Candra told herself. *At last.*

This was the place where the most wealthy, powerful, glamorous people in the world lived and worked. And she was among them, about to come into her own fortune after so many difficult years. She felt dizzy with anticipation, and she wanted desperately to stand still and savor the moment that had been so long in coming.

But her grandmother tugged her sleeve and pulled her along toward a long corridor. "Come on, this way, Meg."

Moments later, they were stepping through wooden-paned doors. While her grandmother stopped and put up an enormous black umbrella, Candra glanced around and saw a sign that read, "Vanderbilt Avenue."

Vanderbilt, she thought—wasn't that the name of an American tycoon?

Someday, she wondered dreamily, would there be an avenue named after her?

"The bank is around that corner, on Park Avenue," her grandmother

said, pointing, and holding the umbrella over both their heads as the
rain poured down around them.

Candra could only nod again, not trusting her voice to conceal her
excitement. Park Avenue! Everyone knew that was the stomping
grounds of the richest of New York's rich. She thought back to the
days, not so long ago, of living in the Drayers' servant quarters and
wearing secondhand clothes, and wanted to pinch herself. Could this
be real? Was she, Candra Bowen, actually here at last?

Too soon, they had been swept a few blocks along the sidewalk
among fast-paced walkers, and her grandmother was saying, "This
is it."

Candra wished she could protest, wanting only to keep walking
along the vibrant city streets, feeling like a part of the city's rhythm.
But then she looked up at the large stone bank building, and was instantly reminded of the reason for this trip.

The money.

Jittery excitement pulsed through her veins as she followed her
grandmother up the steps and into the vast lobby. "Wait right here,
Meg," the woman said, pointing to a row of chairs.

"Okay." Candra took a seat and watched as her grandmother approached a woman seated behind a lamp-lit desk.

The two of them conferred for a moment, and then her grandmother
turned and beckoned to her.

Five minutes later, they were both seated across from a short, bald-
ing man in a well-cut gray suit, who introduced himself as Mr. Warner.

"And how do you like school this year, Miss McKenna?" he asked
jovially, forming a steeple with his fingers on the polished desk in
front of him.

"It's fine, thank you."

"And let's see, today you're turning eighteen, is that right? Happy
birthday!"

"Thank you," Candra said again, trying not to sound impatient.

He turned to her grandmother. "It's always good to see you, Hope."

Hope? So that was her name. Candra had been wondering.

"It's good to see you, too, Mortimer," her grandmother said, fiddling with the raspberry-colored chiffon scarf around her neck.

"I do miss Harry. We always used to have a good laugh when he
came in to take care of business, didn't we?"

Candra noticed that her grandmother had stiffened at his words.
Harry had been her husband—Meg's grandfather.

And mine, Candra reminded herself.

"It seems like only yesterday that I last saw him—hard to believe it's been two years," Mr. Warner—Mortimer—went on.

He chatted for another few moments about what a terrific guy Harry had been, apparently oblivious to Hope's increasingly strained expression.

Candra wanted to reach out and shake him, to tell him to shut up. Couldn't he see he was upsetting her grandmother? Feeling a sudden and surprisingly fierce protective instinct, she laid a hand over her grandmother's frail, blue-veined one that clutched the arm of her chair.

Hope looked up gratefully, and Candra smiled at her, feeling a disturbing sense of warmth toward the woman.

And guilt—she felt guilty, again, at the thought of what she was about to do.

Take the money and run.

Well, so what? Didn't she deserve it as much as Meg would have? She was Harry McKenna's granddaughter, too. And the money wouldn't make up for all the lonely years she'd spent in Jamaica, unaware that she had a family somewhere—a family that had given her up without looking back.

So, when Mortimer reached for a file at last and took out a stack of paperwork to begin the financial transaction, Candra pushed the nagging guilt aside.

This was her birthright, and nothing was going to stop her from claiming it.

Mirabelle opened her eyes abruptly.

She was still in the same white-walled, fluorescent-lit room, but Ben was gone.

At first she thought she was alone. She managed to turn her head slightly, then, and realized that someone was sitting in the chair beside her bed. It was a male someone, and his dark head was buried in his hands.

"Shea . . ." she whispered.

His head jerked up and he stared at her. "You're awake!"

She could only nod, and barely managed that. She was still so weak.

Shea jumped out of his chair and stood over her. "Are you all right?" he asked tentatively, and looked over his shoulder. "Do you want me to call someone? The nurse is right—"

"No!" she forced out, through lips that felt parched and stiff.

"Okay, okay, don't worry—I won't." He sat down again, but leaned forward so that his face was close to hers.

"What time . . . ?" she began.

"Almost noon," he told her quickly. "I didn't go to school today."

"How did you . . . ?"

As though he were reading her mind, Shea said, "Your roommate, Char. She told me you were here—I called the dorm this morning, looking for you. Mirabelle, they're saying you must have a severe case of the flu, because they can't find any other explanation for your symptoms. But you seemed fine yesterday. What happened?"

She lifted her shoulders in a weak shrug, and the effort drained her. There was no way she could go into the whole story without risking losing consciousness again. She had to conserve her strength.

"Shea," she said raggedly, "we have to . . ."

She stopped as a wave of numbing exhaustion swept over her, closing her eyes briefly as she fought it off.

When she opened them again, she saw that he'd bent closer still, and was watching her worriedly.

"What is it, Mirabelle?" he asked. "Are you all right?"

"Call . . ." she began, and her voice faded into a hoarse croak. She struggled to get it back, to stay awake.

She did, but only long enough to utter three more words. "Call the police."

"Would you like more tea, ladies?" the waiter asked, discreetly appearing at the table again.

"No, thank you," Hope told him. "Meg?"

Candra shook her head, and watched as he slipped away, his jacket as starkly white and impeccably pressed as the linen napkins and cloth on the small round table.

Never in her life had Candra been to a restaurant as elegant as this one was. Never had she been treated so well, her every whim catered to by the attentive staff and by her grandmother, who kept telling her to order whatever she wanted.

After all, you are the birthday girl, Hope had said more than once, and every time she did, Candra was reminded of Meg—her twin— who shared this day with her. Eighteen years ago today, the two of them had come into the world together.

Tonight, only one of them would leave it.

Candra wanted to be able to enjoy the rich, crumbly pastry and succulent light souffle that sat in front of her, but all of it was sodden in her mouth.

Meg. Her twin sister. Her own flesh and blood. How could she knowingly send her to her death in only a few more hours? Especially on this day, of all days?

"Meg, you haven't touched your fruit," her grandmother said, pointing at the crystal bowl in front of her.

"Yes, I have," Candra protested, and speared a plump red strawberry with her fork so that its juices spilled out. She put it into her mouth and chewed mechanically.

"You seem awfully quiet today, though. Is everything all right?" Hope asked, watching her.

"Everything's fine."

"You aren't disappointed that we're having breakfast in the city instead of lunch? I just didn't want to risk getting back to Crawford Corners any later, with the weather and everything . . ."

"It's fine, Grandma," Candra assured her, lifting the gold-rimmed porcelain cup and taking a sip of her still-hot tea.

"After all, we still have to get to the bank back home," Hope went on, toying with her own teacup. "You need to deposit your check."

Candra nodded, and again felt the back of her chair to make sure that Meg's purse was still there. Inside, folded safely into the leather wallet, was a cashier's check for one million dollars, made out to Megan McKenna.

All she had to do was put it into Meg's bank account this afternoon, and then withdraw the money later using Meg's photo driver's license and credit cards as identification.

It was so simple.

And yet . . .

Sitting here, in this quiet, refined Manhattan restaurant with her grandmother, Candra couldn't help feeling wistful. Maybe even . . . doubtful?

Would it be so bad to keep things the way they were—to keep posing as Meg, and forget about running away, and about . . . the rest of her plan?

Life would be pretty wonderful if she lived it as Megan McKenna. She could continue to live in the comfortable house on Meadowview Terrace, and go to private school, and wear designer clothes, and have a loving grandmother, not to mention a mother, at last. . . .

But what about Landon?

She couldn't give him up. He was the piece that made her picture puzzle complete.

No, she had to proceed with the plan, she thought reluctantly, as she smiled reassuringly at the woman across the table from her.

She would take the money and leave town with Landon.

But first, she would give Dalila her orders to get rid of Meg.

It was the only way.

Six

This time, when Mirabelle came to again, she saw a whole group of people standing around her bed, conferring quietly.

Shea . . .

And Ben . . .

And a man in a white lab coat . . .

And a uniformed police officer.

"Mirabelle?" The man in the coat was at her side a moment after she opened her eyes. He was young and handsome, and looked almost like he could have been a student on campus. But he said, "I'm Doctor Rapaport. How are you feeling?"

Horrible was how she was feeling, but she wasn't about to tell him that.

"Fine," she said, and was surprised to find that her voice was much stronger than it had been before.

"Fine enough to speak with Officer Garrety, here?" the doctor asked, gesturing over his shoulder at the police officer.

Mirabelle nodded.

The doctor stepped back, whispered something to the officer, and then they both moved out of Mirabelle's line of vision.

She caught Ben's eye, and then Shea's. Both of them looked worried—and relieved.

"What time is it?" she asked, and they both looked at their watches.

"Four-thirty," they said in unison, then glanced at each other and laughed nervously.

Mirabelle frowned. "Four-thirty? The day is almost gone."

"You went out again while I was here earlier," Shea told her, and glanced at Ben, who nodded. "I did what you told me to do, though. I called the police. The officer has been waiting for you to come to so he can ask you some questions."

Mirabelle directed her attention to Ben. "Do you know . . . ?" she asked him.

"Yeah. Shea told me what happened."

"What did he tell you?"

"That his girlfriend is missing, but her twin sister is in her place, impersonating her."

"That's all you told him?" Mirabelle asked Shea, who nodded.

Ben frowned. "What else is there?"

Mirabelle shrugged and opened her mouth to tell him she'd explain the rest later.

She was interrupted by Officer Garrety, who appeared by the bed again.

"Hello, Miss Moreau," he said in a deep voice. He was tall and blond and broad shouldered, and had a pleasant face that was touched with concern. "I'm going to make this quick so you can get your rest. Doctor's orders. Your friend here"—he motioned toward Shea—"says you have something to tell me."

She nodded. "Can I . . . would someone please get me a drink of water before I start talking?" she asked, not trusting her voice to hold up without it. Her throat felt raw and dry, and she couldn't risk fading again.

"I'll get it," Ben said. He reached down to squeeze her hand quickly before he walked away.

"Thanks," Mirabelle whispered, and turned back to the policeman. "Okay. I don't know if you're going to believe this, but I hope you'll hear me out, Officer . . ."

"Dalila?" Candra said into the phone. "It's me."

"Yeah, *mon*," said the voice with its familiar island accent. "I've been waiting for you to call. It's raining like crazy outside, and it's almost four-thirty."

"I know," she said dully, fidgeting with a corner of the comforter on Meg's bed. "I just got back from the bank."

"You have the money for me?"

"Yes," Candra lied. "I'll give it to you tomorrow morning."

The woman started to protest, but Candra interrupted her.

"Dalila, you said you would help me. Now listen carefully."

There was silence on the other end of the line.

Candra started talking, giving her directions to Rocky Forest State Park, and to the spot she'd picked out the other night on the way back from Landon's school.

And she told Dalila exactly what she expected her to do, keeping her voice methodical and her emotions detached.

When she was finished, she said simply, "Did you get that?"

"Yeah, *mon*, I got it."

"Okay, then. Go."

"When?"

"Now," Candra said sharply. "There's no time to waste, Dalila. The sooner you get rid of her, the better."

"Okay, no problem, *mon*. But the money—"

"I said I'll give it to you!"

"Okay, okay . . ."

There was a pause, and when the woman said nothing else, Candra barked, "So go on, get busy, Dalila."

"I will, *mon*. I will. Don't you worry about a thing. Dalila will take care of everything for you."

There was a click, and then Candra heard the dial tone.

Still, she sat frozen, clutching the receiver against her ear, staring off into space.

Then the tears started.

They caught her off guard, huge, heaving sobs that consumed her so that she could barely catch her breath between them.

She huddled there in Meg's shadowy bedroom, rocking back and forth and wailing her sister's name over and over as darkness fell outside and the wind and rain howled around the house.

"You don't believe me, do you," Mirabelle said flatly, watching Officer Garrety.

He shrugged and patted her arm. "I believe that you're truly worried about your friend, Mirabelle, but what you're saying is pretty outrageous."

"But it's true, Officer!" Shea protested. "You've got to believe us. Meg isn't *Meg* anymore, she's Candra, just like Mirabelle said. And Meg is in trouble."

"You want me to believe that your friend is lying there, under a spell, in this woman's apartment?" the policeman said incredulously. "And that the reason you know this is that the spirit of Mirabelle, here, flew over to that apartment last night while her body was in bed in the dorm?"

"It wasn't my *spirit* that went, it was my astral body!" Mirabelle looked from Officer Garrety's doubtful expression to Ben's, then settled her gaze on Shea. "I told you no one would believe us, especially the police," she said bitterly. The burst of energy she'd felt after drinking some water was starting to dribble away. It was no use.

Shea grabbed the officer's arm. "Look, can't you at least check it out? Send someone over to the apartment on Elmont to make sure Meg really isn't there?"

"I'd like to help you kids," Officer Garrety said, "but I don't even have a missing person's report on this girl. As far as I'm concerned, there's no problem."

"Okay, then, how do I file a missing person's report?" Shea asked, his voice rising in anger.

"You can't, unless someone's missing."

"She *is* missing!" Shea exclaimed, then looked at Mirabelle for help.

"Listen, Officer Garrety," she said, desperate to get through to him. "I know how this whole thing must sound to y'all. I mean, we're talking about astral projection and ESP and all this stuff you probably don't believe in the first place. But I swear to you that it's real, and that we wouldn't have come to you if this wasn't a case of life or death."

"I'm sorry, Mirabelle. But there's nothing I can do." The officer picked up his hat from the foot of the bed and took a step backward, toward the door.

"Wait!" Ben said sharply, startling everyone else. "Wait just a second. Remember that kidnapping case in Spring City a few weeks back? A little girl was taken from a park?"

The officer frowned. "What does that have to do with anything? I suppose you're going to tell me now that Meg McKenna was kidnapped."

"I am not," Ben said, looking insulted. "I'm going to tell you to think about how the cops managed to solve the case."

"How?" Shea asked, and Mirabelle echoed him.

"They used a psychic," Ben said triumphantly.

Officer Garrety shrugged.

"You have to admit that if the police were willing to listen to a psychic in that case, the least you could do is listen to one in this case."

Mirabelle shot a grateful glance at Ben. So he didn't think she was strange, after all, despite everything she'd said about magical powers and astral projection. She never would have expected him to not only take it in stride, but jump to her defense where the police were concerned.

If only Officer Garrety were as easy to win over. But he just stood there, clutching his navy cap and wearing the same expression of skepticism.

Then it dawned on Mirabelle. She knew exactly how to convince the man that she was telling the truth.

"Would you mind giving me your hat?" she asked him abruptly, propping herself up on her elbows.

He looked startled. "My hat?"

"Yes. Just for a few seconds. I want to try something."

He hesitated.

"Please," Mirabelle said, and finally he shrugged and handed it to her.

She closed her eyes and stroked it, concentrating.

It wasn't easy. She was still so weak, and she hadn't done this in a long time. But she had to . . .

Do it for Meg, a voice whispered somewhere in her mind, and she struggled to focus.

After a moment, images began to come to her.

She studied them intently, and the room was silent around her.

Finally, satisfied that she'd seen enough, she opened her eyes and looked at the policeman.

"You can have your hat back," she told him, and handed it over.

"What was that all about?" he asked, examining it suspiciously before settling it on his blond head.

Ben and Shea looked at each other, and then at her.

Mirabelle shrugged. "I wanted to find out more about you, Officer. And I did."

"What do you mean?"

"Well, I know that you grew up in the Midwest—right outside of Chicago, right?"

He raised his eyebrows but said nothing.

"And that you loved your father very much," Mirabelle continued. "He was a police officer. But he died when you were ten."

"I was eleven—I'd just turned eleven," Officer Garrety said quietly, a faraway look coming over his face momentarily, then being replaced with a frown. "Who told you about my father? And where I grew up?"

"No one told me. I picked up on it from holding your hat."

The officer made a noise that was a cross between a snort and a laugh. "That's impossible." He started toward the door again.

"But what about the tree?" Mirabelle called after him.

He stopped in his tracks. "What tree?" he asked, still facing the door.

"I'm not sure where it is, but there's a tree that meant a lot to you and to your dad."

The police officer turned slowly back to look at her, and the expression on his face was haunted. "How did you know about that?" he asked in a voice that was nearly a whisper.

"I told you . . ."

"She's psychic," Ben said, beside her.

"No one knows about the tree. It was in the woods behind our house, and it was ours, mine and dad's. He was going to build me a treehouse in it that summer. Then he was killed during that robbery . . . I used to climb the tree and talk to him after he was gone. I was sure he could hear me," Officer Garrety said, shaking his head and staring off into space.

Mirabelle watched him and waited.

Finally, he met her eyes. "I'll see what I can do about checking out that address on Elmont."

Candra tossed the last bag in the backseat of Meg's car. As she reached out to shut the door, the wind picked it up and carried it out of her grasp, slamming it closed.

Candra ran back through the pouring rain to the house. She slipped into the foyer and shook the water out of her hair.

No one was home, and only the ticking of the antique grandfather clock in the next room disturbed the silence. She looked around, remembering how she'd felt the first time she'd stepped into this house.

Had it really only been days ago? It felt like months.

Well, it didn't matter. It was over. She'd never set foot in this place again.

Never meet her mother after all. She felt a pang at the realization, then pushed it away. Meeting Giselle wouldn't have been worthwhile, anyway. After all, she'd just think Candra was Meg, the daughter she'd raised. She'd never know she'd met her other child—the one she'd abandoned.

A sound from above startled Candra, and she glanced up to see the cat watching her from the second-floor balcony.

"What are you looking at?" she snapped.

The animal just stared at her.

Candra stared back, but couldn't help feeling uncomfortable. The cat had never liked her. She was the only one who had guessed that Candra was an imposter.

Good thing you can't talk, Candra told the animal silently.

On second thought, maybe it was too bad the cat couldn't speak. After all, she might be able to tell Candra who had been in Meg's bedroom before she got home the other night, when she'd sensed that presence. And the cat had been in Lester's study when Candra had found the file—and probably when it had been stolen.

What had the animal witnessed?

"You know what?" Candra said aloud to the cat. "It doesn't even matter. You know why, *mon*? Because I'm out of here for good. See you."

It wasn't until she'd walked out the front door that she realized she'd reverted back to her Jamaican accent without thinking. She cringed. She wouldn't let that happen again.

Now that she was starting her new life—a life of privilege—she was cutting all ties to the old one. In no time, she'd forget that she'd ever lived in poverty in Jamaica, that she'd ever wanted for anything.

She would be a wealthy American, and that was that.

She reached into her pocket and took out the note she'd written earlier, then propped it on the hall table near the door.

Then, smiling, she splashed back through the downpour, got into the car, and started the engine.

She didn't allow herself a backward glance in the rearview mirror as she drove away. She was afraid that if she looked, she'd feel regret, and she didn't want to feel that.

She didn't want to feel *anything,* she reminded herself firmly. Steeling herself against emotion was the only way she'd be able to get through this night, knowing what Dalila was up to.

Mirabelle sat propped against a pile of pillows, brooding. In chairs on either side of the bed, Shea and Ben slouched, both staring off into space.

They were waiting for Officer Garrety to come back. He'd left to make arrangements for someone to check out Dalila's apartment on Elmont, as well as Meg's house in Crawford Corners.

Mirabelle closed her eyes, then opened them again.

"It's too late," she said abruptly, shaking her head.

"What?" Shea asked, sitting up straighter.

Ben did the same. "What do you mean, it's too late?"

"Meg's gone."

"Gone?" Shea echoed.

Mirabelle nodded. "I'm getting this feeling that they're not going to find her in that apartment. She's been moved."

"Moved where?" Ben asked.

"I don't know. I'm still not feeling a hundred percent like myself. Everything I'm getting on Meg seems fuzzy, but . . ." She shrugged. "I just know she's not on Elmont anymore."

Shea stood and started pacing, raking a hand through his dark hair.

Ben looked at him, then at Mirabelle. "Do you want me to go find Officer Garrety?"

"Would you?"

"Sure."

She looked into his eyes. "Ben, thank you so much for . . . everything."

He flashed a brief smile and reached out to squeeze her hand. "No problem. I'm glad you're all right . . . and glad I know the truth about what's going on with you."

"I should have told you all along. I don't know why I didn't trust you. I *wanted* to."

"You didn't want me to get involved," Ben said simply.

"I was an idiot," she told him, then looked over her shoulder at Shea, who had stopped in front of the window and was watching the dreary, stormy dusk settle in.

"I'll be right back," Ben said, standing and starting for the door.

Before he got any farther, Officer Garrety appeared.

"I was just coming to find you," Ben told him.

"Well, here I am . . . I must be psychic," the policeman said, and cracked a grin. Then he became serious again. "I just spoke to the officers in Spring City, and they went over to that address on Elmont. No one was there."

Shea groaned. "Mirabelle just told us Meg had been moved."

The officer raised an eyebrow in her direction, but said only, "There's something else." He looked around at the three of them. "A source in the vicinity of the Parker woman's apartment revealed that a short time ago, she hired two men to move a heavy cabinet or chest out of her apartment and into a rented vehicle."

"Oh my God," Mirabelle said quietly. "Meg."

"We have someone in Crawford Corners checking out that address on Meadowview Terrace," the officer went on, not meeting her eyes. He turned and headed for the door again. "I'll be back when I know what they've found."

"They're not going to find Meg there!" Shea said, looking disgusted. "She's been abducted!"

"Unfortunately, there's been no indication of that up until this time. We've been trying to track her parents down in Fiji, but so far we've had no luck. And her sister, Carrie Hudson, hasn't shown up either. So, until someone in her family can confirm that she's missing we can't be sure of anything." Officer Garrety said. "However . . ."

"What?"

"We checked with the Adamson-Swift School. Megan McKenna was absent today, without an excuse."

"Would that make her a missing person?"

"Not until she's been unaccounted for after twenty-four hours. Unfortunately, she's eighteen years old as of today. If she were a minor, we wouldn't have to wait the twenty-four hours."

"That's ridiculous!" Shea exclaimed.

"Look, I know you're upset, and I'm doing what I can to help you," the policeman said. He left the room again, calling over his shoulder, "I'll be back. Just sit tight."

Traffic on I-95 was horrendous because of the weather. There were accidents all over the place, and according to the meteorologist's report on the radio, the worst was yet to come. The storm had been downgraded from a hurricane, but it was still headed for the New England coast, bringing a promise of stronger winds and heavier rain yet.

By the time Candra reached the exit for The Lawson School, her hands ached from clenching the wheel and her nerves were shot. The only positive thing about the horrible driving conditions was that they forced her to concentrate on the road. She couldn't let her attention shift to the disturbing thoughts that flitted on the fringes of her mind.

Thoughts about Meg.

As she turned onto the private drive that led to the school, she spotted a figure huddled outside the main gate up ahead. An enormous black umbrella shielded the top of his body from her, but she knew it was Landon even before she drew closer.

She saw that a large duffel bag was slung over his shoulder, and relaxed. Until now, she hadn't realized she'd been subconsciously worried that he wasn't going to show, or that if he did, he wouldn't want to go away with her.

But he's here, waiting, she told herself as she pulled to a stop beside the gate. *Everything's going to be fine now. You'll see.*

He waved and opened the back door, tossing his duffel bag onto the seat beside her luggage. Then he got into the front and turned to her.

"Candra!" he exclaimed, pulling her into his arms. He was damp and his cheek against hers was icy, but she burrowed against him anyway.

"I was worried about you," he told her, pulling back to look at her face in the dim interior of the car.

"Worried about me? Why?"

"Driving alone in this weather. I would have called to tell you not to come if I'd had a number where I could reach you."

"You didn't want to see me?" she asked, narrowing her eyes at him.

"Of course I wanted to see you. But I didn't think it was safe for you to make the trip."

"Oh." Relieved, she gave him what she hoped was a sunny smile. "Well, here I am, safe and sound."

"Thank God." He settled back in the seat and said, "Mind if I turn up the heat? I'm chilled through."

"Go ahead." She put the car into Drive and pulled out into the road to turn around.

"So where are we going?" Landon asked, after he'd adjusted the temperature control on the dashboard.

"Away," she said lightly, casting a sideways glance at him.

"I know that, but where?"

"Does it matter?"

He hesitated, then shrugged. "No. As long as I'm with you, I don't care where we go." He reached out and trailed a finger along her cheek.

His touch sent shivers of pleasure through her—and something else. She pushed her misgivings aside and said simply, "I'm glad you feel that way, Landon."

She turned her attention to the road ahead. The windshield wipers were on at top speed, but still it was difficult to see through the downpour. She would have to really concentrate on driving.

But as the school fell into the distance in the rearview mirror, and her eyes got used to the darkness and rain and wipers again, she couldn't help letting her mind stray back to yet another thought she wanted to avoid.

It's only the spell.

The spell she'd cast on Landon—that was the reason he was going along with her so willingly. How would he feel about her if his feelings were under his own control?

She would never know.

Just be glad he's with you, she told herself. *This way, he's not going to put up any fight when he realizes we're leaving for good.*

Yet again, she felt a pang of regret. She had what she wanted—but not the *way* she wanted it. She hadn't realized it would matter to her whether Landon was with her of his own free will, or not.

Well, there could be no backing out now. There was nothing to do but move forward with the plan.

* * *

"I've never seen anything like it," Dr. Rapaport said, sitting back and putting his stethoscope aside. His brown eyes were focused intently on Mirabelle.

"I *told* you I feel fine."

"Your temperature and blood pressure are back to normal, all your vitals are good, the color's back in your face—basically, you've made the speediest recovery I've ever seen," he told her, and shook his head.

"So I can leave the infirmary, right?"

He hesitated. "Well, you look a little tired. Maybe—"

"No, I feel great. Really."

A nurse stuck her head in the door. "Doctor Rapaport? You have a phone call."

"Tell them I'll call back."

"It's your wife. It's kind of urgent. She said a tree branch came down on the roof and now there's water coming in the baby's room."

"Oh, great," he muttered, glancing at the window. Darkness had fallen outside, and the rain and wind seemed to have grown more violent.

He stood and looked at Mirabelle, distracted, as though he'd forgotten she was there.

She silently thanked his wife and the fallen branch.

"You're free, if you want to go," he said quickly, and on the way out the door, added, "Just take good care of yourself over the next few days, okay? Nothing too strenuous. Promise?"

"I promise."

As soon as he closed the door, she got out of bed. For a moment, she had to grasp the back of the chair for support. Her legs were wobbly and she felt light-headed.

But after a moment, she felt better, and swiftly got dressed in the clothes Ben had picked up from Char. As soon as she was ready, she opened the door and found Shea, Ben, and Officer Garrety waiting for her, looking anxious.

Something had happened. She could tell.

"What? What is it?" she asked, looking from one to the others.

"We're going down to the station," Officer Garrety told her. "Right away."

"Why?"

"We just linked Meg with a report that came in at Crawford Corners—"

"One of Candra's friends saw her driving Meg's car yesterday afternoon!" Shea cut in. "This girl—Kim something—thought it was suspicious, since Candra had supposedly gone back to Jamaica earlier this week. She said she acted strange when she realized she'd been recognized, and drove off in a hurry."

"And this girl called the police?"

"Yes, this afternoon," Officer Garrety told Mirabelle. "She noted the license plate of the car, figuring Candra may have stolen it, and it's been traced to Meg. The only thing is, we have no real proof that it wasn't Meg driving the car—"

"Except that this girl, Kim, didn't know Meg existed," Ben pointed out. "She swears it was Candra."

"The Crawford Corners police are in the process of questioning Kim Williams—that's the girl who called in the report—and investigating this Candra person right now," the officer said. "No one's home at the McKenna place. They want to talk to you and Shea."

"Well then, let's go," Mirabelle said, and started down the hall.

She'd only taken a few steps when a surge of dizziness came over her. She blinked and reached out to steady herself against the wall.

Ben was at her side in an instant, putting his arm around her. "Mirabelle, are you sure you're all right?"

Behind her, she heard Shea and Officer Garrety echoing his concern.

"I'm fine," she murmured, taking a deep breath and closing her eyes for a moment, then forcing them open again. "Come on. We've got to hurry."

She started walking again, and Ben kept a steadying grip across her shoulders as they made their way to the police car parked out front.

Seven

"Do you want me to drive for a while?"

Landon's voice startled Candra out of her faraway thoughts, and she shook her head. "No . . . No, I'm fine," she muttered, and forced her full attention back to the Interstate ahead. Traffic was crawling and she'd been in the right lane, following the same set of headlights, for over an hour now.

"How far is it?" Landon asked.

"How far is what?"

"The place where we're spending the weekend."

"Oh, that." She hesitated.

Was now the time to tell him that they weren't just spending the weekend together? That they were running off to start a new life, someplace out west? Candra had no idea where . . . she hadn't gotten that far in her plan.

All she knew was that they had to get rid of the car and buy a couple of plane tickets first thing in the morning. And as for tonight . . . well, she'd just assumed they'd stop at some hotel later, near the airport.

Before, she'd been electrified at the thought of being alone, overnight, in a hotel room with Landon. Now, she felt only dread over the evening ahead.

Why can't you forget about why he's with you, and just enjoy the fact that he is? she berated herself.

But she couldn't.

And it wasn't just that.

How could she concentrate on being alone with Landon when she knew that Meg was out there somewhere in the storm, dying?

Being murdered, she corrected herself bluntly.

Because of you, your sister is going to die. And for what?

For being the one our mother chose.

But Meg couldn't help that, any more than Candra had been able to help being left behind.

Tears sprang to her eyes, blurring the road through the windshield even more. She reached up and hurriedly wiped at them, but not before Landon noticed.

"Hey, Candra . . . are you okay?" He reached out and touched her shoulder.

She flinched. "I'm fine."

"No, you're not. Your eyes . . . are you *crying*?"

"No. It's just . . . they're just strained, from driving."

"Pull over," he said firmly. "I'll take over."

"But you don't know where we're going."

"So you can give me directions. Come on, pull off."

It *would* be a relief to sit back and let him take over, she thought, noticing for the first time that her shoulders ached and her hands were sore from clenching the wheel so tightly.

She glanced at the side of the road, then at the steady line of headlights in the rearview mirror. "We can't just pull off to the side of the road, Landon. It's too dangerous . . . the weather's too bad. Someone could hit us."

"Well, fine. Get off the highway at the next exit, and we'll switch places there."

She nodded, then allowed herself to recognize something she'd been fighting to ignore.

They were approaching the area of the Rocky Forest State Park. The exit couldn't be more than a few miles ahead.

Right at this very minute, Dalila should be someplace nearby, either hiking to the spot Candra had described, or maybe even digging in the ground, which had to be pure mud at this point.

You can stop her, a voice whispered in Candra's mind. *There's still time, and you're close enough.*

Stop her? Why would I want to do that? If I stop her, and let Meg live, everything will be ruined.

She bit her lower lip.

If she didn't stop Dalila, Meg would be dead.

Meg.

Her twin sister.

Candra didn't realize she was pushing down on the accelerator until Landon shouted, "Hey, slow down!"

Startled, she saw that she was right on the tail of the car in front of them, and she lifted her foot from the pedal.

"What are you doing tailgating in this weather, Candra?" Landon asked. "It's dangerous. And anyway, what's your hurry? It's like you're suddenly in a race or something. Relax."

"Sorry," she muttered, not looking at him. What *was* she doing?

"I know you're tired, but don't get us into an accident trying to make it to the next exit. Look—we're almost there. See that green sign?"

She knew what it would say even before she glanced at it.

Rocky Forest State Park, Exit 1 Mile.

Mirabelle looked from Officer Garrety, who stood beside her, to the man seated behind the desk.

His name was Sergeant Scovall, and he was the grandfatherly type, with a fringe of white hair and bright blue eyes.

Mirabelle had liked him immediately, even more so when he didn't seem to doubt her story.

But now, she had to convince him to go a few steps further and do something about it. There was no time to waste.

"So you're saying"—he said thoughtfully, resting his chin on his hand—"that you want to track your friend down using ESP."

"It's the only way," she said again, glancing at Officer Garrety for backup. "She's in danger. I know she is."

Officer Garrety cleared his throat. "I think we have no choice but to listen to Miss Moreau, here, and follow up on this, Sergeant. Remember the case last month with the kidnapped child in Spring City? A psychic found her."

"I know, I know," Scovall said impatiently. "I'm not denying that. But until we get a solid lead on this Candra person, there's not much to go on. And the officers who went out to Jonas Drayer's house on Soundview found that no one was home."

Mirabelle glanced over her shoulder. Through the office's glass window, she could see Ben leaning on the wall in the corridor, while Shea paced anxiously. The poor guy was at his wits' end, frantic with worry over Meg.

Just as Mirabelle was.

She closed her eyes and bent her head, tuning out the voices of the two men, concentrating on Meg.

Where are you?

A series of images flashed before her so swiftly and sharply that she was caught off guard. She gasped and clutched the armrests of the chair.

"What is it?" Officer Garrety asked, grabbing her elbow. "Are you all right, Mirabelle?"

"I saw her!" she announced, her eyes snapping open. "I saw Meg.

Her hands and feet are tied, and she's unconscious. She's in a blue van parked in the woods."

"A blue van?" Officer Garrety repeated, and looked at the sergeant. "I didn't tell her that."

"You didn't tell me what?"

"That the vehicle Dalila Parker had rented and had those men load the cabinet into was a blue van."

"I swear he didn't tell me!" Mirabelle turned to Sergeant Scovall. "I saw it. You've got to believe me. And it's still here in Connecticut— I'm sure of that, too. In the woods someplace. If you'll just give me a chance, I can figure out exactly where. *Please!*"

The sergeant studied her. "Wait right here," he said after a long moment, and stood up. He left the office, closing the door behind him.

"Where do you think he's going?" Mirabelle asked Officer Garrety.

Out of the corner of her eye, she saw Shea and Ben looking after the sergeant as he strode down the hall, then facing her expectantly through the office window.

"I have no idea," the policeman said. "But I wouldn't be surprised if you just got through to him. This is exactly what happened with that psychic who was used in the kidnapping case, from what I hear. She knew details that no one had been told."

"I've got to figure out the rest," Mirabelle said, closing her eyes again and concentrating.

After a moment, she murmured, "East. And south. I'm getting those directions clearly . . . Meg's southeast of here."

"In the woods?"

"In the woods. But—"

Just then the office door opened again. Sergeant Scovall stood there with several other uniformed men.

"All right, Miss Moreau," he said abruptly. "I'm convinced. Help us locate Megan McKenna."

The exit road was familiar. Candra followed its curve to a two-lane highway and a sign with an arrow.

Rocky Forest State Park, 2 Miles.

"Just pull off in that convenience store parking lot," Landon said, pointing.

Candra glanced at it. It was where she had bought the flashlight the other night. She eyed the gas pumps in front of the store, and said, "You know what? We need gas. Let's fill up while we're here."

Landon peered at the sign in front of the store. "Okay. It says that it's self-serve only. Figures. I'll get out and do it."

"Thanks." She drove over and pulled up in front of the pumps. Her hand was shaking badly as she reached for the button that released the tank panel. She heard it pop open.

Landon put up the leather collar on his blue Nautica jacket and reached for the door handle. "That sign says 'Pay before you Pump,'" he told Mirabelle. "Do you want anything from inside? Something to drink?"

"Uh, yeah. I'll have a bottle of iced tea," she said impulsively. "And a bag of potato chips. And one of those little fruit pies. Cherry."

"Thirsty *and* hungry, huh?" He grinned. "Me, too. Be right back."

She nodded and turned away from him, not wanting to watch him walk away.

Setting her face grimly, she took a deep breath and counted to ten.

Then, telling herself she was doing the right thing, she shifted the car into Drive and pulled out onto the highway.

She headed, as fast as she could drive on the wet, bumpy road, in the direction of the park.

Mirabelle opened her eyes, shook her head, and sat up on the couch. She turned and knocked on the glass partition above her head, and a moment later, the office door opened.

"It's no use," she told Sergeant Scovall, who poked his head in. He had been waiting outside with the other officers.

"What's the matter?" he asked.

"I can't do it this way. I keep getting the same images—Meg, the van, the trees—but I can't get past that enough to tell exactly where she is, let alone to project myself there."

"But you still say she's someplace southeast of here, right?"

She nodded. "You know what would work? If I could be driven in that general direction, my instincts might take over so that I could lead you right to the spot."

"The roads are a mess—weekend rush hour traffic is still going strong, and everything's backed up because of the weather. That would take forever. But let me see what I can do. Just sit tight for a minute, okay?"

"Sure." She sighed and leaned back as he disappeared, tailed by the officers who had been clustered outside the door.

Moments later, Ben asked from the doorway, "What's going on?"

"Nothing yet. It's not working. I can't seem to concentrate enough to figure out exactly where Meg is. If I could just get closer to her, I have a feeling I'd be able to tell a lot more."

"Where'd the sergeant run off to?"

She shook her head. "I have no idea. He said he's going to see what he can do."

Ben came over and perched on the arm of the couch, looking down into her face. "You're exhausted."

"I'm fine," she lied. She was starting to feel awful again, but she couldn't give in to that. Meg needed her.

"Where's Shea?" she asked, to change the subject.

"Still out in the hallway. He's really upset."

"I know." Frustrated, Mirabelle banged a fist on the cushion beside her and said, "If I could just get closer . . . Ben, I know I'm capable of finding her! She's still alive—"

"Are you sure?"

"Positive. But not for long. That woman is going to murder her, Ben." Saying the words aloud for the first time seemed to make it real, and Mirabelle felt a lump rise swiftly in her throat.

Ben patted her shoulder in silence.

There seemed to be nothing else to say.

After what seemed like hours, but was probably no more than ten minutes, Sergeant Scovall reappeared. "Mirabelle?"

"Yes?"

"I need you to come with me, please."

She jumped up.

So did Ben. "Where are you going?" he asked the sergeant.

"We're going to do what we did in the kidnapping case last month. That time, we flew the psychic over the area in a helicopter until she was able to pinpoint the site where the child was being held."

Mirabelle froze halfway to the door. "A helicopter?" she echoed weakly.

"Yes. I've lined it up. They're waiting for you."

She swallowed hard over the lump that had become solid fear.

Cecile's words echoed back at her.

I see danger for you if you fly, Mirabelle.

The maid's premonition of something terrible happening to her while she was flying was one Mirabelle had shared on more than one occasion. For years, it had kept her from taking plane trips.

Now, in the space of a few seconds, she had to decide whether to risk her life by boarding a helicopter tonight to look for Meg.

There might be nothing to this whole thing about me flying, she told herself, trying to be reasonable.

But she wasn't convinced. Too often, she'd had shattering visions of danger involving planes.

But this isn't a plane—it's a helicopter. That's different.

Is it?

As she hesitated, barely aware of the puzzled looks she was getting from Scovall and Ben, she glimpsed Shea through the open door over the sergeant's shoulder. He was sitting on the floor in the corridor, his face buried in his hands, his shoulders quaking.

He was crying, Mirabelle realized.

She made her decision in that instant.

"Okay, let's go," she said, lifting her chin and clenching her hands into fists at her sides.

Candra slowed the car at the entrance to the park. The rain had let up a little, and in the murky glare of the headlights, she could make out a chain stretched across the road, beside the deserted gatehouse. It had been there the other night, along with the sign that said *Park Closed After Dark.*

Just as she had then, she jumped out of the car and unfastened the chain, moving it out of the way. After she'd driven through, she got out again and grabbed the chain fumbling clumsily until she got it hooked.

Getting back in the driver's seat, she clenched the wheel and pulled forward. Her fingers were stiff and her hands were icy, not as much from the raw weather as from the dread that was building in the pit of her stomach.

How much time did she have? It could be mere minutes.

But Meg was still alive. She was positive of that.

She knew it, she realized with sudden clarity, the way she would know the instant her twin died.

She's a part of me . . . my other half, she told herself bitterly. *How could I have done this to her? I need her.*

A sob escaped her throat as she drove forward, following the narrow, tree-sheltered road in the direction she had taken the other night. It was nearly underwater in spots, and as she approached the turnoff up ahead, the car hydroplaned. Candra fought to get it back under control, then forged ahead.

As soon as she'd turned onto the side road that led to the hiking trail she'd taken, she realized she was in trouble. It wasn't paved, and the rain had turned it into a marsh. There were deep ruts where a vehicle had recently passed.

Dalila had come this way with Meg, recently enough for the tracks to still be evident.

Candra followed the tire marks as fast as she could, but the road was mostly uphill and it was rough going. Several times, she started to skid, but managed to stop.

Then it happened—she skidded, lost control, and ended up veering off the road.

"No!" she screamed, not so much out of fear for herself, but because she couldn't get stuck now. She had to get to Meg.

The car narrowly missed hitting a stand of trees, and when she'd brought it to a stop, she surveyed her position. She might be able to steer out of here.

She put the car into reverse, but as soon as she put her foot on the gas, the wheels spun noisily. She shifted into Drive, but that was no better. After a few minutes of shifting back and forth, she realized it was no use. The tires were mired in dense mud, and there was no way she was going to be able to move it.

Peering out into the darkness, she tried to figure out how far she was from the trail. The other night, it had taken her only moments to drive up this road and park. Now that she'd been forced to go so slowly, there was no way to tell where she was.

But there was no time to waste, and she had only one option.

She'd have to start hiking from here, and pray that she got there in time.

She opened the car door and stepped out.

Instantly, her foot, clad in Meg's Italian leather boot, sank into slimy muck. She winced and silently promised to buy her sister another pair . . . if she saw her again.

No . . . not if . . . when *I see her again,* she corrected herself.

Then, her jaw set grimly, she began hiking as fast as she could through the black, rainy, windswept forest.

Mirabelle felt hot and sweaty despite the chill in the aircraft as the motors revved on the launch pad. She rubbed her forehead, willing the light-headed feeling that had increasingly come over her to go away.

She needed to stay alert if she was going to find Meg.

"All set?" the uniformed pilot called over the roar of the engines, turning to look at her.

She nodded and checked her seat belt again with trembling hands, then folded them in her lap so that the pilot and Sergeant Scovell, who sat beside her, wouldn't notice.

She wanted to ask whether it was safe to take off in rain and wind like this, but told herself not to be ridiculous. Of course it was safe, otherwise they wouldn't be doing it.

All you have to worry about is Meg, Mirabelle reminded herself. *Just concentrate on Meg.*

The whir of the engines grew louder, and the pilot said, "Here we go."

Mirabelle turned and looked out the window. In the dark, rainy mist, she saw Ben and Shea standing off to the side with Officer Garrety. The officer had a hand on Shea's shoulder and was saying something to him, probably reassuring him that Meg was going to be all right.

Ben was watching the copter, and his eyes locked with Mirabelle's through the window.

Good-bye, Ben, she told him silently, wishing she could touch him one last time. He'd given her a brief hug and told her to be careful before she'd boarded the helicopter, and his arms around her had been such a comfort. . . .

You'll feel them again, she promised herself as the aircraft gave a little lurch.

But as it lifted off the ground, buffeted by wind and water, Mirabelle wasn't so sure.

Cecile's warning, and her own terrifying premonitions, shot through her mind again.

She fixed her gaze on Ben, watching as he fell away below her, telling herself that this might be the last time she would ever see him.

Suddenly, she realized she'd been a fool to have resisted getting involved with him. Why had she fought her feelings for him? Life was too short.

When she did come back from this helicopter ride, she promised herself, the first thing she would do was throw her arms around Ben and tell him how much he meant to her.

If she came back.

Candra found an abandoned blue rental van about a quarter of a mile away from where she'd left Meg's car in the mud. As soon as she spotted the van, she ran toward it, briefly seized by the hope that Dalila might have abandoned Meg in it while she went up the trail to dig.

But even as she drew closer, Candra instinctively knew that the vehicle was empty. She peered in the windshield anyway, then pounded on the locked doors and metal sides of the van, calling her sister's name vainly.

After a moment, she got hold of herself and knew she had to press on.

Leaving the van behind without a backward glance, she continued to move through the dark forest. Finally, she turned off the road at the hiking trail she'd followed the other night, the one she'd instructed Dalila to take.

The woods were heavy with shadows and mist, and she plunged ahead with her arms stretched out in front of her, pushing away the branches and stalks that crowded the narrow trail. Every so often she stopped to listen, but the steadily moaning wind made it impossible to hear anything, even if there had been anything to hear.

What was she expecting?

Dalila's voice?

Or Meg's?

What she wouldn't give to hear Meg's voice, she thought, pressing on desperately. How could she have blamed her sister for her own misfortune? How could she have schemed to kill her own flesh and blood?

Tears rolled down Candra's cheeks, mingling with the raindrops.

She was beginning to lose hope that her sister was still alive. She hadn't yet felt the stab of knowledge she felt certain would come over her at the moment Meg died, but she knew time was running out. Even now, Dalila might be pushing Meg's limp body into the trench she'd dug in the clearing. . . .

Even now, the black, slimy mud might be smothering the life out of Meg. . . .

The going was becoming more and more difficult as the trail grew steeper. It was impossible to tell in the darkness how far she still had to go.

Suddenly, Candra slipped and fell onto her knees and outstretched hands on the muddy ground, and for a moment, she wanted to just stay there, and sob, and sleep . . .

Escape this nightmare.

But as she lay trying to find the energy and will to move on, the wind died down momentarily.

In that lull, she heard something just ahead.

A voice . . .

Dalila's voice, chanting.

Candra scrambled to her feet and rushed forward, clawing her way to the top of the trail to rescue her sister.

* * *

"Nervous flier?" Sergeant Scovall asked above the roar of the engines, eyeing Mirabelle across the tiny cabin of the helicopter.

As he spoke, a gust of wind slammed into the aircraft.

She merely nodded, her throat choked with fear.

"Me, too. Takeoffs are the worst," he told her. She noticed that he was clutching his armrests so hard that his knuckles were a mottled pinkish white. The sight did nothing to reassure her.

She nodded again, and turned away to look back out the window.

Behind her, the sergeant said, "Don't worry, you'll relax in a few minutes. I always do. Gordy's an excellent pilot."

That doesn't matter, Mirabelle wanted to tell him. If something was going to happen, it was going to happen despite Gordy's skill.

The copter lurched again, and Mirabelle bit down hard on her lower lip to keep from crying out.

Why had she ignored her own sense of foreboding and flown after all these years?

How could she have been so foolish?

She knew, with growing certainty, that they weren't going to come down safely tonight. Her premonitions were rarely wrong, and they wouldn't be this time.

"Miss Moreau? We're headed southeast," Gordy said over his shoulder.

"Go to it, Mirabelle," Sergeant Scovall said, reaching across to touch her arm.

She nodded, closed her eyes, and struggled to concentrate.

After a few moments, she opened them again. "We're getting closer to her, but we're still not in the right territory. There are too many buildings and roads."

"In a few minutes we'll be away from the urban area," Gordy told her. "We're about to move into a region of several large wooded expanses that stretches from here to the shore—whoops, that's some wind," he said, adjusting a control on the panel in front of him as the copter pitched again.

Grimly, Mirabelle nodded, squeezed her eyes closed again, and tried to tune out everything but the thought of Meg.

At the top of the trail, Candra moved stealthily through the undergrowth, creeping toward the small clearing at the edge of the ravine several hundred feet away.

She could no longer hear Dalila, but whether it was because she'd stopped chanting or because her voice was drowned out by the wind, Candra wasn't sure.

She saw marks on the ground now, where something heavy had been dragged recently. She knew that it had been her sister's unconscious body, probably concealed in the canvas tarp she herself had advised Dalila to use.

As she moved slowly closer to the spot she had chosen—had it only been days ago?—for Meg's execution, Candra became aware of something hovering nearby. It was nothing tangible, just an aura, and yet it was so real—so ominous and evil—that she had to fight for control over her instincts, forcing herself not to turn and flee.

Only the knowledge that her sister's life was hanging in the balance kept her moving toward it.

That, and the realization that she, herself, had conjured the dark power.

As she slipped toward the edge of the tangled undergrowth and braced herself for whatever it was that she was about to find, Candra fully acknowledged her responsibility for the first time.

If anyone was to die here tonight, it should—and *would*—be her.

"There," Mirabelle shouted across the roar of the helicopter engines, pointing, for Gordy, in the right direction. "Keep going . . . she's down in those woods somewhere. We're almost there."

She felt as though she couldn't breathe as the helicopter flew lower, toward the spot that was drawing her instincts like a magnet, and yet somehow repelling her at the same time.

The images of Meg that kept flitting through her mind were shrouded now in a haze of murky darkness. There was a negative energy emanating from that wooded spot that made Mirabelle shudder in its very intensity.

Evil.

Pure evil, and it was stalking helpless Meg.

"We're getting closer. Come on! We have to get to her before it's too late!" Mirabelle practically screamed at the pilot.

"It's all right, Mirabelle, don't worry. We'll make it." Sergeant Scovall's tone was soothing, but she couldn't let it comfort her.

The copter flew lower still, fighting the stormy weather, and Mirabelle's eyes were riveted out the window on the black woods below.

Just as she was about to announce to the pilot that they were closing in on the spot where Meg was, the aircraft rolled crazily, then careened out of control.

It all happened in a fraction of a second—the pilot's panicked curse as he grappled with the controls, Sergeant Scovall's terrified shout, and a horrible, high-pitched shriek that encompassed a single, futile word.

"Nooooooo!"

That's me—that ungodly scream is coming from me, was Mirabelle's last startled, conscious thought before the unforgiving ground abruptly rose to meet them.

Eight

Candra carefully started to part the dense leaves that shielded her view of the clearing, then froze.

Something had just reverberated through the woods.

Something distant, yet more violent than the storm, something she couldn't put her finger on.

Her hands kept moving the branches aside even as her brain tried to imagine what it had been, and she realized, with a start, that she was looking right at Dalila Parker, who stood less than ten feet away.

The woman was motionless, her head cocked to one side, as though she, too, had sensed whatever it was that had just startled Candra.

Candra saw that Dalila was wearing a long, hooded robe made of some inky fabric. The hood concealed her face from Candra, who forced her gaze to travel downward, to the long, lumpy bundle on the ground beside the trench the woman had dug a few yards from the edge of a steep ravine.

Inside that filthy canvas tarp was her twin sister.

Now Dalila shrugged and turned her attention back to Meg. She stooped and removed something from the folds of her robe. It glinted, and Candra realized, with numbing horror, what it was.

Dalila stooped over the bundle on the ground, and then, in one sudden, violent motion, swooped in with the blade before Candra could react.

The ropes . . . she's just cutting the ropes, Candra realized after a chilling instant, watching as the woman sliced away at the cords that encircled the tarp.

She stood again and tossed the knife aside, then bent and grabbed the edge of the canvas and pulled at it roughly, causing the bundle on the ground to flip over. Dalila tugged again, and unwrapped the tarp until Candra spotted a long strand of dark hair poking out from beneath it, and then a waxen-looking hand.

Moments later, Dalila had pulled the rest of the shroud away so that Meg's outstretched, unconscious form was revealed on the ground.

For a moment, as Dalila pushed the sleeves back on her robe and reached down again, Candra thought the woman was going to simply nudge the body until it tumbled into the shallow grave she'd dug.

But then, in a blur, she spotted Dalila's hand closing over the handle of the knife again, and she realized that she was going to stab Meg, killing her before she buried her.

Candra moved instinctively as Dalila raised the blade.

Leaping forward, out of the bushes that had concealed her, she cried out, "Dalila, no! Stop!"

"Candra?" the woman looked up, the knife poised inches from Meg's stomach. "What are you doing here?"

Her voice was different, Candra realized—not her own. It was more guttural, and her words were monotone.

"I came to stop you," Candra said, and stifled a gasp as the woman raised her head farther, and the folds of the hood revealed her face.

Dalila's eyes betrayed the diabolic powers that had taken over her body, just as Candra had willed them to when she'd cast her spell.

This isn't Dalila, Candra realized with a stab of utter terror. *This is my worst nightmare come to life.*

"Stop me?" the strange voice echoed, and then laughed. "Why would you want to stop me? You were the one who wanted this. You were the one who made this happen."

"Well, I've changed my mind. I don't want Meg to die."

"Oh, you've changed your mind." The words were mocking. "You don't want Meg to die. Well, it's too late for that. *I* want Meg to die. She's going to die." The hand that held the knife raised menacingly again, hovering over Meg's body.

"No, please . . . she's my sister," Candra said, her voice coming out a whimper.

She expected to see the blade flash downward, but it remained poised, and the figure before her spoke again. "That's true. She's your sister. Your other half. And in ordering her death, *mon,* you have committed the most heinous crime of all: the destruction of your own flesh and blood."

"I know." It came out a sob, and Candra pressed a trembling fist against her lips. "I can't let you do it. I was wrong."

"No. She's responsible for your misery. She has stolen everything you should have had—the wealth, the comforts . . . your mother."

The words were an echo of Candra's own, spoken only yesterday. But she no longer believed them. Maybe she never had . . . maybe she'd only been trying to convince herself all along.

Now she only knew that she desperately needed her sister. Meg was all she had left . . . all that really mattered, anyway.

Meg was what she had been missing all her life, not the rest of it—not the wealthy lifestyle she'd thought could make her happy.

Dalila's eyes were fixed on Candra's, and in their depths she saw glittering hatred. It was as though that hatred, along with bitter resentment and vengeance, had been transferred there from Candra's very soul. And in purging herself of those vile emotions, she had been left with something stronger.

A feeling more intense than any she had ever known swept over Candra as she moved her gaze from Dalila's face down to the figure on the ground. She wanted to reach out and stroke Meg's bruised forehead, to brush her tangled, matted hair back from her face, to whisper that everything was going to be all right.

But with a strangled cry, Dalila suddenly brought the knife straight downward.

Without thinking, Candra reached out and caught the woman's wrist, fighting with every ounce of strength to keep her from jabbing Meg with the deadly blade.

She reached out with her foot and wrapped it around Dalila's ankle, sending the woman tumbling backward onto the marshy ground. Candra pounced on her as she scrambled toward Meg, still brandishing the knife.

She clawed at Dalila through the folds of the robe, grabbing for the blade as it went by in a blur. The fingers of her left hand grazed the edge of it and she vaguely realized she'd been cut.

But Dalila still had the knife, and she had to stop her.

Impulsively, as the sleeve of the woman's robe bared her forearm, Candra bent and swiftly sank her teeth into the smooth brown flesh.

Dalila let out a howl, and her grasp on the knife went slack. Candra seized the handle and, clutching it tightly, scrambled to her feet and stepped back.

She held it up threateningly as Dalila rolled onto her back and pushed herself to a standing position. She glanced down at Meg, who still lay unconscious behind Candra.

"Don't go near her," Candra warned. "If you do, I swear I'll kill you."

The woman laughed, an eerie sound that was barely human. "Go ahead," she taunted. "Even if you do kill me, you'll still be in danger. Both of you," she added, with a dark glance at Meg. "You'll never be safe."

"What do you mean?"

"Someone is after you. Someone who is far more powerful than either of you. Someone who will stop at nothing to get what he wants."

"What are you talking about?" Candra demanded. She waved the knife slightly and hoped her hand didn't appear to be trembling. She felt as though her entire body was shaking, on the verge of collapse. "Who's after me?"

"He's after you *and* your sister. And . . . never mind," Dalila said, taking a step backward and shrugging. "Why should I tell you?"

"Dalila, listen to me. . . . You're not yourself. You're under my spell. I can take it off of you, and you can help me. We can help each other. You have to tell me what you're talking about."

The response was another laugh and another step backward. But this time, Dalila lost her footing.

Candra realized, in the instant the woman stumbled toward the ground, that she was too close to the edge of the ravine.

She dropped the knife and sprang forward to grab Dalila, but she wasn't fast enough.

With a cry of terror—or was it rage?—the woman went tumbling backward down the steep, rocky cliff.

Candra could do nothing but stop at the edge and listen and watch until the terrible dull thuds had ceased and Dalila's body lay broken and limp far below.

Forces of goodness
Powers of light
work with me
with all your might . . .
To break the spell
that has been cast
so that she
may rise at last.

Kneeling on the wet ground beside Meg, Candra stopped chanting and, with her hands still outstretched across her sister's prone body, bowed her head.

The rain still poured down from the unforgiving skies, and she was drenched and chilled through, but that didn't matter. Nothing mattered but bringing her sister back.

But she couldn't help wondering, again, whether it was any use to keep on trying. She'd been at it for what felt like hours, and still Meg hadn't moved.

Stubbornly, she told herself that she couldn't give up. She owed it to Meg.

And to herself.

Come on, she silently begged her twin. *I need you so much . . .*

With a heavy sigh, Candra lifted her head and began the chant yet again, not knowing what else she could do.

Forces of goodness
Powers of light
work with—

She froze and stared down into Meg's face. Was it her imagination, or had her sister's eyelids just fluttered?

She waited, holding her breath, but nothing happened.

Grimly, she began again.

"Forces of good—"

Yes! This time, she was positive that Meg's eyelashes had moved slightly.

"Meg!" Candra called, grabbing her sister's shoulders and giving her a little shake. "Can you hear me? It's me, Candra . . . your twin. Meg, please come back. I need you so much. I—I love you, Meg. Please . . ."

Suddenly, with a shudder that racked her whole body, Meg moaned and opened her eyes.

Candra gasped.

For a moment, she couldn't speak, could do nothing but stare down into the face that was a mirror image of her own.

Then, with a sob, she reached up to smooth the tangled strands of wet dark hair off her rain-drenched face. "Oh, Meg," she whispered raggedly, shaking her head.

"Candra?"

Hearing her name slip past those parched lips was a wonder. She had been waiting so long, hoping against hope. . . .

Candra looked gratefully into her sister's bewildered eyes. "Yes, it's me," she told her, and added, "I'm your twin."

Meg nodded, and, wincing, lifted her head. Candra slipped her arms beneath Meg's and helped prop her into a sitting position.

Her sister glanced around, appearing dazed. "Where am I?"

Candra hesitated.

"It's a long story," she finally said. "I'll tell you later. Right now, we've got to get out of here. It's kind of far. Do you think you can get up and walk?"

"If you help me," Meg said simply, looking at her with trusting dark eyes.

Candra had to swallow over a sudden lump in her throat before she could reply.

"Sure, I'll help you. Come on—we'll do it together," she promised, and, reaching out, she slipped her hand into her sister's at last.

The back room of the small occult shop on Elmont Avenue was tiny and overpowered with the scent of exotic herbs and powders, damp wooden floorboards, and age.

The lone occupant, a dark-skinned, strong-bodied young man, didn't notice the close, stale atmosphere or the violent sounds of the storm that raged outside in the night.

He stood, clad in a long black hooded robe, before the Obeah altar he had prepared on top of several stacked packing crates.

Flickering candlelight danced on the walls, casting eerie shadows and mingling occasionally with bright flashes of lightning that slashed through the one small window on the back wall.

He lit the incense burner on the altar, and a pungent wisp of smoke rose to blend with the already musty air.

Raising his arms and closing his eyes, he began to chant silently, invoking the forces of evil. Then he reached with one hand for a shallow pottery bowl on the altar, pulling it closer, as the long, dark fingers of his other hand disappeared in the folds of his robe, and, a moment later, produced two cardboard rectangles.

He stared at them for a long moment, then shook his head as if to clear it. Holding the rectangles above his head in both hands, he began muttering a new chant, each phrase growing more feverish and punctuated by claps of thunder from above.

Finally, with a flourish, he dropped them so that they fluttered into the shallow bowl, landing face up.

Identical pairs of eyes stared at him from the photographs—black, almond-shaped, exotic eyes.

One pair belonged to Megan McKenna, and the formal school picture was one he had stolen from her own bedroom.

The other pair of eyes were Candra Bowen's, captured in a shot he had snapped surreptitiously on the street just the other day.

He met their unsuspecting, frozen stares with a narrowed gaze and reached for a small vial on the altar. He poured the few ounces of liquid it contained into the bowl. Now the familiar faces watched him from beneath the watery surface.

A long black candle burned beside him, and he carefully removed it from its holder. In one swift movement, he passed the flame over the bowl, then watched as the contents ignited.

He had only one last fleeting glimpse of the faces of the twin sisters before both photographs were obliterated to ashes in the furious orange and yellow inferno.

A sinister smile curled his lips.

Nine

"Just a little farther . . . can you make it?" Candra asked Meg, shouting to be heard above the wind and rain that swirled around them.

"I think so." Meg was clutching Candra's arm so hard that it hurt.

Her flesh was probably actually going to be bruised, Candra realized, as Meg stumbled a little and tightened her grasp even more.

Grimly, Candra looked straight ahead along the dark trail, thinking that she deserved the pain after what she had done. She deserved a far worse punishment.

Oh, Meg, how could I have done it?

She bit down on her lip to keep from saying the words aloud, instead telling her sister, "We're almost there."

"But where are we going?" Meg asked, stopping for a moment and pushing her long, soggy hair from her face. "We're in the middle of nowhere."

Candra stopped, too, and peered at her twin in the darkness.

It was still so startling to stare at a mirror image of her own features. Meg had the same large, almond-shaped dark eyes, the same full lips and exotic bone structure, the same olive-toned skin. She even wore her straight black hair the same, parted in the middle and hanging down her back.

"We're in Rocky Forest State Park," she told Meg patiently, as she shoved her own dripping tresses out of her eyes. "Remember? I told you that when you asked a few minutes ago."

"I know, but . . . why?"

Candra hesitated. She knew her sister didn't have any memory of how she'd gotten here. She couldn't know that Dalila Parker had driven her unconscious body in a rented blue van from her apartment in Spring City, Connecticut.

She couldn't know *anything* that had happened to her, in fact, from the moment Dalila had slipped the powerful potion into Meg's tea and cast a spell on her that afternoon almost a week ago.

As Candra locked into her sister's blank, confused expression, she knew what she *should* do.

She should tell Meg the truth.

That she, Candra, had been behind the whole scheme. That she had not only bribed Dalila to get Meg out of the way for a while so that Candra could step into her charmed world . . .

But that Candra, caught up in a frenzy of greed and fury, had also cast a spell on Dalila. She had beckoned the forces of evil to over-power Dalila so that she would agree to bring Meg to this desolate spot for one diabolical reason.

Candra had wanted Meg murdered.

But you changed your mind! she told herself, fighting to control the wave of near-hysteria that rose in her gut. *You're the one who saved her from Dalila. If you hadn't gotten here when you did, Meg wouldn't be alive.*

Instead, it was Dalila who had been killed, in a fall over the edge of a steep ravine a few miles up the trail.

And she's the only one who knew, Candra reminded herself. *With her out of the way, there's no way Meg can find out what you did— what you* almost *did.*

"Candra?" Meg asked, reaching out and taking her arm again. Her other hand clenched the stiff canvas tarp that Candra had wrapped around her, since Meg was wearing only a T-shirt and jeans.

Meanwhile, Candra was wearing Meg's clothes, just as she had been all week. If Meg had recognized the black jeans or storm coat, she hadn't said anything. And the Italian leather boots on Candra's feet were so coated in mud that they were well beyond easy identification.

"Candra?" Meg repeated. "Are you okay?"

"Yeah, *mon,*" Candra said vaguely, automatically taking on the Jamaican dialect she had fought so hard to lose over the past several weeks.

Meg smiled faintly. "You have an island accent."

"No, I don't," Candra denied quickly, realizing what she had done and slipping back into the smooth Connecticut speech pattern that had become second nature while she was posing as Meg.

"I didn't mean it in a bad way," Meg said. "Actually, I think it sounds cool."

Candra said nothing, just looked away.

She couldn't bear that her sister was being so kind. After what she'd done—what she'd *tried* to do to Meg.

Tell her! her conscience demanded. *Tell her right now. Get it over with.*

But she couldn't bring herself to confess.

Instead, she said, "Come on, let's keep going. I think it's starting to rain harder."

Meg didn't protest, just grabbed Candra's sore arm again, causing her to wince slightly as they trudged on through the stormy woods.

Meg's mind was spinning.

Was she really hiking through the woods at night in the middle of a downpour . . . with her long-lost twin sister at her side?

The whole thing was surreal, and yet, somehow, she accepted it.

It was Candra's presence that reassured her. Though they were strangers, she felt an odd sense of comfort at finally coming face-to-face with her sister after a lifetime apart. It was as though, bewildering as it had been to regain consciousness in this bizarre setting, nothing seemed to matter for now but the fact that she had found her other half.

Eventually, Meg knew, Candra would tell her what was going on.

Until then, there was nothing to do but follow her sister over the narrow, uneven trail toward wherever it was that they were going.

She trusted Candra instinctively, in a way that she had never trusted another person in her life. With Candra, she knew she was safe.

How could it be otherwise? Candra was a part of her. They had been formed from the same cells, had been carried, intertwined, for nine months in the intimate confines of their mother's womb.

Until somehow, something had wrenched them apart.

Someone, Meg told herself, and thought of her mother.

Giselle was weak—she'd always known that. But Meg had never doubted that her mother loved her. And she wondered, not for the first time, how the same woman who had raised her could have denied her twin.

How must Candra feel, knowing that their mother had given her up? Did Candra know why? Or was their past as much a mystery to her as it was to Meg?

Meg pushed away the endless questions that coursed through her mind, telling herself that soon, when they were warm and dry and back home, her sister would provide some answers.

Or if Candra knew nothing more than she did, at least they could unravel the secrets of their past, together.

And now that they'd found each other, they wouldn't let anything— *anyone* tear them apart again.

For now, Meg kept her mouth shut and her eyes focused on Candra's dark silhouette in front of her as they made their way out of the woods.

* * *

"There it is," Candra announced to Meg as they emerged from the trail at last onto the muddy road that wound through the park. She pointed to Meg's black Honda, which was mired where Candra had deserted it . . . could it have only been a short hour or two ago?

"My car . . . what's it doing there? I don't remember driving it here," Meg said, her voice a high-pitched protest that mingled with the rising wind.

"You didn't," Candra said simply. "I did."

"But how did *I* get here?"

"Dalila Parker drove you here in that van," Candra said, pointing at the second abandoned vehicle nearby. "You don't remember it, do you?"

"No." Meg shook her head slowly, frowning as though she was trying to come up with some recollection.

"Do you know who Dalila is?"

"She's the woman who lives over on Elmont Avenue . . . the one I met at that carnival with Zoe. The one who brought us back together . . . right?"

Candra turned her head so she wouldn't have to see Meg searching her face for answers.

"Right," she mumbled, and tugged Meg along the last few yards to the car.

"Let's get in and warm up for a few minutes," Candra said, her teeth suddenly chattering. She reached into her pocket for the keys and unlocked the driver's side door with shaking fingers.

Only when she'd pulled the door open did she realize that it was Meg, and not her, who belonged behind the wheel. This was Meg's car, not Candra's.

The masquerade was over. It was time for Candra to step back into her rightful place.

"Here, go ahead," she said, moving away from the door and motioning for Meg to get in.

Her sister shook her head. "You drive," she told Candra, and added, "I mean, if you don't mind. I still feel too out of it. And besides, I still have no idea where we are."

Without protest, Candra climbed behind the wheel and pressed the button to unlock the passenger's side door. Guiltily, she fingered Meg's silver Tiffany key ring before jabbing it into the ignition and turning on the engine. She busied herself pushing the heat control onto the highest setting as Meg got in beside her and closed her door, shutting out the roar of the wind.

"It takes a few minutes for the heat to get going," Meg said, settling back against the seat with a sigh. "It'll kick in soon. It always does."

And again Candra was reminded that the car belonged to Meg, not to her.

Meg had no idea that Candra had been driving it for the past week, or that Candra had been living in her home, sleeping in her bed, inhabiting every part of her privileged world.

She had no way of even suspecting what had been going on.

No one knows the truth, except Dalila, Candra thought again, and lifted her gaze from the dashboard to look out through the rain-drenched windshield into the darkness that surrounded them.

And with Dalila gone, there's only one way Meg is going to find out what I've done.

I have to tell her.

I have to tell her now, *before I change my mind.*

And of course, Candra knew she couldn't change her mind. She couldn't lie to her sister about what had happened over the past week.

Could she?

Of course, she *could.*

It was *possible* that she could get away with what she had done.

But she *wouldn't* do something like that.

It was time to stop living a lie.

Time to do what was right.

Time to tell the truth and face the consequences.

"Candra," Meg said beside her, and reached across the seat to grasp Candra's cold, damp hand in her own.

A lump rose suddenly and violently in Candra's throat at the contact with her sister's bare skin.

"Please tell me," Meg said quietly. "What's going on? Why are we here? Where did I get these clothes that I'm wearing? I've never seen them before in my life. I feel so strange . . . like I'm losing my mind, or something. Why can't I remember anything?"

Something in Meg's voice reached down into Candra's soul, and she felt herself quaking inside, too overcome with emotion to speak right away. Meg sounded uncertain, and frightened, and yet there was an unsettling intimacy in the way she had spoken to Candra.

It was as though she trusted Candra to make everything all right, the way she had blindly trusted Candra to guide her out of the woods just now.

But how can she trust me after what I've done?

I have to tell her.
No more putting it off.
I have to confess . . .

"Candra, come on, you have to tell me what's going on. I have to know. Please . . ."

Miserably, Candra turned to look at her sister.

Meg's eyes fastened immediately on her own, and even in the shadowy interior of the car, Candra could read the expression on her sister's face.

It was one of utter faith.

"I . . ."

Candra stopped, took a deep breath, and started again. "Dalila . . ." she said, and forced herself to go on. "Dalila brought you here to kill you, Meg."

Though her sister gasped at the words and her free hand flew up to press against her mouth, Candra saw in her eyes that she wasn't entirely shocked.

She paused, searching for the words to convey the rest of the story.

Before she could go on, Meg said, "I knew there was something about that woman . . . from the moment I met her, she gave me the creeps, Candra. Thank God you saved me from her."

Wide-eyed, Candra asked, "But . . . how did you know that?"

"I just assumed . . . I mean, isn't that what happened? Didn't you save me?"

Slowly, Candra nodded.

She felt Meg's grasp tighten around her hand. Somehow, Meg's flesh was warm, and Candra vaguely willed her sister's body heat to banish the chill from her own icy hands.

"But why did Dalila want to kill me?" Meg asked. "I mean, she was odd, but she didn't seem evil. And she promised to introduce me to you. She brought us together, didn't she?"

Without waiting for a reply, Meg added, "But I can't even remember what happened after I went over to her apartment to meet you this afternoon."

"This after . . ." Candra echoed, staring at her sister. The rain-spattered windshield cast her face in an eerie polka-dot pattern. "Meg, that wasn't this afternoon."

"What do you mean?"

Candra couldn't reply. Her mind was racing.

"You mean," Meg said slowly, frowning, "that I've blanked out more than a few *hours*? Oh, God . . . What day is it?"

"It's Friday. Actually, not anymore," Candra said, glancing at the dashboard clock, which told her that it was well after midnight. "It's Saturday."

"Which . . . which Saturday? How much time has passed since that day at Dalila's?"

"Almost a week."

Meg nodded, looking too stunned to speak again.

Candra's thoughts tumbled over each other.

Not only didn't Meg realize what Candra had been up to, but she now seemed to think she was suffering from some form of amnesia.

Which was true, actually.

The spell Dalila had cast had rendered Meg into a state of suspended animation. For her, time had obviously stood still from the moment she'd lost consciousness after drinking that tea Monday afternoon.

She'll never know if you don't tell her, Candra thought again, staring out at the storm through the windshield.

"So," Meg said in a small, hollow-sounding voice, "I've been out of it for almost a week. What happened during that time?"

Candra found herself shrugging.

How could she tell Meg what had happened? How could she say, *You've been lying unconscious in Dalila's apartment since Monday?*

After another moment's hesitation, she lied, "I have no idea what you did during most of that time, Meg."

"But you do remember that we were supposed to meet in Dalila's apartment on Monday afternoon, right?" Meg asked. "Please tell me I didn't imagine that whole thing."

"No, you didn't imagine it."

"Thank God I'm not a total nut case." Meg smiled faintly. "So we met . . . I wish I could remember it. Ever since I found out you existed, I fantasized about what it would be like to come face to face with you. I can't believe that when it actually happened, I somehow zoned out."

"Maybe that's why," Candra found herself blurting. "Maybe it was too much for you, emotionally. Maybe you couldn't handle something like that—so you sort of . . . lost it for a while."

"You think?" Meg looked relieved.

Candra nodded, ignoring the protests of her conscience, which was warning her to confess. "I know what it was like for me, meeting you," she told Meg. "Intense."

At least that was the truth.

And Meg was bobbing her head up and down, like she understood. "When did you find out that I existed?" she asked Candra. "Did you know when you were living back in Jamaica?"

"No. I didn't find out until I came to Crawford Corners."

"But that's such an unbelievable coincidence, isn't it?" Meg asked. "That you would end up here, in Crawford Corners, out of all the towns in the whole country? Dalila said you were living on an estate with . . . your grandmother."

"Not my grandmother," Candra corrected swiftly, and bitterly. "Rosamund Bowen isn't related to me in any way. But yes, I did think she was my grandmother. She was a housekeeper for the Drayers . . . Jonas Drayer." She paused, and when Meg didn't say anything, went on. "He's an American. Gran—Rosamund worked for him in Jamaica, where he was a developer for SNE Real Estate. Then—"

"SNE?" Meg interrupted. "As in, Southern New England? My grandfather worked for them, too. The company is based here in Crawford Corners. I guess that explains the coincidence. His job was the reason my mother—sorry, *our* mother—was in Jamaica in the first place back when we were born."

"So obviously, she left me behind and brought you back here to the States with her," Candra said, unable to keep the chill out of her voice.

Meg looked troubled. "I guess," she said quietly, her eyebrows furrowing.

"Anyway"—Candra went on, shrugging as though it didn't bring fresh pain every time she acknowledged what Giselle had done— "when Jonas decided to move his family back home, he brought Rosamund and me with him. We've been living at the Drayers' place out on Soundview Road."

A flicker of recognition lit Meg's eyes. "I know where that is," she said, nodding. "Mom mentioned something about them being back in town, and one night, Shea and I turned around in the driveway of their house. A big white place with a curved driveway, right?"

"Right."

"Shea's my boyfriend—did you know that?" Meg asked, her expression clouding over again. She didn't wait for an answer. "At least, he *was*. We've been having trouble lately. I hope . . . I wonder what's going on with us now. It's so weird that I can't remember . . . Oh, God, Candra, you have to tell me everything you know."

"I will," Candra assured her, even as guilt stole over her again, stronger than ever. "Don't worry, Meg. I'll tell you everything."

You can't do this. You have to tell her the truth.

It's now or never.

You won't be able to live with yourself if you don't confess.

And she realized it was true.

She hated herself for what she had done.

She owed it to Meg, and to herself, to tell the truth.

There was only one way to pay the price for the sins she had committed against her sister. She had to own up to what she had done, and she had to do it now.

She opened her mouth and forced herself to speak. "Meg, there's something I have to—"

"What was that? Did you hear it?" Meg interrupted, and both sisters looked around, startled, as a blinding beam of light suddenly came out of nowhere and swept through the car.

"Oh, thank God. Look—it's the police." Meg squinted into the misty darkness and glimpsed two men in uniforms stepping out of the car that had pulled up behind the Honda.

There was a third person with them, she noted—another man. Or, rather, a guy about Meg's age, she revised as he drew closer. He was tall and broad shouldered. Meg sensed the hurry in his pace as he and the officers approached the car, but she saw one of the cops put a hand on his arm and caution him to stay behind them.

Frowning, she looked at Candra. "Who's that guy with them?"

Her sister was just staring out the back window of the car, a strange, unreadable expression on her face.

A moment later, there was a cop on each side of the car, opening both doors and jerking blinding flashlight beams into the interior.

"Candra Bowen?" the officer on Meg's side asked, peering at her.

And Meg heard the officer on Candra's side ask the same thing. *How strange,* she thought fleetingly, *that they don't know the difference. We could switch places and no one would ever know . . .*

"No, I'm Meg," she heard herself say, and the officer looked relieved.

"Megan McKenna?"

"Uh-huh."

"Are you all right, miss?" he asked, and she noticed that he was young and baby-faced, probably not much older than his midtwenties.

"I'm fine." Obviously, they knew that she had been in danger. "My sister got to me in time," she added, and looked over to see that Candra was being helped—or pulled?—out of the car by the other officer, who was bigger and older and gruffer looking.

Meg heard him say, "You have a lot of explaining to do."

And then the young guy in the down jacket was there, too, pushing his way in and asking, "Candra, are you all right? I thought you'd been kidnapped when I came out of the store and—"

"Mr. Keller," the other officer cut in, "would you please step back and be quiet?"

"Sorry, Officer, I just—"

"It's okay, Landon," Candra interrupted. "I'm fine."

Bewildered, Meg turned to the policeman on her side of the car. "What happened?"

"We were hoping you'd be able to tell us," he said, leaning into the car so that his head was out of the downpour. He seemed to be waiting for her to reply.

"I . . . I can't," she admitted slowly. "I have no idea how I got here. All I know is that my sister saved me from that woman."

"What woman?"

"Dalila Parker."

The officer nodded, as though he recognized the name. "And where is she now?"

Meg jerked her head in the direction of the trail. "Up there, somewhere. She tripped and fell over the edge of the ravine. Candra said she's dead."

The officer's jaw stiffened and he lifted his head to call to his partner. "Hey, Chuck? Can I talk to you a minute?" He looked back at Meg and said sternly but not unkindly, "You stay put right in this car, okay?"

"Okay."

She watched as the two policemen walked around to the back of the car, one of them dragging Candra along by the arm. The guy she'd called Landon stood a few yards away, apparently focused intently on the conversation they were having.

Meg wished she could hear what was being said, but even with her door open, it was impossible with the storm raging around them. The cops were doing a lot of finger pointing and arm waving at Candra, and she seemed to be cooperating calmly, nodding or shaking her head or shrugging.

After what seemed like an eternity, the cop Meg had been talking to came back over to the car and bent to look at her again. She saw that his dark hair was now plastered to the sides of his wet face, and his uniform was soaked.

"Miss McKenna? I'd like to ask you a few questions," he said grimly.

* * *

It seemed like the younger officer had been in the car for hours, questioning Meg. Candra stood stiffly, watching, her arm—the same sore arm Meg had clung to earlier—imprisoned in the officer's iron grasp.

Relax, she told herself, not for the first time since the cops had approached the car. *They can't prove anything. As far as they know, as far as anyone knows, you did nothing wrong.*

She felt Landon's gaze on her, and deliberately kept her attention focused on the car. She didn't want to acknowledge the questions she'd seen when she'd looked into his eyes before.

He hadn't seemed accusing, like the policemen, but maybe the fact that he wasn't suspicious of her was even worse.

He'd looked at her with bewilderment and anxiety and, mostly, concern. But Candra knew why. His emotions weren't coming from his heart, they were coming from the spell she'd placed on him. The spell that made him want her, passionately and blindly.

It was the only reason he'd ever wanted to be with her, the only reason he'd agreed to go away with her tonight, no questions asked.

And obviously, he wasn't even daunted by the fact that she'd taken off and left him while he was paying for gasoline in that convenience store back on the highway. No, he'd actually thought she'd been kidnapped.

He'd called the police from a pay phone in front of the store, the officers had told her, and reported that his girlfriend had been abducted.

His *girlfriend.*

What Candra wouldn't have given, just a short time ago, to hear him call her that.

A guy like Landon Keller—with his all-American good looks, private school education, and easygoing popularity—a guy like him shouldn't have noticed someone like Candra Bowen. All right, most males *did* look twice at her, but once Landon realized that she was merely the Jamaican immigrant who lived in the servants' quarters at his friend Craig's home, he should have moved on.

She had made sure that wouldn't happen.

And now, knowing that what he felt for her wasn't real, she wished more than anything that she had simply left him alone in the first place. Indifference—or even Craig Drayer's brand of mocking sarcasm— would be better than magically manufactured care and concern.

"All right, Miss McKenna," the young officer finally said. "If you're sure you don't remember anything else, we'll have to give it up for tonight."

"I don't remember anything that happened after Monday afternoon," Meg insisted, feeling like a broken record.

"And I believe you, okay? Temporary amnesia is a typical response after trauma. We want to have you checked out by paramedics to make sure you're all right. And then we'll arrange to get you back to Crawford Corners so that—"

"And my sister, too," Meg cut in quickly, casting a glance at Candra, who still stood out in the pouring rain, flanked by the burly cop.

"I'm not sure what's going to happen to your sister," the policeman said, opening the car door. "We have to radio in for backup, and— look, we'll know more in a little while. You stay here."

"Can't I get out and talk to Candra for a second? I just want to make sure she's all right."

"I'm afraid not. And don't worry, she's fine."

"But she's getting soaked out in the rain."

The officer shrugged. With a brief wave, he was gone, leaving Meg alone in the dark again.

She twisted in her seat and watched him going back over to his partner. The two conferred briefly before the younger one apparently took over guarding Candra as the older one went to the police car.

Oh, Candra, what's going on? Meg wondered, and sighed. *Are you in some sort of trouble?*

But if her sister was in trouble, Meg vowed fiercely that she'd do everything she could to help.

After all, she and Candra were a team, and she wasn't about to let anything come between them ever again.

"I'm exhausted," Meg said, yawning and stretching as the police car left I-95 on the exit leading to Crawford Corners at dawn. She turned to Candra, who sat beside her on the backseat. "Aren't you beat?"

Candra nodded. It had been a few hours since she had been cleared of any wrongdoing, but she still felt edgy, especially since the two police officers in the front seat seemed to regard her with undercurrents of suspicion anyway.

But there was nothing they could pin on her. No one could prove that she had tried to harm Meg, especially with Meg vehemently insisting that if it weren't for Candra, Dalila Parker would have killed her.

All they could do was ask Candra to point the backup squad in the direction of Dalila's body.

Then an emergency rescue truck had arrived on the scene, and the paramedics had wrapped Candra and Meg in thick blankets and examined them both.

The whole time, Landon had hovered, looking worried and mostly staying silent. Luckily, it was hard for him to get close enough to speak to Candra, with Meg pretty much clinging to her side, and all the police officers and rescue workers bustling around.

Finally, the two original cops announced that they would be transporting Candra and Meg back to Crawford Corners, and that they had arranged for another officer to drive Landon back to The Lawson School. Meg's car, which was still mired in mud, would be left behind for now.

As the officers prepared to escort Meg and Candra to their car, Landon had touched Candra's shoulder gently and whispered, "Call me in the morning, okay?"

She'd simply nodded, and tore her gaze from his—though not before seeing the tender expression in them.

"It's Meadowview Terrace, the next one up." Meg's voice crashed into Candra's thoughts, and she realized they were almost home.

Home? It's not your home. Not anymore, though it was fun pretending for a while ...

"Too bad Mom isn't here—but she'll be back from Fiji sometime tomorrow," Meg told Candra as the car made the turn onto the quiet, familiar street.

The houses here were large and upscale and set far back from the road, with well-tended, sweeping lawns. Candra remembered how satisfying it had been to pretend she belonged here during these last fleeting days.

"I can't wait until she finds out about you. She's going to—"

When Meg stopped short, Candra looked up and followed her gaze to number forty-one, a familiar red brick colonial. And she saw what had startled her sister. A police car was parked in the driveway.

"What are the cops doing at my house? What's going on?" Meg asked, sounding panicky and leaning toward the two cops in the front seat.

"I don't know," the younger one, Officer Hammond, said with a frown. He looked at his partner, who was behind the wheel. "What do you think, Chuck?"

The older officer shrugged and pulled the car to a stop at the curb.

"I hope it's not about my sister ... I mean Carrie, my other sister," Meg added with a quick, almost apologetic glance at Candra before she opened the door and jumped out. She raced across the lawn as a cop got out of the car in the driveway.

Candra and the two officers followed, arriving just in time to see Meg burst into tears.

"What is it?" Candra asked, a sick feeling in her stomach.

"An accident," the uniformed officer said.

"Her sister?" Officer Hammond asked.

"No, it's my friend Mirabelle," Meg wailed. "Oh, God . . ."

Mirabelle.

Candra's gut twisted with recognition at the name.

Mirabelle Moreau was the girl who, along with Shea, had followed Candra when she'd been driving Meg's car the other day. It was Dalila Parker who had told her that Mirabelle was Meg's friend, and that she, too, had powers.

She forced her attention back on the situation at hand.

"I'm Officer Garrety," the cop was saying. Candra felt his eyes sweeping over her and sensed the same aura of suspicion she had gotten from the other two men.

She met his gaze head-on and straightened her shoulders. After a moment, she was pleased to see that he seemed uncomfortable and looked away, addressing the other two men.

"I heard you were on your way here and I was sent over to meet you. I've been working with Mirabelle and a few of Meg's other friends, who were concerned that she was in danger. You don't know how relieved we were when we got the call a few hours ago that she'd been located."

Officer Hammond nodded. "Did they tell you what had happened?"

"I know she had been kidnapped by the Parker woman, who then tried to kill her. That was what Mirabelle said. She knew the Parker woman's plans, though we still have no clear motive."

Again, Candra was aware of Officer Garrety flicking a distrustful glance in her direction.

"But how did Mirabelle find out what was going on?" Meg asked.

Officer Garrety hesitated, then said, mostly to the other two officers, "Uh, we don't normally use psychics to locate missing persons, but this girl knew what she was talking about."

Candra stiffened. So Mirabelle had figured out what Dalila was up to. What else had she known?

"Anyway," the officer continued, "she was up in a police chopper, leading the pilot and our sergeant to Rocky Forest, when it went down. Weather like this, they shouldn't have been flying," he added, shaking his head and gesturing at the sky, which was still gray-black and spilling torrents of rain.

"You said she was in critical condition. Is she going to pull through?" Meg asked, sniffling and calming down.

"I don't know. She's at Spring City General."

Candra caught her lower lip in her front teeth and pondered that. If Mirabelle lived, she might implicate Candra. And yet, what evidence could she possibly have that Candra had schemed to have Meg killed?

Beside her, she suddenly realized, Meg was shivering violently.

Candra instinctively put an arm around her twin's shoulder and said, both for her sister's benefit and for the officers', "We have to get inside. After everything she's been through, she needs to rest."

She flashed a brief smile at Meg's grateful, exhausted expression, then turned back to the three policemen.

"I'm sure you'll keep us posted on Mirabelle's condition," Candra informed Officer Garrety in a no-nonsense voice, then added to the other two men, "And thank you for driving us back here, and for everything else."

They nodded, all three of them.

Her arm still around Meg's shoulder, she started leading her sister up the walk to the front porch.

It wasn't until they were in the foyer, with the door closed and locked against the storm and the three pairs of suspicious eyes, that Candra realized she'd been holding her breath.

She let it out in a sigh of relief.

"Are you okay, Candra?" Meg asked.

"I'm fine." *Now that that's over,* she added silently.

And it *was* over.

Case closed.

"You know"—Meg said, looking closely at her in the bright overhead light—"you really do look exactly like me. I even have a coat like that."

"It's yours," Candra said truthfully, and impulsively added, "you loaned it to me the other day. Remember?"

"No." Meg's eyes were sleepy-looking, and she yawned. "I can't remember anything . . ."

"Come on," Candra told Meg, and gestured at the balcony above, where the bedrooms were. "You have to get upstairs."

"I don't know if I can walk another step," Meg said wearily. "I feel like I want to just drop right here and curl up on the floor."

"No, don't do that," Candra told her firmly.

Meg protested with a weary groan and really did look like she was going to collapse on the spot.

"Listen, Meg, I'll help you. Come on."

She was grateful when Meg allowed herself to be led across the foyer, with its polished honey-hued wooden floors, framed original watercolors, and delicate crystal chandelier that was suspended from the twenty-foot ceiling.

"You've been so great to me, Candra," Meg murmured.

"You're my sister," Candra said simply.

You're my sister, but I can't bring myself to tell you the truth. And now you think I'm your savior, instead of the person who tried to kill you.

But, she promised herself, as she and Meg started up the curved staircase, that starting this moment, she'd make it up to Meg.

She'd do whatever it took . . . as long as she didn't have to tell her the truth.

Ten

Saturday morning dawned gray and rainy on Elmont Avenue in Spring City, making the seedy neighborhood appear more dismal than ever. The storm had stalled just off the New England coast, and it wasn't expected to move out of the area for several hours.

The Closed sign was still hanging on the glass door pane of the tiny occult shop down the block from Rivera's Newsstand. But the place wasn't deserted.

The young man who had spent the last few hours sleeping on a woven mat in the cramped back storeroom emerged into the front of the store and walked over to the window.

He looked down the street and saw that two patrol cars were parked in front of Rivera's, their domed red lights spinning silently.

The sight didn't surprise him.

He had been awakened from a sound sleep by the sudden, certain knowledge that something had happened to Dalila Parker.

And he knew, just as clearly, that both Candra and Meg were still alive.

Oh, well.

There was still time. Still plenty of time.

Although, it was a pity that Dalila Parker wouldn't be able to tell him whatever it was that she'd been hiding from him. He'd sensed that she had some kind of secret when he'd first spoken to her. But the woman had insisted on keeping it to herself.

He'd figured he would force her, in time, to tell him whatever it was. Especially once he had her under his power.

He smiled, thinking about the monster he'd created in the middle-aged woman. Candra had thought she was so clever, casting that small spell on Dalila so that the woman would destroy Meg for her.

Little did the girl know that Dalila was under a much more powerful spell—or that someone else wanted Meg dead.

And he'd wanted Candra dead, too.

Now it appeared that he'd have to accomplish both deeds by himself. He hated to do it. Things could get messy that way.

He sighed and calmly ran his strong, ebony-skinned hands over his head to pat his close-cropped dark hair into place. He removed his long black coat from a hook, slipped into it, then unlocked the door and pushed it open.

The chill in the air took his breath away momentarily, accustomed as he was to the hot, balmy mornings back in Jamaica. But he plunged into the clammy weather anyway, striding along the sidewalk, focused on the building on the opposite corner.

A small crowd had gathered beside the patrol cars. He scanned it and noted that one could find two types of people out in this neighborhood at this early hour. One group consisted of the bleary-eyed barhoppers, drug users, and streetwalkers who prowled Elmont until the sun came up. The others were the poor-but-respectable men, women, and children who actually lived and worked here, most of them transplants from the Caribbean islands.

He crossed the street and sidled up to the fringes of the group that had gathered on the corner.

"What happened?" he asked the person directly to his right, a middle-aged black man who flashed a gold front tooth the moment he opened his mouth to answer.

"The woman who lived up there," the man said, and pointed to the row of windows above the newsstand. "Her name was Parker. They say she was killed last night, someplace out in the woods. Now the cops are searching her apartment."

"She was up to no good, that one," a dark-skinned woman commented, looking over her shoulder. She wore large gold hoop earrings and a bright pink turban. "I don't know what happened. Until a few days ago, she was okay. But I passed her on the street yesterday, and her eyes, *mon*—they were filled with—evil."

Gold-tooth nodded until the woman had faced the building again, then turned back to him and snickered. "Evil. Yeah, sure, evil. So, you know the Parker lady, kid?"

"No," he lied. "Just curious."

There was no way, right now, to get into the apartment and find what he needed.

He slipped out of the crowd and made his way along the street until he came to a storefront deli that was open. There, he bought the Spring City *Morning Herald* and a cup of coffee, knowing it would be disappointingly weak and bitter compared with the rich Blue Mountain blend he was used to. But he'd be back in Jamaica soon enough, he promised himself. Just as soon as he'd taken care of business.

As he headed back along Elmont toward the occult shop, he saw that the crowd had dispersed and that one of the patrol cars had left. Inside the other, two officers sat filling out information on a clipboard.

They didn't notice him, but he kept his head down just the same.

He was on the corner, about to cross back to his block, when something soft bumped against his calves.

He looked down to see a sleek black cat staring up at him. The animal's eyes were narrowed and it hissed threateningly. It hadn't liked him from the start.

"Now, now, Erzulie," he said in his smooth, rich voice, reaching down and scooping Dalila's pet into his arms. He darted a glance at the cops to make sure they hadn't noticed. "How did you get out? Did you sneak through the door when they weren't looking?"

The animal squirmed in his grasp, but he easily balanced his coffee and paper and held the cat firmly against his chest. The light changed and he crossed the street in a few quick strides.

"What's the matter? Don't you like me?" he murmured to the hissing, twitching cat, who was trying to escape his grasp as he walked swiftly toward the shop. "And why is that? You know I had nothing to do with your mistress's unfortunate . . . demise. I am truly sorry to hear about it."

And that, he acknowledged to himself with a cunning smile, *is the truth.*

He would miss Dalila, if only because she would no longer be available to help him with his little . . . mission. He had found her by chance, having followed Candra to the woman's apartment one day. In no time, he had Dalila Parker mesmerized and willing to do whatever he asked.

Such a shame, he thought now, clucking his tongue and shaking his head, that he could no longer rely on her.

A few moments later, he unlocked the door again and entered the occult shop. The cat squirmed in his arms as he turned the latch behind him, deposited the coffee and newspaper on the counter, and headed for the back room.

"What's the matter, Erzulie?" he asked, looking down at the animal with mock concern. "Are you frightened? Don't be. You see, I need you."

He walked over to the makeshift altar he'd arranged on top of some crates.

Then, still holding the cat firmly against his chest with one strong hand, he stroked the thick folds of fur beneath the cat's tense head with the other and crooned, "Are you ready to help me? Good. Just relax."

In one swift, violent motion, he clamped his fingers around the thin, bony feline neck and wrenched it. There was a high-pitched, staccato cry and then a pleasing snap before Erzulie went limp against him.

"See? That wasn't so bad, was it?" he asked in his thick Jamaican *patois.* "And now you can help me. You see, the ceremony I'm about to conduct calls for fresh blood. And yours will do perfectly."

With a chuckle, he laid the animal on the altar and removed a gleaming dagger from the folds of his long black coat.

Giselle McKenna Hudson was fully aware of the attention she was attracting from males and females alike as she moved through the waiting area at Los Angeles airport.

She was pleased, as always, to notice the envious glares from the women, and the admiring stares from the men. She had been the target of those same reactions repeatedly over the years, in more places than she could recall.

In the South Pacific, where she had been until yesterday, her fair coloring had been a rarity, and some of the native men had practically treated her like a goddess.

Even here in L.A., where every other woman seemed to be as blond and willowy as she was, Giselle knew she stood out. She was wearing an expensive copper-colored sleeveless sheath that complimented her coloring. Her skin was honey-bronzed from the vacation in Fiji. Her long, light hair was worn loose and was more sun-streaked than ever.

As she approached the bank of pay telephones on the wall, she allowed her pale green eyes to meet and hold the appreciative gaze of a particularly good-looking blond man who was passing by. She realized that he was the star of last winter's biggest box office smash, a movie that had been shown on their flight out from New York last week.

He raised his eyebrow suggestively at her, and Giselle's delicate mouth curved into a knowing smile.

It was so tempting to simply stop and flirt with this man—to bask in the attention from one of the world's hottest sex symbols. She even allowed herself to imagine his strong hands roaming over her body as they had done to the actress in the movie during a steamy love scene. She would tilt her head back in ecstasy, and when she did, he would kiss the hollow of her throat, and . . .

Reality intruded.

Out of the corner of her eye, Giselle spotted Lester coming out of the men's room.

Reluctantly, she tore her eyes away from the movie star and kept walking toward the telephones, pretending she didn't see her husband.

"Giselle," Lester said, catching up to her and grabbing her arm. "Who's watching the carry-on luggage?"

She shrugged. "I left it on the seat over there by the counter. It's fine."

A look of panic came over Lester's thin face, and his watery eyes widened behind their wire-framed glasses. Giselle stifled the urge to grin at his distress.

"You can't just leave brand new Vuitton luggage sitting in the middle of an airport!" he said frantically. "What's the matter with you, Giselle?"

She shrugged airily and pointed toward the phones. "I'm going to call the girls and tell them the flight was delayed because of the weather there."

Lester was already gone, scurrying through the boarding area to where she had left their bags. Actually, she *had* asked the middle-aged nun who was sitting beside her to watch them. But Giselle got such perverse pleasure out of watching Lester fret . . . why ruin the fun?

He's a weenie, she told herself as she covered the last few feet and picked up the receiver of a pay telephone. *You're married to a total weenie.*

How had it happened? She'd been so young when they met, so young and blind. Had she actually found Lester attractive? Now, with his limp reddish mustache and receding hairline, it was hard to believe.

But then, back then, she hadn't been all there. She was still too out of sorts, trying to forget what had happened in Jamaica, doing her best to raise Meg as a single mom.

And she'd been so young, really—so naive. Naive enough to be dazzled by the way Lester had treated her. The man had practically thrown himself at her feet and begged her to use him as a doormat. He had obviously worshiped everything about her, and Giselle had found herself addicted to his constant praise.

Unfortunately for him, her addiction hadn't lasted. And now that she could see things clearly, she couldn't imagine how she had stayed with him for so long.

Oh well, Giselle thought as she punched in the familiar number of the house back in Connecticut; she wouldn't be Mrs. Lester Hudson for long. She wanted a divorce—had wanted one for a long time now, in fact. But lately, she had decided the time had come to do something about it.

As the phone rang, she checked her Rolex and saw that it was ten o'clock back on the East Coast. She never bothered to change her watch to reflect the current time zone when she traveled. It was too complicated, and besides, Giselle wasn't one to worry about something as superfluous as time.

She wasn't one to call and check in on her daughters, either—she figured they were old enough to take care of themselves. At least, Meg was. And she looked out for Carrie, who was more trouble-prone. Besides, Giselle's mother lived nearby if anything went wrong.

Lord knew Hope McKenna worried enough for both of them. Giselle had vowed, growing up, that she would never be anything like her basket case of a mother, and thank God, she wasn't. No, she breezed through life with devil-may-care aplomb.

The only reason she was calling home now was to see what the story was with the weather. The airlines wouldn't give a straight answer—they'd just announced that the flight to New York was delayed indefinitely because of some storm.

Giselle had been counting on getting home in time for her standing manicure appointment later today.

As the phone continued to ring in her ear, she examined her nails and decided that she'd be in big trouble if she didn't make the appointment. The creamy coral polish was chipped and scarred in a number of places.

After four rings, the answering machine clicked on, and Giselle heard her own cheerful voice saying, "Hi! Lester, Giselle, Meg and Carrie can't come to the phone right now. Please leave a message, and we'll get back to you as soon as we can. Thanks!"

At the sound of the beep, she said, "Meg? Carrie? It's me, Mom. Are you guys there and screening calls? If you are, pick up. Come on, guys. . . . I'm on a pay phone at LAX." She waited another second or two, then sighed and said, "Okay, our flight is delayed and I don't know what time we're going to get home. We'll see you when we see you. Bye."

She hung up and frowned momentarily. Odd that no one would be home at this hour on a Saturday morning. Neither Meg nor Carrie was exactly an early riser—a trait they had undoubtedly inherited from her.

Giselle didn't allow herself to contemplate the situation for more than another second, though.

As she turned and made her way back to Lester and the luggage, she pushed the vague sense of curiosity out of her head. Life was too short to spend time wondering about such things.

Instead, she scanned the waiting area for another sign of that hunky movie star.

Eleven

Meg and Candra had been running through the dark, scary woods, fleeing from something dark and sinister that wasn't quite tangible. Just when they seemed to be hopelessly lost, they'd stumbled across a glass telephone booth.

For some reason, Meg wasn't surprised to see it there, in the middle of nowhere.

"Quick," Candra shouted, "let's call nine-one-one."

But when Meg lifted the receiver, she couldn't get a dial tone. Desperately, she kept putting it into the cradle and lifting it again, as Candra looked over her shoulder and pleaded, "Hurry . . . before it's too late. We have to get someone to help us. Hurry!"

Then, as Meg held the phone helplessly in her hand, it started to ring.

But it can't be ringing when it's off the hook, she thought dazedly in the dream.

It wasn't until she heard Candra's groggy moan beside her that she snapped out of it and realized where she was, and that the ringing phone was real.

But when she moved to get out of bed to answer the extension on her desk across the room, she found that her legs were too stiff and weak to function. She nearly fell, and had to sit quickly again on the edge of the mattress.

"Are you okay, Meg?" Candra asked.

She turned to see her twin lying beside her in the wide, queen-size bed, snuggled beneath the rose-patterned comforter. Candra's hair was tangled on the puffy goose-down pillow and her eyes were rimmed with dark circles.

"I'm just a little woozy, that's all," Meg said, and smiled. "It's so great waking up and seeing you here."

"You, too," Candra said, but she didn't smile back. Her dark eyes were solemn. "Was the phone ringing?"

"It was, but the machine must have picked it up downstairs. It's no big deal. They'll leave a message. Did you sleep all right?"

Candra nodded and yawned.

Meg thought about how the two of them had staggered up to bed as it was getting light out this morning, both utterly exhausted. Candra had wanted to sleep in the guest room, but Meg had begged her to stay here in her room.

Somehow, she'd been seized by the irrational fear that if she let her twin out of her sight for even an instant, she would vanish again—this time, for good.

"Maybe someone was calling with news about Mirabelle," Candra suggested.

Meg's stomach turned over with a sickening thud. Mirabelle. The helicopter accident. She'd forgotten all about it.

"I'm sorry I reminded you," Candra said quietly, as if she could read Meg's mind.

"It's okay."

"Was she . . . a good friend?"

Meg hesitated. "Well, I haven't known her for very long. But she was the kind of person who you have an instant connection with . . . you know what I mean?"

Candra nodded but said nothing.

"She's the one who told me I have . . ."

"What?"

"Powers," Meg said reluctantly, and waited for Candra's reaction.

Either she was going to think Meg was completely crazy, or she would understand . . . because she had powers, too.

But once again, Candra didn't reply, and it was impossible to read the closed-mouthed, veiled expression on her face.

Meg hastily said, "I guess 'powers' is a strong word for it."

Still, Candra was silent.

"It's just that sometimes," Meg went on cautiously, "I seem to . . . know things. Like, I'll be aware of something before it happens. Does that ever happen to you?"

After what seemed like a long time, Candra said slowly, "Yeah. It happens to me. And other stuff, too."

"Like what?"

"There have been times when I sense things about people . . . you know, things I couldn't possibly know because they're strangers, or whatever."

"Me, too," Meg said excitedly. "When did you realize you had the . . ."

"Powers?" Candra supplied with a tight-lipped smile.

"I guess it's as good a word as any, right? So when did you figure it out?"

"I've always known I had certain . . . capabilities. But I didn't really start to develop my skills until Rosamund—" She broke off, as though she'd caught herself saying something she shouldn't have said.

Meg saw the way her sister's expression clouded when she mentioned the name of the woman she'd believed was her grandmother.

"What did she do?" Meg asked gently when her sister remained silent.

Candra shrugged and turned her head on the pillow so that she was staring up at the ceiling.

And Meg knew the conversation was over.

When Candra came downstairs an hour later, her hair still damp from her shower, she found Meg in the enormous kitchen at the back of the house. She was dressed in jeans and a simple but expensive-looking navy sweater, sitting at the oak table eating a bowl of granola.

"Oh, good, you found the stuff I left out for you," she said, looking up when Candra walked in. "Does it fit okay?"

"Yeah, thanks," Candra said, feeling uncomfortable as Meg sized her up. She was wearing her sister's black leggings and a charcoal-colored top—one she'd already worn earlier this week when she was posing as Meg.

"God, it's so strange," Meg said, shaking her head. "You look exactly like me, especially dressed in my clothes."

"Any news about Mirabelle?" Candra asked abruptly, to change the subject.

"Not yet. It was my mother . . . I mean, Mom . . . who called before."

Candra flinched at the word *mom*. It implied a cozy intimacy that was the last thing she felt when she thought of Giselle—who was, after all, in addition to everything she'd done, a total stranger.

Meg apparently sensed her discomfort, because she quickly added, "She's not sure when she'll get home. She and Lester are stuck in L.A. because of the weather here."

Candra looked toward the double windows over the sink. Outside, the world was still gray and dreary. Even the kitchen, with its pristine white walls and appliances and bright track lighting, looked somehow dark and dismal.

Suddenly, she heard an angry *meow*.

"Hey, C-A-T," Meg said sternly, "cut that out."

Candra stared at the familiar cat who had appeared in the doorway of the kitchen. The animal's green feline eyes were focused knowingly on hers.

"She's really a good kitty," Meg said, getting up and going over to scoop the cat into her arms. "It just takes her awhile to get used to strangers."

"Most cats are like that."

"Yeah, they are. You can pet her, though, and she'll warm right up to you."

"It's okay," Candra told her quickly when Meg came closer to her. "I'm allergic to cats anyway."

"You are? Oh, God, sorry. I'll let her outside for a while."

Candra didn't argue, just watched as Meg planted a kiss on the cat's furry head and carried her to the door.

"What other allergies do you have?" Meg asked, when she'd returned to the table.

"Hmm? Oh, none that I know of."

"God, I'm glad we're not *totally* alike. I'd hate to be allergic to cats. Sometimes I feel like C-A-T's the only one around here who understands me. . . . Want some?" she asked, holding up the cereal box and peering inside. "There's a little left."

"No, thanks."

"I'm starving." She refilled her bowl. "I feel like I haven't eaten in a week."

You haven't, Candra thought, as she glanced at the light green ceramic tile counter and saw that there was a pot of coffee waiting.

"I don't usually drink coffee," Meg said, following her gaze, "but I feel so exhausted today that I figured I needed a shot of caffeine. Have some if you want . . . it's kind of strong, though. I didn't know how much to put in."

"I like strong coffee," Candra said, suddenly thinking of the all the warm, breezy mornings in Jamaica when she'd sipped her favorite Blue Mountain blend.

A wave of homesickness came over her, so acute that she had to turn away from Meg so that her sister wouldn't spot the sudden tears that filled her eyes.

Behind her, Meg said casually, "The mugs are up in that cupboard to your right."

Candra nodded and reached blindly for one.

She was seeing the glistening, translucent aqua waters of the Caribbean, and the waxy blue blossoms of the lignum-vitae trees in the garden of the Drayers' home in Ocho Rios, and the dazzling feathers of the exotic island birds: the Red-billed Streamertails and Jamaican Mangoes . . .

And Rosamund's lined chocolate-colored face, stern but so familiar that Candra was filled with an inexplicable ache to see the woman again.

Even though she had lied all those years, pretending to be someone she wasn't.

Why, Grandmother? Candra wondered, before catching herself.

Ironic, that she was no relation to Rosamund, yet still automatically referred to her as *Grandmother.* Meanwhile, Giselle was the woman who had given birth to her, and she couldn't bring herself to consider her as *Mom.*

Candra's hand shook as she reached for the pot and poured steaming black liquid into her cup. She forced her thoughts away from Giselle, not wanting to arouse any more of the anger that had caused her to resent Meg so fiercely. That was behind her now.

So, for that matter, was Rosamund, but . . .

Why did you pose as my grandmother and raise me? What was your connection to Giselle?

She thought back to the day Dalila Parker had told her the truth. *Your whole life is a lie,* the woman had said. *You aren't who you think you are.*

Candra had been raised under the impression that her white mother had died in childbirth and her black father, supposedly Rosamund's son, had been killed shortly after. The moment Dalila told her that wasn't the case, she had been overcome by curiosity.

It came back at her full force now.

"It's time we figured out what happened in our past," Meg's voice interrupted her thoughts abruptly. "Don't you think?"

Startled, Candra wondered, not for the first time, if her twin could read her mind. Slowly, she turned, both hands wrapped around her mug.

"I mean, obviously something happened back in Jamaica when we were born—something that no one wanted us to know about," Meg said, and spooned more cereal into her mouth.

"Yeah, I know what happened." Candra sipped the acrid coffee, felt it burning her throat.

Meg put her spoon down. "You do? What?"

"She had two daughters, and gave one up. She chose to keep you and not me. *That's* what happened."

It was what Dalila had told her that day.

She didn't want to choose, but she had to—one for her, one for him . . .

But instinctively, Candra knew now that Dalila hadn't been telling her the whole truth. Giselle had chosen Meg, but Candra hadn't been given to her father. Somehow, she'd wound up with Rosamund.

And when she'd asked Dalila about her father, the woman had grown insistent that she couldn't reveal anything more.

Odd, Candra thought now, looking back, that Dalila had been so forthcoming about everything else in her past.

She glanced at Meg, who was staring off into space.

Candra went over to the table, pulled out a chair, and sat down heavily.

"She may not be a perfect mother." Meg's voice, when she spoke again, was reserved. "But believe it or not, she's not a terrible person, Candra. I don't think she *wanted* to keep just one of us. I think that for some reason, she had no choice. And that's what we need to find out."

"If you're so curious," Candra bit out, "why don't you just *ask* her?"

"Because she won't talk about it. I've asked her all my life about my past, and it's like it's this forbidden thing. No one talks about it. Even my grandfather, before he died, refused to tell me anything about how I got here. I used to think it was because my mother had been wild when she was a teenager, and everyone was ashamed when she got herself knocked up at sixteen. But that's not all there is to it . . . I'm positive of that."

It was Candra's turn to remain silent. She thought about the beautiful blond woman she'd only seen in the photographs that were scattered around this house.

And though she'd thought she could put her resentment behind her, it returned full force, more bitter than the muddy coffee Meg had made.

You gave me away, she accused the smiling, pretty face she could see clearly in her mind's eye. *How could you?*

"If you knew what she was like . . . She's weak, Candra," Meg said wistfully. "Weak and vain and self-centered and sometimes really . . . foolish."

"Sounds like the perfect mom," Candra replied on a caustic laugh.

"Who is?" Meg shot back. "Look, all I'm saying is that whatever she did, she obviously did for a reason. Maybe not the best of reasons, but we need to find out what it was. Something happened to her in Jamaica. She was just a kid, younger than we are now, and she got pregnant while she was there. I had always thought my real father was this guy, Stu Kingman, who lived here in Crawford Corners and was her high school boyfriend. But Dalila told me that wasn't true. She said the guy who got her pregnant was someone she met in Jamaica. And that wasn't all she told me."

"What else?" Candra prodded when Meg hesitated.

"She said that Mom got involved in something that was way over her head while she was down there. And she said 'she paid the price,' but she wouldn't tell me anything more than that. Something strange happened, Candra. I guess, deep down, I've always known it, too. Maybe that's why I never pressed her for the details. But now I have to know. Candra, we *have* to figure out what happened."

Candra looked into Meg's earnest almond-shaped eyes. Her sister was silently begging her to put aside her spite, at least until she understood what, exactly, had happened all those years ago.

Another little piece of Candra's hardened heart melted. She allowed more of her anger to dribble away.

After all, you owe her, she reminded herself sternly. *What you really owe her is a confession, but since you didn't go through with that, your cooperation and kindness would be a good substitute . . . for a start.*

Besides, Meg was the one person in the world who shared her past . . . and who wanted to unlock the mystery.

"Don't you wonder about our father?" Meg went on. "Like, who he was? *Where* he is? Dalila wouldn't tell me. She got all silent and weird about it when I asked."

Candra thought about Dalila's similar reaction to her own questions about their father.

"And my grandmother acted funny about him, too. I mean, it isn't strange that she wouldn't want to admit that my mother got pregnant by some stranger who lived in another country, because she can be kind of . . . basically, she's a prude. But she got really upset when I kept pressing her for information about him."

An image of Hope McKenna, Meg's thin, perpetually nervous grandmother, popped into Candra's mind. Had it been only yesterday that Candra had ridden the train into Manhattan with her, to get the million-dollar check that had been left to Meg by her grandfather?

That money was supposed to give Candra a fresh start. At this moment, she and Landon were supposed to be on their way to a new life together.

Now it was sitting in Meg's bank account, where it rightfully belonged. And despite a flinch of regret that so much money had slipped through her fingers, Candra was relieved that it hadn't worked out that way . . . that Meg was still alive.

She focused her attention on her sister again.

"Isn't he just as much at fault as she is?" Meg was saying.

"Who?"

"Our father! After all, Mom at least raised *one* of us. I mean, where the hell is he?" Meg asked with uncharacteristic vehemence. "I think that our first step is to find out . . . and find him."

"You would think," Candra said slowly, after absorbing her sister's words, "that since we both have some kind of—you know, *powers,* as you put it . . . that one of us would be able to figure something out, here. You'd think that we have an edge over the average person."

"We do," Meg said excitedly. "Especially now that we're together. We can figure this out, Candra."

"How? It's not as though there's some trail of clues that's going to lead us right to the answers."

"No, but there's something. Last week, I found a box of my mother's things in my grandparents' attic. There was a sketchpad that had a picture of us, together when we were newborn babies—that was how I knew I had a twin. How . . . how did you find out?"

"Dalila told me," Candra said briefly. "What else was in the box, Meg?"

"Some other stuff, from the time when she spent in Jamaica. Weird stuff."

"Like what?" Candra reached for her coffee mug again, trying to act nonchalant.

"A little red drawstring bag," Meg said, frowning slightly.

Startled, Candra glanced up. "A conjure bag?"

"Mirabelle called it a *gris-gris* bag."

That was the voodoo version of the charm, Candra noted. "Same thing," she told Meg. "What was in it?"

"Some powdered herbs and baby hair."

"Baby hair?"

"I guess it was mine . . . or maybe yours. It was tied with a ribbon. Mirabelle told me that the bag was a charm and that my mother had probably made it to attract something."

Candra thought of the bag she had worn pinned over her heart, the one that had succeeded in winning Landon Keller's affection.

"Or," Meg continued hesitantly, "she said the charm could keep something away. Like evil spirits. And there was a blue candle in the box, too—Mirabelle said it symbolizes protection. And a doll."

"What kind of doll?"

"It was like . . . you know, a voodoo doll. Made out of clay, dressed in scraps of fabric that looked like they had been made from baby clothes. And there was more hair—dark hair, like ours—embedded in the head of the doll."

Candra's heart was pounding. "Where's this box you found?"

"In my room. I hid it in my closet."

Then why didn't I find it last week when I went through your stuff? Candra wondered, puzzled.

Aloud, she said, "Let's go get it. I want to see the stuff that's in it."

"Okay, come on." Meg pushed her chair back from the table and led the way upstairs.

A minute later, standing inside her closet, she turned and looked at Candra, her eyes wide with disbelief. "It's gone!"

"Are you sure?"

"I'm positive. It was right here. How could it just vanish?"

Candra thought about what had happened to her a few nights earlier, when she had been snooping through Lester Hudson's office down the hall. She'd found a file labeled *Merriweather,* and inside, a confidential report along with a scribbled phone number that had a Jamaican exchange. But before she could react, she'd had to leave the office for a few minutes. And when she'd returned, the file was gone.

"Someone must have taken the box," she told Meg now. "Do you have any idea who it could have been?"

Meg frowned. "No one even knew it was here. But I think there's some other stuff missing, too—my burgundy leather boots, and . . . my leather coat, and . . . who would snoop through my—Carrie!" she interrupted herself.

"What?" Candra asked, thinking of the missing clothing. She knew exactly where it was. Stashed in the trunk of the Honda, packed neatly into Meg's luggage. Meg, of course, had no idea the bags were there. Candra had been planning to take everything along when she started her new life with Landon.

"Carrie's my sister. *Half*-sister, actually. She's always doing something obnoxious. She probably came in here to borrow my clothes and boots, and found the box."

Candra contemplated that. She couldn't tell Meg, but she was sure Carrie hadn't been behind the theft of the box—or the file.

She was sure, because of what had happened the other night.

She recalled, with a chill, how she had entered Meg's bedroom after midnight, and had been instantly struck by the knowledge that someone else had been there. And she had been aware, in the way she had always *known* things, that it wasn't Carrie, or Sophie, the housekeeper. This was a dark, threatening presence.

She had felt it since that incident, too. The creepy feeling had descended over her again a few days ago, when she was on her way to Dalila's. She'd sensed someone watching her. The only person around had been a stranger . . . a young, dark-skinned guy dressed in black. He hadn't said anything, or done anything unusual, but something about him had made Candra uneasy.

She'd pushed that episode, and the others, out of her mind.

Now she wondered what it all meant—whether the sinister stranger had something to do with the missing box.

If so, how much did he know about Meg and Candra . . .

And why did he care?

Meg was about to ask Candra what she was thinking—she was wearing the oddest expression, and her dark eyes almost looked frightened—when the front door banged open downstairs.

They both jumped.

"Someone's here," Meg said, coming out of her closet and quickly closing the door behind her. Since it couldn't be her mom and Lester, and Sophie didn't work on Saturdays, there was only one possibility. "It must be Carrie."

Sure enough . . .

"Meg?" The familiar voice bellowed from downstairs.

"Up here," she called back, looking at Candra and rolling her eyes.

Then it struck her, as she heard Carrie's feet pounding up the stairs, that she had no idea whether her sister even knew about Candra's existence.

Had she told Carrie?

Had Carrie and Candra met?

Again, she felt the numbing chill that pervaded her mind whenever she thought about the fact that she couldn't remember anything that had happened over the past week.

A moment later, Carrie was standing in the doorway of her room. Her sister's pale hair was unkempt and her face, with its delicate features that were so like Giselle's, seemed drawn and pasty. Baggy jeans and an enormous navy plaid flannel shirt hung on her tiny frame.

"Meg, I—"

Carrie stopped in midsentence and stood there, frozen, staring.

Well, there's your answer, Meg told herself, watching her sister's startled, light green eyes darting from her own face, to Candra's, and back again.

Until this moment, Carrie had obviously had no inkling that Candra existed.

"Carrie"—she said gently, and moved forward to put a steadying hand on her sister's bony wrist—"this is Candra. She's my twin."

Finally, Carrie blinked and made a sound—a faint gasp.

"I know it's a shock, Carrie," Meg told her. "Believe me, I was just as stunned as you are when I found out. I was thrilled, though." She looked at Candra and smiled.

Candra, however, was focused intently on Carrie.

Carrie opened her mouth, closed it again, then began, "Mom—"

"She doesn't know that Candra's back," Meg cut in quickly.

"Back from where?" Carrie's gaze darted to Candra again. "Where did she *come* from?"

"Jamaica," Candra said simply.

Carrie frowned.

Meg told her, "I was born there . . . you knew that, right?" At Carrie's nod, she went on, "Obviously, Mom had two babies, and for some reason" —she looked at Candra, hoping she wouldn't interrupt, and continued—"she had to leave Candra behind. She never told me about Candra, and Candra never knew about me, either . . . until recently."

"This is totally unbelievable," Carrie said, shaking her head. "I mean . . . I just can't *believe* it. Does my dad know?"

"I have no idea," Meg told her shortly.

"If he doesn't, he's going to go nuts."

As far as Meg was concerned, who cared if Lester went nuts? Her stepfather doted on Carrie, his "real" daughter, but there was no love lost between him and Meg. Even Giselle seemed to have cooled toward her husband lately, which Meg took as a hopeful sign. Maybe her mom would wise up and dump the guy.

"So you just popped up recently, huh?" Carrie asked, and Meg saw that she was eyeing Candra shrewdly.

Candra nodded. "That's right."

"Interesting." Carrie looked thoughtful.

Meg cleared her throat. "Carrie," she said, "did you by any chance take some stuff out of my closet?"

"Like what?"

"My burgundy leather boots, for one thing. And . . . I had this metal box . . ."

"Meg, are you accusing me of stealing your stuff?"

"Not *stealing*. Borrowing. The way you borrowed my No Doubt CD and my Coach shoulder bag and my—"

"I haven't taken anything from your closet, Meg. Not your burgundy boots, and not some stupid box." Carrie lifted her chin, glanced at Candra, and asked Meg pointedly, "Are you sure you didn't pack them?"

"Huh?"

"You know. The other night, you were packing your bags for some trip to see a friend."

Startled, Meg said, "What friend?"

"You wouldn't tell me."

"Well, why would I?" Meg shot back, struggling not to let Carrie know she had no idea what she was talking about.

She snuck a glance at Candra, who seemed to be watching Carrie closely.

"Forget it, Meg." Carrie rolled her eyes. "I'm out of here."

"Fine. Go."

"I will. I just came home to change my clothes, anyway. When Mom and Dad get home, tell them I'm at Terry's. I won't be late, though. I need to talk to them."

"Mom called. She and Lester are stranded in L.A. and they don't know when they're coming home."

Carrie stopped in the doorway, and Meg saw her back stiffen. Slowly, she turned around. "You mean, they might not be back tonight?"

"I have no idea. Why? Hoping to get away with something else while they're still out of town?" Meg knew her sister had been running around with a wild crowd lately. Lord knew what Carrie had been up to ever since their parents had left for Fiji. Especially since Meg hadn't been able to keep an eye on her . . . or had she?

"No, it's not that . . ."

Surprised at Carrie's suddenly subdued tone, Meg looked closely at her. "What's wrong?"

"I just . . . something happened last night, that's all."

"What was it?" Meg walked over to her sister and put a hand on her bony wrist. She was shocked when she realized that Carrie was shaking. "Come on, Carrie, tell me—what happened?"

"Meg . . ."

"Tell me! I mean it!"

Carrie hesitated, her eyes sliding to Candra, whose expression remained veiled, and back to Meg again. "It's just . . . I mean, it's probably not—"

"Carrie!"

"Okay, I'll tell you. It was really late. I was here by myself, in bed—I couldn't sleep 'cause of the storm—when I heard something downstairs. I thought it was you. But then I remembered that you'd said you were going away overnight, so I snuck down . . . and I found someone creeping around the living room."

Meg felt sick. She glanced at Candra, and saw that she, too, was focused intently on what Carrie was saying.

"Someone had broken into the house?" Meg asked, and Carrie nodded. "Who was it?"

"I have no idea. He was a black guy, about your age, and he was dressed in dark clothes—he had on this creepy long coat, and he was just . . ." Carrie shook her head and shuddered. "When he saw me, he got this terrible look in his eyes, like he was going to hurt me."

"But he didn't, right?" Meg asked, suddenly feeling protective of poor frail, fragile Carrie. "He didn't do anything to you, did he?"

"No. He just *smiled*. It was so . . . eerie. I mean, the guy just smiled and looked at me in that terrible way, and then he turned around and disappeared."

"Did he, like, run out the front door, or out a window, or what?"

"No, Meg, I said he *disappeared!*" Carrie's voice rose shrilly. "As in, *poof*, he was gone!"

Meg stared at her, then sighed wearily. "What were you on last night, Carrie?"

"Nothing!"

"Yeah, right."

"I swear, Meg, I wasn't on anything. Okay, so I smoked a little dope and had a few beers at a party earlier, but I was fine when I got home. And it wasn't my imagination. This guy just vanished."

Meg hesitated.

Chances were that Carrie had been so stoned she'd been hallucinating.

But still, Meg couldn't help thinking about something Mirabelle had told her. About how people could use something called astral projection to experience out-of-body travel. Mirabelle said she'd done it herself.

Candra asked Carrie, "This guy didn't steal anything?"

Carrie shrugged. "Who knows? I didn't stick around to figure it out. I called Eddie, and he came and got me, and I spent the night with him."

Ordinarily, Meg would have been distressed to hear that her sister was still hanging around with a low-life dropout drug dealer like Eddie. But that was the least of her worries now.

Something told her that whoever had been in the house last night was no ordinary prowler.

She saw the contemplative look on Candra's face and sensed that her twin was thinking the same thing.

Twelve

"Any news?" Giselle asked Lester, as he plopped down in the seat next to her.

"Same story. There's a big storm on the East Coast, and everything's delayed. They have no idea how long. I demanded to speak with the supervisor, and that idiot behind the counter said she *is* the supervisor. I don't believe her."

Giselle rolled her eyes, feeling sorry for the girl behind the airline's boarding counter. Lester had been up there every fifteen minutes for the past two hours.

Giselle was half-embarrassed by the scenes he kept causing, and half-amused.

Lester was always demanding to see supervisors, wherever they went. If a waiter brought him something he didn't like, he demanded to speak with the supervisor. If a flight attendant told him that, unfortunately, all the pillows and blankets were being used, Lester demanded to speak with the supervisor.

It rarely got him anywhere, but he liked to think he could throw his weight around.

"Do you have any more Tums?" Lester asked her, moaning a little. "My ulcer's acting up again."

"You don't *have* an ulcer, Lester. Doctor Yoon said you're fine."

"What does he know? As soon as we get back home, I'm going to make an appointment with a specialist. How about those Tums?"

"I'm all out," Giselle lied. "You'll have to go buy some. And while you're at it, see if they have the new *Vogue* yet."

Naturally, Lester wasn't thrilled about having to go "all the way back" to the main terminal.

Giselle watched him trudge away, relieved to be rid of him for even a short while.

As soon as we get home to Crawford Corners, she promised herself, *I'm going to make an appointment to see a lawyer.*

She leaned back against the seat and closed her eyes, thinking about how free she would feel the day she said good-bye, forever, to Lester.

Then she thought about Carrie. Her younger daughter wasn't going to take the divorce lightly, she knew. Carrie worshiped her father, and vice versa.

But Meg . . . Meg would be as thrilled as Giselle would be to see him go.

Giselle knew Lester considered himself a terrific stepfather. He was always telling people how he treated the girls equally—how whenever he bought something for Carrie, he bought something for Meg. How "the poor kid" was lucky to have a "caring" father figure in her life.

Whenever he brought that up, he would give Giselle a *look*, as if to remind her that it was her fault Meg didn't have a real father.

Until recently, Lester hadn't even known the whole story about Giselle's past. He'd believed what she'd told him when they first met over fifteen years ago . . . that she'd gotten pregnant after a one-night stand with an American tourist in Jamaica. That she hadn't even known his last name or bothered to try and track him down when she'd discovered she was expecting.

Giselle had never planned or wanted to tell Lester the terrible truth.

But she'd finally broken down this summer, when she'd started planning their annual trip to the South Pacific, and Lester had launched a campaign to go to the Caribbean instead. Several of his colleagues were planning to tour the islands for two weeks on someone's yacht, and Lester was determined to go.

"It'll be great for my career, babe," he'd told her. "These guys really look up to me. I can't let them down. I can get some great deals out of this trip."

Giselle knew he fancied himself a flourishing financier. The reality was that he was mediocre at best. In fact, he wouldn't even have a job if Giselle's father hadn't conceded to getting him the brokerage job back when she'd first started dating him.

Of course, Harry McKenna had first tried to convince Giselle that Lester was a gold-digging opportunist. But somehow, she had been caught up in his flat-out adulation of her to see him for what he really was. Being out-and-out worshiped wasn't such a bad thing.

Besides, she had seen bland, bespectacled Lester as *safe*. And after what she had been through in Jamaica, she wanted nothing more.

Jamaica.

Giselle had vowed, the day she left eighteen years ago, that she would never return.

So when Lester had repeatedly pestered her to make the trip with his colleagues, Giselle had steadfastly refused. And when he had badgered her for days, then ultimately demanded a rational explanation, what else could she do?

She had finally broken down and told him exactly why she didn't want to go.

Giselle knew the story was bizarre, and she hadn't entirely expected him to believe it.

But apparently, Lester had.

He had met her heart-wrenching confession with silence at first, and then with several questions—some she couldn't answer, and others she didn't want to consider.

And while he didn't seem sympathetic over what had happened to her during that terrible, long-ago year in Jamaica, he hadn't forced the issue of going to the Caribbean, either.

In fact, he hadn't mentioned it again.

But something told Giselle he hadn't forgotten what she'd told him.

Sometimes, in the past several weeks, she had caught him looking at her with a strange, thoughtful expression in his watery gray eyes.

Whenever that happened, she got the feeling that there was more to Lester than she'd ever suspected.

And that made her all the more eager to leave him.

She sighed and opened her eyes, looking around the crowded boarding area. No sign of him yet, but any minute now, she'd spot his familiar dull reddish hair and skinny frame making its way toward her.

Oh, well.

Soon, Giselle promised herself. *Soon, Lester Hudson will be history.*

He slipped through the misty rain to the back door of the Drayers' big white house and knocked. With cold, clammy hands, he wrapped his long black coat more tightly around him as he waited, cursing the nasty New England climate.

It would be good to get this prolonged mission over with and get back home to Jamaica's blue skies and soothing sunshine.

After a few moments, the door opened and Rosamund stood there, holding a dish towel. "Yes?" she asked briefly, barely glancing at him as she dried her hands.

"Hello, Rosamund," he said evenly.

She gasped as soon as he spoke, and peered more closely at him, her eyes wide with disbelief. "What are *you* doing here?"

Taking pleasure from the flicker of fear in her expression, he said smoothly, "Oh, I think you know."

"I have no idea, *mon*."

"I have a little bone to pick with you," he said, stepping into the house and leaning against the wall. He folded his arms and looked at her, waiting.

"I don't know what you're talking about," she protested, retreating a few steps back, toward the kitchen.

He uttered a single word. "Meg."

At the mention of the name, Rosamund opened her mouth in surprise, then quickly closed it again.

"The baby you said was sacrificed? The way she was supposed to be?" he asked, enjoying the torment in her dark gaze.

The woman stiffened at his words, but said nothing.

"She's alive. Her mother brought her back to Connecticut. You lied to me, Rosamund. You said she was dead."

He watched her carefully. Her quivering lips were clamped shut.

"Meg's death in exchange for Candra. That was the deal you made. You were desperate to get your hands on that baby girl, weren't you, Rosamund? You had lost your own child, a little girl, too. Do you remember that awful day when you found her dead in her crib? No explanation. Poor little baby . . . a victim of crib death." He smiled. "Those things happen. But you always wanted another baby. And finally, you got Candra. A precious baby girl to raise as your own. It would be a shame to lose her now."

Her black eyes were defiant, but a violent trembling in her jaw betrayed her fear. "Candra isn't here. She ran away."

It was the truth—he already knew it, of course. But he feigned surprise. It was more fun that way. "Where is she?"

"I don't know."

"You're lying again, Rosamund." He kept his voice quiet and chillingly calm. "You know, you're not very good at it."

"But I'm not lying. I haven't seen Candra since last weekend. She's gone, and I don't think she's coming back."

He smiled. Torturing her was even more entertaining than he'd anticipated.

She took a step back. "You'll have to go now. Mrs. Drayer doesn't like me to have visitors here."

"We both know Mrs. Drayer's not home. Nobody's home except you."

"Well, I have someplace to go," she retorted, obviously trying not to seem fazed, but failing miserably.

His lips curved into a smile. "Oh? Where are you going? To your sister's apartment on Elmont Avenue?"

"How did you know that?" she blurted.

"I know everything, Rosamund. I know that you and Tish are in a coven, and that it meets on Saturday nights. I know *where* it meets. And"—he paused and looked her in the eye—"I know where Candra is."

Now her fright was plainly visible as she gazed at him. Her voice shook as she said, "Get out of here. Go on, go away. You don't belong here."

"I think I do. You've kept the truth about Meg from me. And there's more, isn't there?"

"I don't know what you're talking about."

"I'm talking about your other secrets, Rosamund. Dalila Parker told me that you're hiding something else from me. She suspected that the secret could be found among Giselle's things. I sent her there just the other night, to Giselle's home, to see what she could find out. Unfortunately, whatever she came up with is unavailable to me at this time."

"What do you mean?"

"Dalila Parker is dead."

Rosamund gasped and brought a fist to her lips. "You killed her," she said in a whisper.

"No. It was an accident. Imagine that! Life is startlingly cruel at times. First, your baby daughter is stricken by crib death. Now Dalila Parker has an accident . . ." He chuckled softly, marveling at fate, then hardened his eyes. "Now, since I can't yet get into Dalila's apartment to see what she found, there's only one way for me to find out what it is that you're keeping from me."

He took a step closer and reached out for her.

Then froze.

They both heard it.

A door slamming somewhere in the front of the house. A moment later, a man's voice called, "Anybody home? Rosamund?"

After a moment's hesitation, she said, her voice high pitched and unnatural, "In here, Mr. Drayer."

As footsteps approached the kitchen, he moved swiftly away, through the door and back out into the rain. His long coat whipped around his legs in a sudden gust of wind.

He slipped across the landscaped yard and into the trees, then turned and looked over his shoulder.

Rosamund was just closing the back door.

And even from this distance, he could see the expression of terror on her face.

Good, he thought contentedly, as a smile played over his lips. *I've gotten to her.*

And though his objective had been interrupted this time, he knew there were other ways to get the information he wanted.

He always got what he wanted, sooner or later.

Thirteen

"She's still in critical condition," Meg reported to Candra, hanging up the cordless telephone and putting it on the polished coffee table. "They said there's been no change and she's still in a coma."

"That's too bad." Candra had been looking absently through the Irish lace curtained window, listening to Meg's conversation with the hospital. Now as she turned toward her sister, she kept her expression concerned and a little detached, the way anyone would be if something terrible happened to someone they didn't know.

It wasn't that she wanted Mirabelle to *die* . . .

Of course she didn't.

It was just that she knew that if Mirabelle *lived*, she could—and would—tell Meg what Candra had done.

If she even knows what you did, Candra reminded herself. She had no doubt that the girl had suspected she was impersonating Meg, but really, what proof did she have?

And even if she went to Meg with her suspicions, Candra could simply deny them. Meg would have to believe her over Mirabelle, wouldn't she?

Of course she would.

After all, we're flesh and blood, Candra reminded herself as her sister flopped down beside her on the floral chinz couch and sighed.

"So what do you think, Candra?" Meg asked in a subdued tone.

"About what?"

"About everything. Especially what Carrie told us about that intruder."

"I don't know what to think about that," Candra told her truthfully. "But the description of the guy sounds a lot like someone who was following me to Dalila's the other day."

Meg's eyes widened. "You're kidding."

"No. He was . . . bad," she said slowly, remembering. "I sensed that he was there, on the street, even before I turned around and saw him. He sent off dark, evil vibrations."

"Who was he?"

"I have no idea. I'd never seen him before in my life. But there's something else . . ."

"What?"

"Right before Dalila died, when I was struggling with her, she said that someone was after me—and you, too. That we were in danger. She said the person is more powerful than both of us."

"Do you think she was telling the truth? Maybe she was just desperate and . . . I don't know." Meg looked frightened. "Who could be after us?"

Candra shook her head. She was racking her brain, trying to come up with something . . . anything. But she kept drawing blanks.

"Why did Dalila try to kill me, Candra?" Meg asked suddenly.

"I . . . I have no idea, Meg."

"It just doesn't make sense. Nothing makes sense. How did you know where to find me last night?"

Candra paused for only the briefest moment before saying, "Instinct."

Meg nodded. "That's what I figured. You know, I've read that the bond between twins is psychic, anyway. Since you and I seem to have stronger psychic abilities than most people, I guess it makes sense that we'd be able to find each other and help each other under dire circumstances. I feel safer, somehow, knowing that. Don't you?"

Candra merely nodded, then quickly changed the subject. "I wish we could find that metal box."

"I was thinking . . . maybe I'm the one who took it," Meg said. "After all, I can't remember anything about this past week. How do we know that I didn't just move the box and put it someplace else for safekeeping?"

"We don't *know* that," Candra said carefully, "but how likely is it?"

Meg shrugged. "We should probably search the entire house, just to make sure it isn't around someplace."

"You think so?" Candra asked, knowing it would be a waste of time. The box was gone. She was as certain about that as she was of the fact that the Merriweather Investigations file had disappeared the other night.

At the sudden sound of footsteps on the porch outside the living room window, she glanced at Meg.

"Someone's here," Meg said, a split second before the doorbell rang.

"Aren't you going to get it?" Candra asked, when her sister didn't move.

"I'm afraid."

"Oh, Meg, I'm sure that whoever's after us isn't going to come ringing the bell," Candra said, trying to make her voice light. But in reality, she wasn't so sure about that. She wasn't sure of anything anymore, and that bothered her. Candra liked to be in control.

"Will you get it?" Meg asked in a small voice.

Candra nodded, got off the couch, and went into the foyer. She opened the door and found herself face to face with Shea Alcott.

"Meg!" he said, and immediately grabbed her into a bear hug. "Thank God you're okay. You have no idea how crazy I've been the last twenty-four hours."

Before Candra could reply, a voice behind her said, "Shea? That's my twin sister. *I'm* Meg."

He released Candra instantly, and she saw the displeasure in his eyes. She wondered what he was thinking. She'd forgotten all about the fact that he had been with Mirabelle, following Candra, the other day. Did he, too, have suspicions about what she had been up to?

The look on his face told her that he did, but he quickly looked past her to Meg. "I was so worried about you," he said, and moved toward her.

Candra watched as Shea pulled her twin into his arms. He held her tightly for a long time, and she saw Meg's hands wandering up around his neck, clinging there naturally as she rested her head on his shoulder.

It's so unfair, Candra found herself thinking. *Why can't someone care about me that much?*

Again, her thoughts flew to Landon Keller, but she forced herself to put him out of her mind. What he'd felt for her wasn't real. And it was over, anyway. She would never see him again.

"Shea, I want you to meet someone," Meg said, finally pulling back from him and glancing in Candra's direction. "This is Candra Bowen."

"I know. We've already met, haven't we, Candra?" Shea's eyes on her were cold. His hands were still possessively resting on Meg's waist.

Candra felt a little prickle of trepidation, but kept her face blank.

"You've met," Meg repeated, and looked upset. "God, I didn't even remember. I can't take this. When am I going to get my memory back?"

"What are you talking about?" Shea asked, turning his attention back to her.

"It's the strangest thing. I have amnesia," Meg told him. "I can't remember anything that happened to me since Monday afternoon, when

I met Candra for the first time. I guess the experience was so intense that some part of my mind totally shut down."

"Oh, Meg, get real," Shea said. "You know who's behind this, don't you?"

"Behind what?"

"This whole memory loss, or whatever it is that you think you have."

"What do you mean?"

"It's her," he said, pointing at Candra. "She did something to you."

Meg wrenched herself out of his grasp. "What are you talking about?"

"Candra has been posing as you, that's what I'm talking about. She's been wearing your clothes—"

"Oh, please," Meg interrupted. "I loaned her some stuff. Big deal. She's my sister."

"It's not just that, Meg. She's crazy."

"What are you talking about?" Meg looked over her shoulder at Candra, who made sure she wore a wounded expression. Meg saw it and said, "It's okay, Candra, don't—"

"Meg, are you crazy, too?" Shea demanded, waving a finger in her face. "She's no good. I swear, Meg. She even tried to kill you!"

"Shut up!" Meg shouted at him, shaking her head and stepping back from him, toward Candra, who remained silent. "You're the one who's crazy, Shea! Candra didn't try to kill me—she saved me from Dalila Parker."

Shea shook his head. "You're wrong."

"No, *you're* wrong. She's my twin sister, for God's sake. Why would she try to kill me?"

"Ask her," Shea said, turning his gaze on Candra.

So did Meg.

Candra looked at her sister and shook her head. "Meg, I have no idea what he's talking about."

"Of course you don't, Candra. He and I haven't been getting along lately, and he can't stand the fact that I might be close to anyone other than him. Just ignore him."

"Jesus, Meg, you've got to be—"

"You know what, Shea?" she interrupted him. "Why don't you just get the hell out of here."

"But Meg—"

"I don't want to hear it," she said, holding up a hand and turning her back on him. "Your jealousy has totally ruined this relationship. First you accused me of going out with someone else behind your back, which was a total lie. And now you can't stand the fact that I have a sister who might take up some of my time, so you make up some crazy story about her. You want me all to yourself, and you're smothering me. I can't take it anymore. So just go."

Shea stared at Meg's back, and the look in his eyes filled Candra with guilt. He cared about her sister, she realized. A lot. He really, truly, loved Meg.

And Candra was the cause of the pain that was clearly eating away at him.

You should do it now, she told herself, as she looked from Shea to Meg. *Tell her the truth. Confess. Tell her that he's right.*

But again, somehow, she couldn't bring herself to do it.

Shea turned away from Meg and walked toward the door, passing Candra without meeting her eyes.

A moment later he was gone, closing the door quietly behind him.

"Slamming's not his style," Meg said in an odd, choked voice, and Candra looked up to see her looking at the door. "He's not the type to make a scene."

Candra didn't know what to say. Her sister's expression was a mirror of Shea's. She was in love with the guy, and he had broken her heart.

No.

Candra had. She was the one who was responsible for Meg's heartache.

Meg let out a shaky sigh, then said, "You know, I'm better off without him. We were too different anyway."

Candra wasn't fooled by her sister's attempt to shrug it off. "Maybe you'll get back together," she suggested, still unable to meet her sister's eyes for fear of what she would see there.

"No. No way. Not after what he said about you. And did you hear that crap about you posing as me? Obviously, since we're identical twins, people are going to mistake us for each other. That's how this whole thing started, you know, with Dalila. She thought I was you at the carnival that day. And then people started telling me they'd seen me in places where I hadn't been . . ."

"I know what you mean," Candra said, nodding. Relief was coursing through her. "It happened to me, too. Some of your friends thought I was you."

"Someday, we really should switch places," Meg said with a smile. "It would be fun."

"Yeah, sure, someday," Candra said, and looked away.

* * *

"This is crazy. I've been through this entire room before, and I never found anything unusual," Meg told Candra an hour later, as they slipped into the master bedroom.

Though her mother had been away for almost two weeks, the scent of her expensive perfume still hung in the air. The huge room looked like an ad out of a home decorating magazine, with its perfectly coordinated chintz bedspread, curtains, and wallpaper.

"Maybe you missed something," Candra said. "Besides, what other way is there to try and figure out what happened? We have to see if we can come up with something—anything at all."

Meg sighed. "You're right. You look in the closet, and I'll take her dresser drawers."

"What about Lester's dresser?"

"Oh, please. Who wants to touch all his underwear and socks and stuff like that?"

"I don't, especially, but we have to search everywhere," Candra said.

"Well, believe me, Lester's too boring to have anything interesting hidden in his dresser."

"Are you sure?"

Meg frowned at her sister. "What do you mean?"

"I mean, maybe he's not as boring as you think. Maybe he's got something to hide."

"Lester? The only thing he has to hide is the stupid bald spot on the top of his stupid head. It drives him crazy. He's always trying to comb his hair so it won't be so noticeable. He's such a dork."

Candra shrugged. "Maybe there's more to Lester than you think, Meg."

"I totally doubt it, but even if there is, he doesn't have anything to do with what happened to Mom in Jamaica," Meg said firmly, wondering why Candra seemed so insistent about Lester. It was almost as if she knew something about him . . .

"Candra," she said, "is there something you're not telling me? About Lester?"

"No. Well, not exactly."

I knew it, Meg thought. "What's up?" she asked aloud.

"I just have this feeling about him, that's all. A really strong feeling. I think he's up to something."

Meg stared at her. "Like what?"

"I have no idea."

"Why do you think so? What happened?"

"I told you. Nothing. It's just a feeling, Meg."

"Well, why don't I have the same feeling?" Meg asked, feeling irrational but unable to help herself. "After all, we both have powers. And I've lived with Lester practically my whole life. I never felt any odd vibes coming from him."

"Well, you might be immune where he's concerned, since you're used to having him around," Candra pointed out. "And," she added bluntly, "my powers are stronger than yours. I've been training myself to use them since I was a little girl."

"Maybe we should search Lester's study," Meg said slowly, after considering her sister's words.

Candra shrugged. "We can, but we might not find anything there."

"Yeah, but we might." Then Meg remembered something. "The only problem is, he keeps everything locked. His desk *and* the file cabinets."

"Locks," Candra said airily, heading for the door, "can be picked."

A few minutes later, Candra and Meg were on their knees in front of a file cabinet in Lester's office. Candra had inserted a bobby pin in the keyhole and was jiggling it around.

"Do you think it'll work?" Meg asked, even as Candra broke into a grin and said, "There it goes."

She pulled the drawer open and gestured. "Be my guest. You start looking through here, and I'll pick the lock on the other cabinet."

"What am I looking for, exactly?" Meg asked, staring at the row of manila file folders.

"I have no idea," Candra told her. "But you'll probably know if you find it."

Meg shook her head and lifted the first folder out. It was labeled AAA, and inside was a collection of canceled checks from Lester's membership fees for the American Automobile Association.

Meg sighed and jammed it back into the drawer.

Lester being involved in anything unusual, she thought, was about as likely as the notion of Candra plotting to kill her.

Still, she kept looking through the file cabinet.

Giselle closed her copy of *Vogue* and sighed moodily, tossing it into a trash can beside her seat.

"Now what?" Lester asked, looking up from the novel he was reading.

Or, Giselle thought, *pretending* to read. Lester, pretentious boor that he was, made a big show of reading the classics whenever anyone was around to see him, like here in the airport, or at the country club pool back in Connecticut. But Giselle knew he'd been on the same page—page thirty—of Tolstoy's *War and Peace* for several months now. And she'd seen the glazed look in his eyes as he stared at the book.

"Now what's the matter with you?" Lester repeated, closing the book over his index finger, to keep his place.

What a joke.

"What do you mean, what's the matter with me?" Giselle asked, frowning.

"You just sighed and tossed that thing like you're mad at the world."

"Don't be ridiculous, Lester," she said irritably. "I didn't toss it."

"Yes, you did. I saw you."

"How could you have seen me? I thought you were busy reading."

He reddened, and she smiled.

She was aware that the middle-aged woman on Lester's other side had looked up from her own magazine and was eavesdropping. So was the elderly couple sitting in the row of seats across from them. They were all poised for the next bit of dialogue, probably hoping for an out-and-out marital spat.

It figured. Everyone in the gate area was bored stiff. The last big event had been the gate attendant's announcement that although the flight was probably going to be delayed at least two more hours, they should all remain in the boarding area in case they suddenly got clearance to board the plane.

Giselle fixed the nosy couple across the way with a steely stare, and they quickly buried their noses in their newspapers again. The woman on Lester's other side got the hint and turned away.

"How much longer do you think it's going to be?" Giselle asked Lester, who had opened his book again.

"Hmmm?"

"Oh, as if," Giselle said, shaking her head.

"As if, what?"

"As if you're so busy reading that stupid book that you didn't hear what I said. Never mind." She stood and was about to walk away—not sure where she was going, only needing to escape Lester's mere presence for a while—when the gate attendant stepped in her path.

"Are you on the flight to New York, ma'am?" she chirped, her round face rosy above her crisp white blouse and the navy bow at her throat.

Giselle wanted to muster every ounce of sarcasm she possessed and say, *No. I'm just hanging around here because it's a fascinating way to spend a Saturday afternoon.*

But instead, she only nodded.

"Then I suggest you stay put for a few minutes. We might be able to board soon."

"Really?" Now *that* was a bit of good news. "How soon?"

The woman shrugged. "Could be only a few minutes, or . . ."

"Or . . . ?"

"Who knows? Why don't you have a seat again? We wouldn't want to lose you."

"No, we wouldn't," Giselle muttered, and went back to Lester.

He glanced up. "Where did you go?"

"Nowhere."

"Oh."

Giselle slumped in her seat and slipped her bare feet out of her copper-colored sandals. She studied her tanned toes, with their coat of coral polish, and thought that if she were any more bored, she'd be asleep.

Her mind drifted, meandering from how irritated she was with Lester, to why she'd married him in the first place. Mentally, she slipped back through the years to those dismal months when she was a stressed new mom being courted by a man who hung on her every word, who thought she was beautiful despite the ten extra pounds she hadn't yet lost from childbirth, despite the disgusting smell of faintly soured milk that seemed to cling to her in those early years of motherhood.

Then she went back further still, to Jamaica.

It wasn't a place she wanted to visit ever again, not even in her mind.

She usually tore her thoughts away whenever they started in that direction.

But somehow, she couldn't seem to help it today. There were no distractions here in the quiet, crowded airport waiting area.

Giselle closed her eyes and remembered what it had been like then . . . back when she was a seventeen-year-old American girl in Ocho Rios.

Paradise.

That had been her first impression of her new island home, with its backdrop of gentle breezes and perpetual sunshine, with its reggae beat and easygoing, black-skinned people who spoke in a lilting *patois.*

There, Giselle knew, her parents had hoped to isolate her from the fast crowd she'd been running with at her own school back in the States. They'd hoped that by taking her away from Stu Kingman, her devil-may-care boyfriend, they might make her into a chaste girl-next-door . . . something she had never been in the first place.

And, for the first week or so that she was a newcomer on the island, she had spent a lot of time hanging around their rented house in the hills above Ocho Rios. She even, for lack of anything better to do, helped her mother and Letitia, the Jamaican housekeeper, get things unpacked and settled.

Giselle had to admit that the place was beautiful, all terra cotta and white stucco, with sweeping views from every window and from the sprawling open air poolside deck. There, a bikini-clad Giselle was able to perfect her tan while sketching the scene that lay before her. She thought she'd never tire of the scene below—the rolling green, flower-dotted foothills leading down to the picturesque, brightly colored buildings of Ocho Rios and the shimmering blue-green water of the Caribbean Sea.

Still, being Giselle, she soon started longing for some action. After all, she couldn't sun herself, sketch, and be a homebody forever. She needed *fun*.

One night, when her parents were at some welcome dinner for the SNE development executives who were temporarily relocating to Jamaica, she had snuck out of the house and borrowed the car her father had leased for her mother to drive. Not that Hope McKenna would have dared venture onto the winding, rutted island roads, particularly in a car where the steering wheel was on the wrong side. She'd already said so.

Giselle had a few close calls as she careened down to town, mostly when she forgot to drive on the left. Breathless and exhilerated from the adventure, she had parked on a narrow dirt street in front of the first nightclub she came to.

She knew it was a club because of the neon sign that read "Evil Annie's" out front and the reggae beat that throbbed into the street. But the building was little more than a low, pink-colored cinderblock shack, really . . . nothing like Studio 54 back in Manhattan, where Giselle and her friends had gone disco dancing several times after seeing *Saturday Night Fever*.

She made her way into the dark, crowded interior of the club, mildly surprised at the familiar, sweet aroma that tinged the air. Ganga, they called it down here, didn't they? She had smoked it on

several occasions with Stu and his friends—not that it ever did anything much for her.

Here, though, the stuff was probably a lot more potent. Feeling a
little dizzy at the heady scent, Giselle pushed her way to the bar.

"What can I get you, milady?" the bartender asked in a singsong
patois.

"Uh, I'll have a Sloe Gin Fizz." Giselle was new at this club stuff,
though she and her friends had gone out a few times back home recently.

"Nah," he said. "Have a hummingbird."

"What's that?"

"You'll see. You'll like it."

She shrugged and watched him move over to a blender behind the
bar. He hadn't bothered to ask her for ID, which was the first sign, to
Giselle's way of thinking, that living in Jamaica for a while wouldn't
be so bad. The fake Wyoming driver's license in her bag wasn't very
convincing, and she'd rather not resort to using it if she didn't have to.

"You a tourist?" the bartender asked, setting a foamy, creamy pink
drink in front of her. Sweat glistened on his dark skin; the place wasn't
air-conditioned.

"No, a native," she'd retorted.

Looking surprised at her quip, he'd flashed a row of straight white
teeth at her.

She'd grinned back, then asked, "So who's Evil Annie?"

"You never heard of the White Witch of Rose Hall?"

"The White Witch?" Giselle had repeated, after deciphering his
rapid-fire island accent.

"Annie Palmer. She was a rich white lady who lived in a Great
House down in Mo-Bay."

"Where?"

"Montego Bay," he clarified. "They say she murdered three of her
husbands and tortured her slaves until they killed her during the upris-
ing in 1833."

"Oh. It was a long time ago," Giselle said, losing interest. She
wasn't crazy about history—in fact, she usually got Ds in it.

"Sure. But everyone who comes to Jamaica hears about the White
Witch."

"She was a witch?" Giselle asked, her curiosity piqued again.

He nodded. "Black Magic. You know?"

She didn't. But she nodded anyway, wondering if Black Magic was
a big thing here in Jamaica. She hadn't ever thought about witchcraft
as being a real thing that people actually practiced. When someone

said witch, she pictured the Halloween costume from Woolworth's that she'd worn in third grade—the pointy black hat and green mask with the long, wart-covered nose.

She wanted to ask the bartender more about it, but someone had called him down to the other end of the bar. It would have to wait.

Swaying slightly to the reggae beat, Giselle tasted her humming-bird. It was delicious, almost like a milk shake. She had only taken a few sips when she'd felt someone watching her.

Looking up, she'd locked eyes with him.

The first thing that struck her was his *darkness*. Virtually everything about him—skin, hair, eyes, even his clothes—was blacker than an asphalt driveway on a sweltering July day. He sat at the far corner of the bar, surrounded by a throng of people, a part of the crowd and yet, somehow, not. His gaze was fixed intently on Giselle.

She couldn't seem to tear her eyes away from his.

They'd watched each other for what felt like an endless interlude, and then the bartender had shattered the spell, asking her if she wanted another drink. She turned to say that she did, then looked back toward the man in black.

He was gone, swallowed up, apparently, in the crowd.

Her hand gripping the icy, fresh drink the bartender slid toward her, Giselle had scanned the smoky, jammed room, looking for him with what felt almost like . . . desperation? But there was no sign of him, and she'd finally left, feeling strangely hollow inside.

It was a full month before she saw him again, though she hadn't forgotten him.

In the interim, she had become friendly with Howard and Raymond, two teenage local boys who tended to the lawn and garden at the house her parents were renting. They introduced her to the pleasures of island rum and Bob Marley music and Jamaican-grown *ganga*. And one night just before dusk, they drove her up into the mountains, speeding along narrow, hairpin curves and swerving to avoid the chickens and goats that wandered in the road. As they drew farther from Ocho Rios, with its brand-new resort hotels and moored cruise ships, the scenery grew more wildly beautiful and more desolate.

Here, a dense tangle of trees and vines shrouded the road, dotted with fragrant blossoms and shielding the birds whose startled, high-pitched calls were accompanied by furiously beating wings as they were disturbed by the passing automobile.

"Where are we going?" Giselle had asked Howard, who was at the wheel.

He hadn't answered, merely looked over his shoulder at Raymond in the backseat. Giselle did the same.

"Ray?" she'd prodded, passing him the open bottle of Appleton's.

"You ever hear of *obeah*?" he'd asked in his thick Jamaican accent.

"Did I ever hear of *a beer*?" she'd repeated incredulously, after struggling to decipher his words.

"*Obeah*," Howard clarified. He was a little easier to understand, having spent several years of his childhood living with an American family his mother had worked for as a housekeeper.

"What's that?" Giselle accepted the bottle back from Ray and took a swig. The liquid sent a pleasant burning sensation down her throat.

"A religion," Ray told her; at the same time Howard said, "Witchcraft."

"Witchcraft?" Giselle echoed, lowering the bottle and staring at Howard. She thought about what the bartender at Evil Annie's had told her.

"In a way, yes. You're familiar with voodoo?"

"Sure. I mean, I'm not *familiar* with it, but a know what it is. Black Magic, right?"

"*Obeah* is like that," Raymond said from the backseat. "It's a religion. We worship—"

"What does that have to do with where we're going now?" Giselle had interrupted impatiently.

"There's a ceremony tonight," Howard told her. "We want to take you there."

"Why?" Giselle swiftly concluded she wasn't crazy about the idea of going to any crazy religious ceremony. She didn't even go to church back home. And anyway, it was dark out here. And the middle of nowhere. Kind of . . . scary.

"We thought you would find it interesting," Ray said simply.

"I doubt it, guys."

Howard slowed the car and pulled off the road, and for a moment, Giselle thought he was going to turn around and take her back home. Instead, he stopped, turned off the motor, and announced, "We're here."

Giselle had looked around, seeing nothing but trees and shadows. Her heart was starting to beat a little frantically. She opened her mouth to demand that they take her home, but was stopped by the sound of thunder.

At least, she thought it was thunder at first.

Then she realized that it was drums.

They were off in the distance, beating a swift, steady rhythm that seemed to echo her own racing heart.

"Come on," Howard said, and he and Raymond climbed out of the car.

There was nothing for Giselle to do but follow suit, clutching the open bottle of rum in her hand.

"Leave that," Raymond told her. "You won't need it."

"What's that supposed to mean?" Giselle asked, but he didn't answer. Shrugging, she screwed the cap on and tossed the bottle back into the front seat through the open window.

Walking single file because the path was narrow, they made their way through the trees. The sound of the drums grew steadily louder and stronger, and Giselle could smell smoke. Not the ever-present marijuana haze that seemed to hover over Ocho Rios, but woodsmoke, reminding her of Girl Scout camp.

Finally, they reached a clearing that glowed from a small fire ringed by large stones. In the orangey light, Giselle could see several people milling around, many of them familiar from the bars in town.

And then she felt it again, for the first time in a month . . . the unsettling sensation that she was being watched. She knew before she turned her head and saw him that it would be the man she'd seen in the club that night—the one who had been cloaked in blackness.

He stood apart from the others in the clearing, watching her. And then Giselle thought—for no reason, really, it just popped into her head—that he'd been waiting for her.

Suddenly he smiled broadly as she stared at him, and his white teeth were a stark contrast to the rest of him.

Unnerved, Giselle clutched Howard's arm. "Who is that?"

"It's Manfred," he said, following her gaze. "He's the high priest."

Manfred.

Even now, years later and hundreds of miles from the mountains of Jamaica, the very name made Giselle shudder.

"It's no use," Meg said, rocking back on her heels and looking up at Candra.

"I know. I can't find anything either." She hated to give up, but there was nothing in this office that was going to incriminate Lester. She knew it.

Meg slid the bottom drawer closed and stood up. "What now?"

"I've been thinking," Candra said slowly, turning away from the file cabinet she'd just finished searching, and looking at her twin. "There's one person who probably knows what we want to find out."

"Who?"

"Rosamund," she said simply, trying to ignore the twinge of pain that jabbed her heart.

"Who?"

"My grandmother . . . I mean, she isn't really, but . . ."

"I know," Meg said, sympathy in her eyes.

And Candra thought again what a marvel it was that she actually had a sister. Someone who cared.

Someone who was there for her, despite what she'd done.

Not that Meg knew . . .

Stop it! she commanded her conscience.

"Anyway," Candra continued after a pause, looking away from Meg, "Rosamund has a . . . meeting every Saturday night. So I'd know where to find her."

"What kind of meeting?"

Again, Candra hesitated. Then she decided she might as well tell the truth. For a change. "It's a coven, actually," she told Meg frankly.

"A coven? You mean, she's a witch?"

"I guess you could say that."

Meg's eyes were big and fixed on Candra's face. And yet, there was something in them, some hint of acceptance, that told Candra her sister wasn't entirely surprised. After all, she had powers of her own, powers she had only recently discovered, and she knew Candra shared them. Was it so odd that Candra's would-be grandmother dabbled in Black Magic?

"So what do you want to do?" Meg asked. "Barge into this coven meeting and demand that Rosemary tell us the truth about our dad?"

"Rosamund," Candra corrected. "And no, we can't just barge in. We have to be careful. This isn't something you mess around with. It might be dangerous."

"Okay," Meg said, looking a little spooked, but game. "Tell me what we do, then."

"We go to where the coven meets, and—"

"Wait," Meg interrupted, holding up a hand. "Why can't we just go to your grandmother's house? I mean, wherever it is that she's living now . . . with the Drayers, right?"

"Because I don't want to set foot there ever again!" Candra thought about the basement servant's quarters where she and her grandmother had lived, and about Craig Drayer and how he had always taunted her, and about Landon, who had kissed her in her room that day that seemed like years ago but had only been weeks.

"Okay, okay," Meg said, shaking her head. "We'll go to where the coven meets. Where is it?"

"Spring City."

Meg nodded. "Near where Dalila lives . . . lived?"

"Not far from there. It's off of Elmont Avenue."

"Okay. When do we go?"

"Tonight."

"Then I have time to go to the hospital," Meg said, looking distracted.

"I guess." Candra wondered about Mirabelle. What if she was awake? What if she told Meg the truth? It would ruin everything.

Well, chances were that she wasn't conscious, Candra comforted herself. Not yet, anyway.

But there's only one way to be sure Mirabelle will never tell Meg what I did, Candra thought, a desolate feeling settling over her.

"I'm going to get ready to go to the hospital," Meg said, and headed out of Lester's office.

Candra nodded absently and stayed there, sitting on the floor in front of the file cabinet, thinking disturbing thoughts that she couldn't seem to evade.

Fourteen

Meg hesitated in the corridor outside the sixth floor intensive care unit of Spring City General Hospital. Her legs felt wobbly, and she wanted to turn around and run in the opposite direction, back along the endless hallways to the main entrance, out into the blowing, icy rain she'd driven through to get here.

She had been here once before, when her grandfather was dying.

Harry McKenna—Harry of the twinkling eyes and easygoing laugh and fighting spirit—had lain in one of the beds beyond those doors. He had been hooked up to tubes and monitors, a pale apparition of the man he had once been. For weeks, he had drifted in and out of the twilight world that eventually claimed him. Even when he was awake, his eyes were often glassy and blank.

And yet, whenever Meg visited him, and he recognized who she was, he grew more lucid. He would beg her to grasp his hands in hers, claiming her touch worked magic, that it made his pain diminish. And after he'd lost his ability to speak, she had always known what he wanted, had always done it instinctively.

She would slip her strong, young hands into his weathered, pathetically thin ones, and she would stay there with him for as long as the nurse would let her. She would chatter to him about school and her cat and her friends, forcing herself to swallow her own sorrow over his condition and make bright conversation. The look that always lit her grandfather's eyes told her what he couldn't say—that having his Meggie there, feeling her touch, was more effective than any medicine the doctors could give him.

But in the end, that hadn't mattered.

Meg couldn't save him from the cancer that had ravaged his body, not any more than the doctors could.

Her beloved grandfather had slipped away, much too soon.

Now it was Meg's friend who lay there beyond the double doors.

And all because of her.

Meg took a deep breath and pushed through the doors, coming face to face with a haggard-looking dark-haired guy who was probably only a year or two older than she was.

"Sorry," they said in unison, and he offered her a brief, sad smile before walking past.

Meg walked the few steps to the desk. The nurse was someone she had never seen before, not one of the staff that had grown so familiar a few years ago when Harry was here.

The woman was looking up at her expectantly.

Meg shoved aside the memory of her grandfather once again and said, "I'm here to see Mirabelle Moreau."

"I'm sorry—she can't have any visitors unless . . . are you immediate family?"

"No."

"I'm sorry," the nurse said again, shaking her head. "It's ICU policy."

"I understand." She should have realized she wouldn't be allowed in. Not when Mirabelle's condition was so critical.

Meg looked over her shoulder slowly, sensing that the guy who'd been on his way out of the ward had hesitated in the doorway behind her.

There he stood, watching her.

At the desk, the phone rang and the nurse picked it up, answering in a muted tone that was probably meant to offer comfort in case the caller had a loved one in the unit.

Meg waited, wanting to ask the nurse about Mirabelle, whether there had been any change—and wondering why the guy in the doorway was just standing there.

"You're Meg," he said flatly after a moment.

Startled, she said, "Do you . . . are you a friend of Mirabelle's?"

"I'm Ben." When she looked at him blankly, he gave a brief, bitter little laugh and said, "She never mentioned me, huh? I'm not surprised."

"I'm not sure . . . she may have," Meg told him truthfully, then wondered how she was going to explain her amnesia to this person.

She didn't have to bother. He didn't ask, only scuffed the toes of his sneakers along the white tile floor in a desolate gesture.

After a few moments, with the nurse involved in a hushed conversation on the phone, Meg said, "Are you and Mirabelle . . . ?" She trailed off, deciding to let him categorize their relationship.

"I don't know what we are, exactly," he said bleakly. "I know what *I* want us to be . . . but now, who knows? There's been no change in her condition."

"Still bad?" Meg asked softly.

He nodded.

"Have you been in to see her?" she asked when he didn't say anything more—probably because he couldn't. He appeared to be on the verge of tears. Clearly, Mirabelle meant an awful lot to him.

He shook his head, then found his voice. "I'm not immediate family, obviously. Just—a friend. Her parents are supposed to be flying in from New Orleans, but the airports are all closed because of the storm."

"I know. My mom . . ." Meg stopped herself again, realizing he wouldn't care that her mother was stranded in an airport somewhere, too. It was a trivial detail, meaningless small talk that had no place in this stark, somber place where lives hung precariously. Where *Mirabelle's* life hung precariously.

Meg and the stranger named Ben eyed each other uncomfortably until the nurse hung up the phone at the desk and cleared her throat.

Relieved, Meg turned back to her. "Can you tell me anything about her condition?" she asked, though it was a moot question now that she'd spoken to Ben.

"I'm sorry," the woman said, her tone kind but professional. "There's been no change. Her condition is critical, and she isn't conscious. Maybe," the nurse added, "the two of you should go down to the cafeteria on the basement level. The coffee isn't bad, and it's usually pretty empty on Saturday afternoons at this hour."

Meg looked back at Ben, wondering if the woman thought they already knew each other. She'd been busy on the phone, so she hadn't heard their conversation, had only seen them talking to each other. Maybe she expected them to cry on each other's shoulders over Mirabelle.

And maybe they should, Meg thought.

"Want to?" Ben asked with a shrug.

"Okay."

Together, they walked back through the double doors and along the hallway toward the elevator. Ben pushed the down button and they waited.

Meg was trying to think of something to say when he turned to her and said, "So you're all right, obviously."

Taken aback, she repeated, "All right? What do you mean?"

"I mean, she didn't get to you."

"Who? What are you talking about?"

"Your sister. Candra." The elevator doors slid open and he motioned for Meg to get on first.

She did, mechanically, positioning herself between two doctors who were having an animated conversation about one of their patients. The elevator was jammed, and Ben squeezed into the corner across from Meg.

As the doors closed and it lurched downward, she wondered what he was talking about. What did he know about Candra? And what did he mean about her getting to Meg?

Unfortunately, Meg thought as the elevator stopped at the fifth floor and two more people crammed their way on, her questions were going to have to wait.

He lay on the mattress of the musty back room of the occult shop on Elmont Avenue, mentally concentrating on Dalila Parker's apartment just a few blocks away.

There was only one way for him to get past the police who were still camped out in the apartment, conducting their investigation.

Closing his eyes, he imagined his astral self separating from his physical self. Years of practice enabled him to project in no time, and moments later he was rising above the body that lay prone on the mattress, gliding away from it and out through the back wall of the shop.

He passed swiftly over the rainy street, noting the squad cars that still sat in front of Rivera's Newsstand. Then, hoping that he could slip into her apartment unnoticed, he went through the outer wall and found himself in her closet, just as he had planned.

An overpowering hunch had drawn him to this very spot.

On the other side of the door, he could hear the television blaring what sounded like a football game from the living room. Two voices were carrying on a jocular conversation about something called the Fighting Irish.

Some investigation, he thought, and after listening to make sure he didn't hear anyone out in the bedroom, he cautiously opened the closet door a crack. Gauzy gray light filtered in and he was able to make out the row of dresses and blouses hanging behind him and the clutter of shoes on the floor.

Guardedly, he reached up and felt along the shelf above his head, beneath the stacks of sweaters and slacks that lined it. His fingers finally found something that didn't belong.

A triumphant smile curved his lips as he realized intuitively that this was the very thing he was looking for.

Ever so quietly, he pulled down the manila folder. In the dim light, he couldn't make out the label. Not that it mattered. This was it. He knew it. And there was more.

He reached up again and rooted among the clothes until his fingers brushed a cold, hard surface. He pulled and found himself holding a metal box.

Trembling with anticipation, he tucked it and the folder under his arm, and swept back through the wall.

The phone rang about a half hour after Meg had left. Candra, lying on her twin sister's bed and staring at the ceiling, was startled by it. She sat up and looked at the extension on Meg's desk, wondering who it could be.

If she didn't get it, the answering machine downstairs would pick it up and take a message.

But what if it was Meg?

What if something had happened to Mirabelle?

Impulsively, Candra reached out and picked up the receiver. "Hello?" she said tentatively, thinking that Meg wouldn't mind her taking the liberty of answering the phone. And anyone else would just assume she was Meg.

Except, she realized belatedly, one person . . .

"Candra? It's me, Landon."

For one wild, troubled moment, she contemplated hanging up on him. Then, if he called back, she could just let it ring.

But then the answering machine would pick up anyway.

And anyway, she had to face him sooner or later. It might as well be now.

"Oh, hi," she said in a detached tone. As if she were bored. As if her heart wasn't throbbing crazily at the mere sound of his voice. As if she weren't sobbing inside at the knowledge that all her dreams about Landon, everything she had imagined for the two of them, had dissolved.

"I was waiting for you to call me, but when you didn't, I thought . . . I don't know, maybe you'd lost the number, or something."

"No," she said indifferently. "I have it."

"Oh . . . were you sleeping, then? I mean, you were probably exhausted after all that happened, and—"

"I've been up," she interrupted him. "I just didn't want to call."

"Why not?"

"Why would I?" she asked, forcing the chilly words past the lump that kept threatening to lodge in her throat.

There was silence on the other end of the line for a long moment.

Then Landon said slowly, "You obviously have no intention of . . . you know. Seeing me?"

"Obviously not."

Again, there was silence.

Candra wanted to sob into the phone, wanted to blurt out the whole sordid story, wanted to tell him that he didn't care about her, not really. He just thought he did, because she'd cast a spell on him.

But she didn't. She didn't say anything at all.

No, she just took the silent receiver away from her ear and replaced it carefully in its cradle. Just like that. Cut him off, and out of her life.

Then, swiping blindly at the tears that trickled down her cheeks, she locked the door. Thinking that there wasn't much time to waste before her sister came back home again, she went over to Meg's dresser and began to clear it off so she could use it, once more, as a makeshift altar.

It was time to remove the spell she had cast on Landon Keller.

Time to let go, once and for all, of the dream.

"Ooohh," Lester moaned, and Giselle glanced up at him. He had closed his book and was clutching his stomach, waiting for her to ask him what was wrong.

She closed her eyes again, not necessarily eager to go back to thinking about Manfred, but not wanting to give Lester the satisfaction of noticing his moan.

"Ooohh," he moaned again.

And again.

And louder.

Finally, Giselle looked at him. "What?" she asked, irritated and conscious that everyone around them was tuned in.

"My stomach. It's that damn ulcer acting up again."

"Take a Tums."

"I don't have any more."

"You just bought a roll."

"I finished it."

Giselle rolled her eyes. "So get another roll, then."

"I can't leave the boarding area now. What if we get clearance to go? Do you want me to get left behind in California?"

Giselle contemplated that briefly and decided to keep her answer to herself. She didn't want the eavesdroppers thinking she was a complete bitch.

"If they board the plane, I'll make sure they wait for you. And anyway, it'll take forever just to get everyone on. You have time to run to the gift shop and back. And this time, why don't you spring for a bottle instead of a roll? You go through those things like candy."

"Are you crazy?" he asked, standing and dumping *War and Peace* onto his seat without marking his place. "Do you know what they charge for a bottle of Tums in this place?"

Giselle shrugged, thinking about the custom-made three-hundred-dollar shirts he claimed were necessary in his line of work, and the outrageously expensive single-malt-scotch he insisted on drinking after dinner in restaurants, though one glass of the stuff cost more than most entrées.

And just a few weeks ago, he'd charged nearly a thousand dollars' worth of clothes at Crawford Corners' finest men's shop just before leaving to go on a business trip. He'd told Giselle he needed a few new suits for a series of meetings in St. Louis, where he wanted to impress some important potential clients.

According to the Weather Channel, there had been so much rain in the Midwest on that particular week that the Mississippi had overrun its banks. When Lester had dutifully called home every night, she had asked him about the weather. He had always told her how lousy it was, how it had been pouring nonstop since he'd arrived, not that he cared since he was in meetings all day, every day.

But when he came home, his bulbous nose bore a telltale red tint. With his fair skin, Giselle knew, Lester never had been able to avoid a sunburn. Even with maximum sunscreen on, all he had to do was step outside for five minutes, and he was fried.

The sun hadn't shown in St. Louis in over a week.

So Old Lester was up to something.

Giselle had wondered who his mistress was, and why on earth she was with Lester. But then, even Giselle had been charmed by him all those years ago. She supposed that somewhere out there, some other woman might, in a weak moment, fall for her husband. Especially if he was whisking her off on tropical vacations under the guise of taking business trips.

And furthermore, Giselle didn't even care. The thought of her husband in another woman's arms left her utterly indifferent. Besides, the fact that Lester had a girlfriend would make it all the easier to dump him.

"I'll be right back, then. Make sure you keep an eye on the bags," Lester said, and walked away.

Giselle watched him. He was slightly doubled over as he left the gate area, but farther down the corridor, he straightened and his step became a purposeful stride.

"*Weenie*," she muttered under her breath, and closed her eyes again.

Instantly, she was transported back to Jamaica, and Manfred.

She had little recollection of that first *obeah* ritual beyond the first moments, when she, flanked by Howard and Raymond, had been invited into the circle of participants. She remembered the constant drumbeat and the high-pitched chanting and Manfred's black eyes glittering in the firelight, always, it seemed, focused on her.

But then it became a blur, probably because of all the rum, she had always comforted herself. Because she didn't want to consider what else it could have been. Didn't want to elaborate on how she'd felt mesmerized by Manfred's gaze, how she'd been powerless to look away or run away, though somewhere in her mind, she heard a warning that this Black Magic stuff could be dangerous, that she might be in over her head.

The next thing she knew, after that first night, she was waking up in the front seat of Howard's car as they pulled up in front of her parents' rented house. And she was sore all over . . . sore in places where she had never ached before. Her upper thighs . . .

Now, she shuddered remembering how she'd tried to ignore the curious discomfort in muscles she'd never realized she had. Tried to ignore what that might mean.

Only later—more than a month later—was she forced to acknowledge what must have happened to her that night at the Black Magic ceremony.

Filled with dread, she realized, when she woke that terrible morning to an overwhelming sensation of nausea, what she'd been trying to deny: that her period was weeks overdue and she was, quite obviously, pregnant.

Meg waited until she and Ben were seated in the hospital cafeteria with two cups of coffee in front of them. The nurse upstairs had been right; the place was deserted except for the occasional orderly or nurse who sat gobbling lunch and constantly checking the large wall clock.

"Okay," Meg said, watching Ben dump three packets of sugar into his coffee, "what were you saying about Candra?"

For a moment, his bloodshot, shadow-rimmed dark eyes looked

blank. Then he said, "You mean back upstairs? I said she obviously didn't hurt you."

"Why would she?"

He gave a bitter little laugh. "Oh, I don't know . . . because she's evil? At least, that was what Mirabelle thought. That was why she was trying to save you. That's why she went up in that damn helicopter in a storm."

"Mirabelle thought Candra was trying to hurt me?" Meg shook her head. "I can't believe she'd think that about my own sister."

"She thought Candra was trying to *kill* you, Meg. She and Shea were doing everything they could to—"

"Shea?" Meg blinked. "How does Mirabelle know Shea? I mean, they met at Zoe's party, but it's not like they pal around together . . . do they?" Suddenly, Meg wondered what had been going on while she—rather, her memory—was out of commission.

He shrugged. "I guess they were both concerned about you, and they said Candra was posing as you, and that she had you tucked away somewhere . . ."

"That's ridiculous!" Meg protested, despite a nagging voice in her mind. A voice that said, *But you have absolutely no recollection of the past week. Why not?* "Candra saved my life. Dalila Parker is the one who tried to kill me."

"Well, Mirabelle said that Candra and that woman were working together."

"They were not!"

"Calm down!" Ben said, looking around.

Meg saw two nurses at a nearby table glance up at them.

She lowered her voice to a fierce near-whisper. "I just don't understand where all this came from," she told Ben. "Why would Mirabelle be suspicious of Candra?"

"How well do you know Mirabelle?"

"Not very," Meg admitted, wanting desperately to believe that her friend might not be as sincere as Meg's instincts had told her she was. Maybe Mirabelle, with all her supposed powers, was just a big fake. But that was hard to believe. . . .

Suddenly, Meg was torn between wanting to believe in poor Mirabelle, who lay in a coma upstairs, and wanting to believe in her sister, her own flesh and blood. One of them, obviously, had been lying.

"Mirabelle *knows* things," Ben told her. "She has a . . . gift, she called it. She can—"

"I know all about her stupid powers," Meg cut in, shoving her untouched coffee away and pushing her chair back. "And as far as I'm concerned, it's all a bunch of bull."

Ben shrugged. "If that's what you want to believe, fine. But she risked her life for you."

"So did Candra," Meg bit out before jumping to her feet and fleeing the cafeteria, scurrying up the stairs and out into the driving rain, not caring when her hair and clothes were immediately soaked or when jagged lightning struck above her.

She's my sister, she kept thinking as she ran blindly through the parking lot toward her car.

She's my sister.

He settled onto the floor of the musty back room of the Elmont Avenue shop, easily wrapping his long dark limbs around each other and leaning back against the wall.

Then he reached for the metal box and the folder. It was labeled, he saw now, inspecting it, with a single word that meant nothing to him. *Merriweather.*

First, he would inspect the box, which wasn't locked. Not that that would have stopped him.

He lifted the lid and gave the contents a cursory glance before picking up the little red drawstring pouch. Instinctively, he knew that Giselle had made this conjure bag. Her very essence clung to it, and he closed his eyes, briefly, remembering what she'd looked like at seventeen. Winsome and sun-kissed, the very picture of wholesome innocence.

He loosened the drawstring, sniffed, and easily identified the powdered herbs inside by their smell. These particular herbs were used for protection.

A sinister smile curved his mouth as he lifted out the tuft of fine black baby hair. She was trying to protect her daughter . . . but which one? Meg? Or Candra?

He had no doubt *who* it was that Giselle feared.

Poor Giselle, he thought wickedly. *Worried that one of your children might be harmed by their very own daddy.*

Fifteen

Meg was pulling out of the hospital parking lot when she saw a familiar car approaching.

It's Zoe, she realized, and honked her horn as the car was about to pass her.

Obviously, her friend was on her way to visit Mirabelle. Meg wondered if a first cousin qualified as immediate family.

In response to the honking, Zoe's red Acura slowed alongside her.

The two cars were only a few feet apart, and despite the nasty weather, Meg saw Zoe's face clearly through the rain-splattered driver's side window.

She looked right at Meg, then turned away and kept driving, pulling away so quickly that her car hit a water-filled pothole with a scrape and a splash.

Meg knew how careful Zoe always was with her Acura these days. She'd already banged it up twice, and her parents had told her if she did it again, they'd take it away from her.

Obviously, her friend was in a big hurry to get away from her.

Meg's eyes narrowed as she looked back over her shoulder, watching Zoe's taillights disappear around a row of parked cars. What had she done to Zoe this past week?

Or . . .

No, she couldn't even think that what Ben had suggested was true.

But still . . .

What had Candra, if she really had been posing as Meg, done to Zoe?

Oblivious to the other passengers and the bustling activity of the airport boarding area, Giselle pressed her tanned, manicured, ring-covered fingers over her flat abdomen, just as she had done that long ago morning.

Of course, back then, a rush of bile had suddenly filled her mouth, and she had gone running for the bathroom. As she choked and spewed the bitter stuff into the toilet, she had wondered if it was mere morning sickness, or if the numbing horror of her realization had made her physically ill.

Even now, she felt a twinge of queasiness, just remembering that awful morning.

Not that she regretted having Meg. Her oldest daughter was dear to her, and as troubled as the circumstances of her birth had been, Giselle had never wished she had never been born. Only that things had been different.

She hadn't told a soul of her condition, but they knew. Everyone, she was convinced, but her parents, was aware that Giselle McKenna was pregnant. Howard and Raymond looked knowingly at her belly when they were around, and the housekeeper, Tish, caught her throwing up more than one morning. Even in town, Giselle was conscious of people staring at her and whispering behind her back.

And no matter how much she tried to convince herself that she was only imagining it, she knew that they knew. She didn't know how, but they did.

She half-dreaded, half-hoped, that she would stumble across *him* again. He consumed her every thought.

Manfred.

And one day, she found him. Rather, he found her.

It happened when she was walking down the winding road toward town about three months after she had discovered her condition; she was planning to buy some larger clothes. Her own waistbands were getting unbearably snug, though she knew she wasn't showing yet. Not in her baggy T-shirts and sundresses. And she had long since stopped wearing a bikini, upset at the mere sight of her own bare stomach, let alone the thought of someone else seeing it.

Her parents didn't suspect a thing, as far as she knew. Her father was too busy with his development project, and her mother was too busy being nervous and miserable about living so far from home.

As Giselle rounded a curve in the road, he suddenly stepped out in front of her, only a few yards away. She stopped and gave a startled little cry, and he simply stood there, looking at her. His black eyes bore into hers, then lowered to stare at her belly with an intensity that made her feel naked and completely vulnerable.

"I know," he said, and she had no doubt as to his meaning.

"Is it yours?"

He only nodded.

She found herself walking toward him as propelled by some force other than her own mind, covering the remaining distance swiftly and throwing herself on him, suddenly sobbing uncontrollably. He opened his arms and took her into his grasp, stroking her hair until she calmed, but still saying nothing.

Finally, she leaned back and looked up into his face. "Why did you rape me?"

"I didn't rape you, Giselle."

She marveled at the sound of her name on his lips, filled with wonder and pleasure that he knew it, that he knew who she was.

"I didn't rape you," he said again. "You were more than willing when I entered you."

Her insides stirred at his words, and she squirmed slightly at the image they created in her mind. "But . . . I can't remember any of it."

He shrugged. "Does it matter?"

"Was everyone there when we . . . did they see . . . ?"

"Of course. It was part of the ritual. And you enjoyed it, Giselle. You wanted me desperately, from the moment you saw me in the club that first night."

She nodded, knowing that what he said was true. She hadn't recognized her own heated desire for what it was. Now she knew that she had wanted him desperately, and she ached for him again.

Slowly, as if sensing what was going through her mind, he reached out and ran a long, tapered black finger down her bare throat. Then he dipped it between his own moist lips before slipping it, moistened with saliva, inside the open collar of her blouse. She trembled as he probed lower, as his cold, wet flesh found her right nipple and caressed it roughly. She felt herself grow painfully stiff beneath his touch, and her whole body tensed with longing.

"Please . . ." she whispered, sinking to her knees in the dusty road. "I want . . ."

"No."

The single word was tossed carelessly from his lips as he withdrew his finger and looked down at her with contempt.

"Please, Manfred. I want you. Inside me. I want you now. Please . . ." She was begging and sobbing, suddenly crazed with need.

"Not now. You carry my child in your womb. You will have me . . . but only if you come to live with me."

Stunned, she whispered, "Live with you? Do you mean . . . you want me to leave my parents?"

He nodded.

"But what do I tell them?"

"What do I care what you tell them? You are going to bear my child. I want you with me."

Dazed, Giselle had watched as he started to walk away. Then, desperate at the thought of losing him, she called recklessly, "I'll do it, Manfred. I'll live with you."

He'd turned and nodded, his face stoic as ever. "I will send someone for you tomorrow at midnight. Be prepared."

From that moment on, Giselle had felt as though she were detached from her own body, watching what happened to herself over the next several months, but never participating.

She had fuzzy memories of a series of events that seemed surreal: stealthily slipping out of her parents' home in the dead of night without a backward glance, being driven by a silent Howard to Manfred's shack in the mountains high above Ocho Rios.

Manfred had been waiting for her, and after Howard left them alone, he had swiftly stripped her clothes off, and then his own, and made passionate love to her on the dirt floor. She was in utter ecstacy as he finally spilled warmly into her, his strong, lean body bucking above her in the dark.

And she thought, as she drifted off to sleep, that this was where she belonged.

The days all blurred together after that. Now, looking back, she semi-remembered the people who came and went, all of them treating Manfred with reverence; and she recalled the midwife, Rosamund, who occasionally came to Manfred's shack to examine her.

More vaguely, she remembered the ritualistic *obeah* ceremonies that took place in the woods under cover of darkness.

She never knew what had happened after they got under way; her mind always seemed to fog over once the drumbeats grew more frenzied and the chanting started.

Her belly protruded as time went on, growing impossibly enormous, and she wore very little clothing in the tropical heat. She didn't recall thinking once of the child she carried or of the parents she had left behind.

She lived only for Manfred, for the exquisite moments when he would grace her with his touch. She thought of nothing else during those hazy summer months. He consumed her very soul, even as his child squirmed and kicked within her.

"How did it go?" Candra asked Meg, hurrying down the stairs the moment she heard the front door open.

"All right." Meg, shrugging out of her navy Burberry trench coat, didn't look up.

Candra's pace slowed as she continued down the stairs, watching her sister.

Meg was at the closet, taking out a wooden hanger and carefully draping her coat over it. But her movements were stiff, and she seemed preoccupied.

"Meg?" Candra asked, frowning slightly. "Is Mirabelle . . . ?"

"There's no change."

"Oh." Candra tried to ignore the flicker of disappointment she felt at her sister's words.

Not that she wanted anything bad to happen to Mirabelle, she told herself. Of course she didn't.

"Well, did you get to see her?"

Meg turned from the closet, but didn't meet Candra's eyes. "No, she can't have visitors. Only immediate family."

Relief coursed over Candra. That meant Mirabelle couldn't have told Meg anything.

But then . . .

Was it her imagination, or did she see a trace of suspicion in her sister's eyes?

It was gone just as quickly as she'd glimpsed it, making her wonder if perhaps she'd been mistaken.

"What did you do while I was out?" Meg asked, sounding—and looking—like herself again.

"Nothing. I read a magazine—there was a copy of *Seventeen* on your nightstand and I figured you wouldn't mind if I borrowed it . . ." She waited for Meg to say no, of course she didn't mind. But Meg didn't say anything. Candra went on, keeping a calculating eye on her sister, ". . . and so I read the magazine and just, you know, hung around."

"Anyone call?" Meg asked, and Candra tensed, thinking of Landon.

"No, no one called," she said hastily.

"Oh. I thought maybe Mom would have. I wish she would get in touch."

"Why? I'm sure there's nothing to worry about. It's probably just the storm that's delaying everything."

"I know that. But I want to tell her about you."

"Why?" Candra asked again, feeling a prickle of alarm. Something in Meg's expression was making her nervous.

Her sister shrugged. "I just want her to know you're here, that's all. She's going to be thrilled."

"Why do you think that?" Candra asked darkly.

"Why wouldn't she be? After all, you're her daughter. Of course Mom's going to be glad you're here. Just like I am."

Those last words sounded hesitant, hollow. Again, Candra caught a fleeting expression of uncertainty in her sister's eyes.

For a moment, their gazes caught and held—Candra's probing, Meg's veiled.

The ringing telephone shattered the moment.

After only a moment's pause, Meg went for it in the next room.

"Hello? Oh, hi, Chasey," Candra heard her say.

Chasey Norman. Meg's nosy, redheaded chatterbox of a friend.

Candra sat absolutely still, straining to hear what she could of the conversation.

"What? When?" Meg asked. "Last night? Oh, right. I forgot all about making plans with you guys. Listen, is Zoe mad? . . . Of course I know how she is . . . I know, I'm sure she's very upset, but I couldn't help it. Something came up."

Suddenly, Candra remembered the plans she, posing as Meg, had made with Chasey and Zoe. They had wanted to take her out for her birthday, had said they would pick her up at eight.

"No, I can't tell you what it was. Not right now . . . Listen, Chasey," Meg was saying. "I don't care. I've had a crazy week, and I'm really not in the mood right now to deal with you and Zoe being annoyed with me for something that isn't even a big deal. . . . It is not. . . . Fine. If that's the way you guys want it."

She slammed down the receiver, and for a moment, there was only silence from the next room.

Then Candra heard it.

The muffled sound of sobbing.

She got up and went to the doorway. Meg sat there beside the telephone, her shoulders shaking and tears rolling down her cheeks. When she saw Candra, she wiped at them and looked away.

"What's wrong, Meg?" Candra asked quietly, taking a few tentative steps into the room.

"Nothing . . . Everything. I feel like I'm losing my mind. I can't remember anything that's happened to me, and my boyfriend and my friends are all upset with me, and I have no idea who to trust—" She broke off there and looked as though she'd said too much.

"You can trust me, Meg," Candra said after a moment, meaning it. "I'm your sister."

"I know. That's what I . . . I know."

"Do you trust me?"

Meg hesitated, and wiped at her eyes again.

Candra waited until her sister looked up at her, and when she did, Candra smiled. It was a sincere smile, one that held a multitude of promises.

Please, Meg, she begged silently. *Give me a chance. I'm your sister. You're mine . . . You're all I have.*

Meg sniffled and then her own mouth curved up. Only slightly, but it was a real smile. She nodded. "I do. I know I don't really know you, and I know you have plenty of reasons to hate me, but I don't think you do. And I trust you."

"I trust you, too," Candra said, and crossed the rest of the way to her sister. She paused awkwardly for a moment, then reached out and put her arm around Meg's shoulders.

"Thanks, Candra," Meg said gratefully, and Candra shoved aside another twinge of guilt.

Even when the sun was shining, there wasn't much light in the small room behind the occult shop. On a day like today, it was filled with shadows that made it difficult to see anything.

But he was young, and his vision was good. Even in the dim light, he could see the items he had found in the metal box.

And after glancing over them, he put them aside. They were interesting, but didn't reveal any secrets.

Like the conjure bag, the clay doll had obviously been fashioned for protection. The blue candle symbolized protection, too. Clearly, Giselle had felt threatened. The thought filled him with pleasure.

And as for the sketch pad—Giselle's, of course—it was filled with drawings of scenery, although there were one or two images that had captured his interest. One was an excellent likeness of himself, the simple line drawing radiating power and passion. The other was a careful depiction of two baby girls, newborn and identical, captured forever on paper by their mother's loving hand.

Meg and Candra.

He chuckled softly, thinking that all of Giselle's protective measures, and her ultimate attempt to flee, had been for nothing.

It was only a matter of time before her daughters met their fate at his hands. And maybe Giselle would, too. It hadn't been his intention to harm her when he'd come here . . .

But then, sometimes impulsive pleasures were the best pleasures of all.

He turned his attention to the file folder.

The first thing he saw, upon opening it, was the pink invoice from

Merriweather Investigative Services in Spring City, Connecticut. It bore Giselle's husband's name, and was stamped *Paid*.

Beneath it was a yellow sheet of legal paper on which was scribbled a phone number with an 809 area code.

His phone number.

Beneath that was a sheaf of bound papers that were labeled *Confidential*.

So. This was the report from that private detective Lester Hudson had hired.

Of course, it had been Lester who had stirred things up after so many years.

He thought back to the day, about a month ago, when his friend Reg, a native Jamaican who worked as a bartender at one of the new resorts in Ocho Rios, had come to tell him that someone had been asking questions.

Strange questions, about the past.

The nosy man was an American who looked like a tourist, according to Reg, but who was clearly in Jamaica for something other than sun and fun.

Hmm.

What was he up to?

It hadn't been too hard for Reg to get the American drunk the next night. After figuring the guy was a cheapskate, considering the meager tips he'd left, all Reg had to do was ply him with free drinks. Once he had grown slap-happy, bragging about his business and his travels, Reg had started asking questions. At first, the guy had been reticent about why he was sniffing around in Ocho Rios, claiming he was just there on vacation. But eventually, with his voice slurred and his eyes starting to look bleary, he'd started talking.

Afterward, when he was safely snoozing back in his room, Reg had driven up into the mountains to reveal what the American had told him.

The man's name was Lester Hudson, Reg reported, and he was from a little town in Connecticut. Crawford Corners.

So that was it. Giselle had been from Crawford Corners. This had something to do with her.

Sure enough, Reg went on to tell him that the man's wife's name was Giselle, and she had borne twin girls eighteen years ago, when she was a teenager living in Jamaica.

According to Lester's wife, one child, Candra, had stayed behind in Jamaica with the father, a local whose name was Manfred. For some reason, Giselle was under the impression that the child had died.

The other child, Meg, had gone back to America with Giselle.

The instant Reg told him that, shock and rage shot through him. He'd known where Candra was all along—that she was being raised by Rosamund, a local woman who had lost her own child in infancy.

But Meg . . .

Meg was supposed to be dead.

Rosamund had told him she was.

Rosamund had *promised* she was.

According to Reg, Lester wanted to talk to the twins' father, Manfred. He had found out, through the private detective he'd hired, that Candra hadn't died shortly after birth after all.

It seemed that Rosamund's sister, Tish, had a big mouth. She had been involved in the coverup, but had blabbed it to someone on the island. Pretty soon, it was common knowledge—although no one, in all these years, had dared to tell Manfred.

Lester had found out that Manfred had wanted Meg dead—and that he had no idea that she wasn't. He also knew that Manfred was quite wealthy.

What he didn't know, according to Reg, was that Manfred was a powerful high priest and that his wealth had come from spells he had cast.

Anyway, what Lester planned to do was blackmail Manfred—and Giselle.

He was going to tell Manfred that if he didn't come up with a considerable amount of money, Lester would tell his wife that her daughter Candra was still alive.

Meanwhile, he was going to tell Giselle that he had tracked down Meg's father, and that if she didn't pay him off, he would reveal to the man that Meg was still alive.

When Reg had asked him why he had to bother blackmailing his own wife, Lester had said, "Because I'm no fool. I know she wants to leave me. And if she does, I'll get nothing, thanks to a prenuptial agreement her father made me sign when I married her. My wife is loaded, and after all these years, I don't deserve to be left high and dry."

Furthermore, Lester had told Reg, he had found out something else. Something neither Giselle nor Manfred knew. And he was safeguarding that secret. Despite the haze of scotch, he had suddenly grown closemouthed. He wasn't going to reveal what he knew.

Poor Lester. The greedy fool had no idea he was dabbling in a dangerous place.

Now, he would find out just what it was that Lester had discovered about the past—the other thing Rosamund had been keeping from him.

He reached for the confidential report, opened it to the first page, and began to read.

And as he read, his eyes narrowed and darkened and his face contorted until he wore hideous mask of fury and hatred.

Now, at last, he knew the truth.

And now he would seek vengeance for this shocking deception.

Yes, all of them would pay for one woman's sins.

Rosamund Bowen would be the first to die.

Giselle would be the last.

"What took you so long?" Giselle asked, hearing Lester sit down in the seat beside her again. She opened her eyes and saw that he was unpeeling the foil end of a new roll of Tums.

He hesitated only a moment before saying, "I had to make a phone call."

Hmm. Why had he decided to be truthful for a change? Maybe he thought she had followed him and seen him. He wouldn't dream that she really could care less what he did.

"Who'd you call?" she asked, because he was obviously waiting for her to.

He popped a pastel green antacid tablet into his mouth. "My voice mail at the office. I needed to see if anyone was trying to reach me."

"On a Saturday?"

He scowled. "I'm a very important man, Giselle. Do you think my job ends at five o'clock on a Friday night? I need to be in contact every minute of every day in case one of my clients needs me."

"Lester, you've been in Fiji for the past week and a half."

"I know, and I've checked my voice mail several times every day."

Giselle wanted to say that he could stop playing at this silly charade, that she knew all about his mistress and that as far as she was concerned, Lester could just call her whenever he felt like it, in front of her. Hell, Giselle would even get on the line and say hello. She'd tell the pitiful woman, whoever she was, that she was more than welcome to Lester Hudson. She'd advise her to stock her medicine cabinet with Tums, and—

"What are you smiling at, Giselle?" Lester sounded irritated, and she shrugged. She noticed that his lips were coated with milky, pale green residue.

"Nothing. I'm not smiling at anything, Lester."

"Have they made any announcements about the flight?"

"Nope."

He sighed and checked his watch, then popped another Tums into his mouth.

Giselle closed her eyes again. Immediately, her thoughts went back to what had happened so long ago in Jamaica. After so many years of trying not to think of it, why was it on her mind so much today?

Because you have nothing else to do in this damn airport, she told herself. *And because yesterday was Meg's eighteenth birthday. Her twin sister would have been eighteen, too, now. What would it have been like if I had been able to bring her home with me, too?*

A lump rose in Giselle's throat, and she swallowed hard over it.

She remembered that terribly muggy September morning when her water had suddenly broken as she made Manfred's breakfast. She hadn't even known what it was, the sudden gush of warm liquid that trickled down her legs. Paralyzed with shame, thinking she had lost control of her bladder, she had given a little moan and stared down at the puddle on the floor.

Manfred had glanced up from his coffee, seen what had happened, and told her to lie down.

As she moved to obey him the first contraction had seized her, a breathtaking cramp that made her cry out and clutch her swollen abdomen.

"Help me, Manfred," she had gasped, suddenly terrified.

But he hadn't.

He had merely left the room, and sent one of the young men who were always hanging around the house to summon the midwife.

By the time Rosamund arrived, Giselle had been writhing on the bed, half-delirious in agony. She was alone in the house, Manfred had left her, saying that it wasn't his place to be here.

Giselle was vaguely aware that Rosamund had brought another woman with her—her sister, Letitia. The two women held a hushed conversation as they poked and prodded at Giselle, and she whimpered and screamed and implored them to make this stop. Her labor had progressed swiftly, and Giselle begged Rosamund to help her, to give her something for the pain.

"Yeah, *mon,* no problem," Rosamund had said, and moments later she was holding a damp, harsh-smelling cloth beneath Giselle's nose. She inhaled and was borne away on a wave of oblivion.

The next thing she remembered was sudden, unbearable pressure, and pushing and writhing, and bellowing at the top of her lungs.

And then, as if across a great distance, she heard a baby's angry cries.

Thank God it's over had been her only thought, as she drifted toward that blessed limbo again.

But there was more pressure, and Rosamund's hurried voice saying, "There's another one. Come on, my lady, push. Push . . ."

And for Giselle, too far gone to comprehend or care, the rest had been a blur. She had slipped in and out of consciousness, fighting the unbearable pain that tortured her body, shutting out the wailing baby, or babies . . .

She didn't care.

She didn't care about anything except ending this terrible suffering. And Manfred . . .

Where was Manfred?

Why had he left her?

She needed him desperately . . .

And then that pungent cloth was pressed to her face again, and there was only darkness, and silence.

When she finally came to, Giselle saw that it was night. She was still lying in the bed, and the lamp was lit, and somewhere nearby she heard the faint whimpering of an infant.

She blinked and looked around, and her gaze came to rest on Rosamund, who sat in a rocking chair across the room crooning softly to the small bundle in her arms.

That's my child, Giselle had thought numbly, but she felt nothing. Nothing but relief . . . and confusion.

Where was Manfred?

And . . .

Hadn't there been two babies?

"Rosamund?" she croaked out. "Where's Manfred? And where's the other child?"

There was only silence for a long time.

Then the woman had stood and walked over to the bed. She had leaned over and deposited the baby in Giselle's arms.

"This is your daughter, my lady," she had said in her singsong Jamaican accent. "She is a beautiful, healthy child."

And in that first moment that she held her baby, Giselle was swamped in a rush of maternal love. This child, this tiny creature with a pinched red face and a headful of black hair, with those dark, solemn eyes that focused unwaveringly on her mother's face, was a part of Giselle . . . and the man she loved.

In wonder, Giselle reached out and caressed the baby's impossibly soft, smooth cheek with her fingertip, and was met with a hushed little coo.

"You're so beautiful," she whispered to her daughter. "I'm your mommy, and I'll always be there for you. Always."

And then, she had looked up at Rosamund, and the woman's eyes met hers with . . . was it guilt? The midwife broke the gaze hastily, looking away as she busied herself smoothing the blanket on the bed and plumping the pillows behind Giselle.

"Rosamund," Giselle said, fighting back an inexplicable rush of panic, "where's the other baby? There were two. I *know* there were two. I heard you say it. I remember . . ."

There was no reply.

Carefully, so she wouldn't jostle the baby in her arms, yet urgently, Giselle reached up and grabbed Rosamund's arm.

"Where is my baby? Tell me!"

"She is gone, my lady. But this child is here, and she is yours."

"She died?"

Again the slight hesitation, the evasive expression in Rosamund's gaze. "She did, yes."

A sob escaped Giselle's throat, and she was enveloped in grief for the daughter she had never even glimpsed. "Where's Manfred? Does he know?"

"He does."

"Where is he? Please, Rosamund," she said, crying now and clutching her baby to her breast, "please tell him I need him."

The woman had nodded and slipped away.

Giselle didn't know how long it was before Manfred came to her, only that it felt like hours, like days had passed as she sat in that bed rocking her daughter. The infant's eyes were closed and she slept soundly, her chest rising and falling in a rhythmic pattern. Giselle wanted to be reassured by those tiny breaths, by the child's warm body against her own, and yet . . .

"I can't lose you, too," she whispered to her daughter. "Please, my little love, please don't leave me, too."

Finally, she heard a sound and saw that Manfred was standing at the foot of her bed. He had always done that—slipped into and out of a room swiftly and silently, startling her with his comings and goings.

Now she burst into fresh tears at the sight of him. "Oh, Manfred," she sobbed, yearning for him to come to her and comfort her, "we've lost our other daughter. She died, and—"

"She didn't die," he cut in.

His words stunned her, filled her with hope, and yet . . .

And yet, his tone was cold. And he hadn't moved to come near her, just stood there, watching her.

And that was when a chill came over her. She realized, in that moment, in a rush of stark revelation, that Manfred didn't love her . . .

And that she was afraid of him.

Deathly afraid.

"She's alive?" she asked hesitantly, watching him.

"No. But she did not 'die.' The other baby was killed, Giselle," Manfred said calmly.

"No . . ." Horrified, and numb with shock, Giselle had tightened her grasp on the baby in her arms, to protect her daughter from the man who had fathered her.

"Yes," Manfred said. "She was sacrificed."

"Oh, God, no . . . oh, please . . . why? Why?"

"Because when I was younger, I made a deal," he said matter-of-factly. "I was born with a gift . . . with power. But always, there was the potential for more . . . for obtaining a force beyond my wildest dreams. All I had to do was promise my firstborn child to the gods and I would rule all who encountered me."

"No . . . oh, Manfred," Giselle protested, unable to grasp what he was telling her. "Why . . . ? Why me?"

"The women here, the ones who partake in our ceremonies, have always been aware of my pledge. Who, of them, would bear my child, knowing its fate?"

The horror of what he was telling her, of what he had done to her, filled Giselle with rage. If not for the helpless child in her arms, she would have lunged at him, clawed at him, beaten him with her fists. But all she could do was stare, and sob, and tremble uncontrollably.

"The moment I saw you, I knew that you were the one who would deliver me to my destiny," he mused. "It wasn't difficult to place you under my spell . . . to make you want me. Women have always wanted me. But you, Giselle, you were the chosen one. You were perfect—an outsider, reckless and vain and naive . . ."

"No, Manfred. Please don't talk this way . . ."

"I gave you a special potion at the ritual that first night," he went on, oblivious to her torment, "the night my children were conceived. A potion that was meant to enhance fertility. It worked, of course, since you have delivered not one, but *two* babies. Such a shame that you won't be able to keep one for yourself."

She couldn't speak, could only cower against the pillows in dread, as he took a step toward her. And then another.

He opened his hands. "Give me the baby."

"No!" she shrieked, clutching her crying daughter against her. "You've already killed one child, Manfred . . . I won't let you have this one!"

"I'm not going to kill her," he said calmly. "I'm going to give her to Rosamund. She wants a child, and I promised to do that, in return for what she has done for me."

"What? What did she do?"

"She disposed of the other one. She made the sacrifice for me."

"You . . . coward!" Giselle's voice was low with fury and disbelief. "You couldn't do it yourself. You were too weak, and—"

She was stopped short by a stinging slap across her cheek.

"*I* am not weak," he thundered. "*I* am not a coward."

In one flurry of movement, he descended on her and wrenched the now screaming baby out of her arms. Before she could react he was gone.

In a panic, Giselle scrambled out of the bed, but her legs seemed to dissolve the moment her feet hit the floor. Suddenly, the trauma of what she had been through, physically and emotionally, took its toll.

She was weak—and disoriented. Blindly, she took a step, and then another.

My baby . . .

I have to save my baby . . .

And then her legs had given out on her and she'd crumpled to the floor in a heap.

Sixteen

The violent storm had finally passed out of the New England region, leaving a surprisingly beautiful sunset in its wake.

Now the last pink-and-peach streaks had faded from the dusky September sky, and the deserted warehouse district in Spring City was cloaked in shadows.

"Are you sure this is the place?" Meg whispered dubiously as she and Candra picked their way across the muddy, shadowy, weed-and-debris-choked railyard.

"Of course I'm sure." Candra was several steps ahead of her, moving with purpose despite the obstacle course underfoot.

Meg scurried to keep up with her sister, trying not to think about snakes and rats and other creatures that might be lurking around them. Overhead, bats swooped across the twilight sky, and Meg kept a wary eye on them to make sure they kept their distance.

"No one's here," Candra called back to her, stopping abruptly a few yards ahead, beside a crumbling shack.

"What?" Meg came to a halt beside her sister and looked around. The shack was little more than a few vertical, rotted boards that had somehow managed to withstand the winds of today's storm.

"I said, they're not here. . . . Shhh." Candra frowned and stood very still, her head cocked as though she were listening for something.

"Where do you think they are?" Meg asked after a moment of silence, knowing Candra was referring to the coven. Her sister only shrugged and didn't move.

Meg felt the hair on her arms prickling with goose bumps, and an eerie sensation was rapidly settling over her. Something was wrong here.

She could sense it.

Did Candra feel it, too?

"Did you hear that?" Candra asked.

"What?" Meg asked, even as a creepy sound reached her ears. It was a moan . . . or a wail. Something in between.

"That." Candra started in the direction from which the noise had come, in a wooded thicket off to the side, near the rusted, gravel-strewn track bed.

Meg hesitated, afraid to follow, afraid to ask Candra what she thought had made that sound. She thought it had come from an animal that had been wounded—or a person. A chill slid down her spine.

"Candra, wait," she called as her sister moved into the trees ahead.

She heard it again—a low-pitched whimper, followed by a gasp that had come from Candra.

"Oh, God, no! Grandmother!"

Meg broke into a run, and when she reached the spot where Candra had disappeared into the woods, she saw her sister crouched on the ground over something white.

A person, Meg realized as she drew closer. A dark-skinned person who was wearing something with a red-and-white pattern, a robe of some sort.

"Oh, Grandmother," Candra sobbed, and Meg stopped just a few feet from them, realizing that the robe wasn't red and white patterned. It was white. The red was blood that seeped from the woman's stomach and shoulders and legs . . . she had been savagely butchered.

And she was still alive, moaning softly, staring up at Candra with wide brown eyes. She appeared startled—not just by what had happened to her, but also by the sight of Candra, here, hovering over her in this remote patch of trees.

"Who did this to you, Grandmother?" Candra asked, her voice choked with emotion, her face twisted in agony as she stared down at the woman who had raised her. Rosamund's head was cradled in her lap, and she stroked the woman's blood-spattered hair. "Who hurt you?"

Meg sank to her knees beside her sister and Rosamund, too shaken to utter a word. She touched Candra's arm in a feeble attempt to offer comfort, but her sister didn't seem to notice; she only went on running her fingers over Rosamund's head.

The woman started to speak, closed her eyes as if in pain, and then tried again.

"He's after you . . . too . . ." she said finally, and Meg saw that she was looking at both Candra and herself.

There was something about Rosamund that reached out to Meg, to some deep, forgotten place in her soul. It was almost as if Meg had known her, once, a long time ago . . . but then, that was impossible. There was only one time in her life when her path could ever have crossed Rosamund's, and she couldn't possibly remember anything that had happened when she was an infant in Jamaica.

And yet . . .

"Both of you," Rosamund went on, her words labored, "He's after you . . . and . . ."

"Who is, Grandmother?" Candra asked, her voice trembling with the barely controlled sorrow and rage that were etched across her face. "Who's after us? Who did this to you?"

Rosamund squeezed her eyes closed, then haltingly said, "After you . . . and your brother."

For a moment, the only sound was Rosamund's struggle to take another breath.

Meg felt as though she were hovering above this surreal scene, watching it happen to someone else.

The old woman's words echoed crazily in her mind.

Your brother . . .

Your brother . . .

Your brother . . .

Finally, Meg dared to tear her eyes away from Rosamund's pain-contorted face to focus on her sister. Candra's wide-eyed gaze met hers, and Meg saw the astonishment there.

Meg couldn't seem to find her voice.

But somehow, Candra found hers. She turned back to Rosamund, and, in a hushed tone, uttered the question that was in Meg's mind.

"Grandmother, are you saying that we have a brother?"

The old woman's head raised, then lowered in an almost imperceptible nod. "There . . . were . . . three babies," she whispered hoarsely. "The boy . . . was . . . first . . . firstborn . . ."

Somewhere, in the fog of confusion and dread that had overtaken Meg's mind, she realized that Rosamund knew she was dying; she was fighting to stay alive long enough to warn them, to tell them . . .

A brother, Meg thought incredulously. *We have a brother.*

"Three," Rosamund croaked again, her pain-racked gaze searching their faces as if for confirmation that they understood what she was saying.

"Three," Candra repeated softly, in wonder. "There were three babies. Me, and Meg, and a brother."

Again, the imperceptible nod. Rosamund closed her eyes as if the effort of even that slight movement had been too much for her.

For a moment, when she didn't move, Meg was seized by the horrible thought that she had died.

But then her eyelids fluttered again, and she opened her mouth to force more words past her parched lips. "Giselle . . . never . . . knew . . ."

"She never knew that there were three of us?" Meg asked, uncertain whether she was more stunned at the fact that she had a brother, or that her mother somehow hadn't realized she'd borne triplets.

But how could that be?

"Must . . . warn your brother."

"Where is he? Who is he?" Candra asked, clutching Rosamund's weathered hands. "Who is he, Grandmother? Please—"

"The one . . . with the . . . amulet."

"Amulet?" Meg repeated. "What do you mean?"

"For . . . protection." Her breaths were coming in short, shallow gasps now, and her expression had grown more tortured. "Sent it with him . . . before I . . . gave him away . . ."

"You gave him away, Grandmother?" Candra asked, leaning her head closer to the old woman's lips. "To who? Where is he?"

"Made of steel . . ." Rosamund said faintly.

"The amulet?" Meg asked, riveted, even as her mind screamed, *This isn't happening. This can't be happening.*

"Engraved . . . pentagram . . . powerful . . ."

"But where is he?" Candra asked urgently. "Where's our brother?"

The only answer was the most terrible thing Meg had ever heard— the gurgling, rasping sound of a human being's dire, futile effort to draw a last breath.

Meg watched in numb horror as Rosamund's eyes widened in frantic protest. The woman realized what was happening, and she was fighting it with everything she had.

"Candra . . . oh, God, do something," Meg sobbed in desperation, turning to her sister. "We have to help her."

But Candra, her face stricken and tears rolling down her cheeks, said nothing, did nothing—only stared in anguish at Rosamund.

And when Meg looked down at the woman again, she saw that her gaze had grown vacant, her battered, bloody body relaxed.

She was gone.

"This sandwich is disgusting," Lester announced, plunking it onto the plastic plate in front of him and making a face.

Giselle noticed that his pale red mustache was dotted with crumbs, and there was a slick of mustard in the corner of his mouth.

She looked away, down at the limp iceberg lettuce salad on her own plate, and poked at the sorry-looking greens with her fork.

"How's yours?" Lester asked, swiping a paper napkin across his lips. He got the mustard, but most of the crumbs remained.

"Mine's fine," she lied.

"I should have ordered a salad. Or something hot."

"Go get something else."

"Are you kidding? Look at that line," he said, gesturing at the crowd of people just inside the cafeteria's doors. "And anyway, airport food costs a fortune. I should go back up to the gate and ask to speak to the supervisor. You know, I think I will. I'm going to demand that they give me another meal voucher."

Giselle rolled her eyes and put her fork down.

"And if they think I'm going to wait in that line again, they've got another thing coming. I'm going to go right to the front, and if they have a problem with that, I'll ask for the supervisor. And while I'm at it, I'm going to ask him why he thinks he can charge an arm and a leg for a sandwich."

"Oh, please, Lester, it's not as if you had to pay for it!"

"That's not the point. I'm going to ask him why, if a goddamn ham and cheese sandwich costs an arm and a leg, it tastes so lousy. How can anyone ruin a ham and cheese sandwich? And then I'm going to—"

"Oh, for God's sake, Lester, why don't you just shut up?" Giselle interrupted, shoving back her chair.

He looked startled.

So did the family of five seated at the next table. Even their toddler was watching Giselle with wide eyes.

She didn't care. Not about Lester, or the family, or what anyone else thought.

She got up and she ran, out of the restaurant and down the carpeted corridor to the ladies' room.

There was a line, she realized in dismay as she walked in the door. There was nothing to do but wait. And do her best not to think about the thing that had been on her mind all afternoon.

But it was no use.

Images kept bombarding her mind.

Manfred . . .

And Rosamund . . .

And the tiny, helpless baby who had died, Meg's identical twin . . .

Luckily, no one in line was paying any attention to her. No one seemed to notice the tears that kept slipping down her cheeks or the way she was trembling all over.

Finally, it was Giselle's turn to slip into one of the stalls.

She closed and locked the door behind her, then wiped at her eyes with a square of cheap, rough toilet paper, hoping that her mascara and eyeliner hadn't poured all over her face. She would check in the mirror before she returned to the gate area, but for now she just needed to be alone, to bury her face in her hands and mourn the baby she had lost so many years ago.

She rarely allowed herself to think of that horrible night; she seldom recollected the atrocious details of what Manfred had done.

Now, huddled in the corner of the tiny cubicle, she was barely aware of the running water and hand-dryers and chattering voices on the other side of the door. She was cut off from the rest of the world, wrapped in her bittersweet memories.

Bitter for the baby who had been murdered at Rosamund's hands.

Sweet for the one who had been saved . . . also at Rosamund's hands.

Giselle would never forget how, after fainting when Manfred had stolen her second daughter, she had awakened to the sound of Rosamund's voice.

"It's all right, my lady," the woman had said, stroking her face with a damp, cool cloth. "He's gone. And I have your daughter."

Everything Manfred had said came rushing back at Giselle, and she'd sat up and lunged for the woman.

"You killed her," she screamed. "You killed her."

Rosamund gripped both her arms with surprising strength. "Yes, one of your children is gone," she told Giselle, "but the other is here. I've brought her back to you. Take her. And leave, now, quickly . . . before he discovers what I've done."

For the first time, Giselle noticed the wicker basket on the floor behind Rosamund, and heard the sweet sound of a baby's sweet gurgling.

"My baby," she cried out, and rushed to the basket. There, curled upon a nest of soft blankets, lay her daughter.

She scooped the infant into her arms and kissed her, over and over, kissed her warm little head and her fat silky cheeks, and even her petal-soft lips.

"Go," Rosamund urged her again, breaking the spell with her abrupt command. "Before he comes back."

"But where do I go?" Giselle had asked helplessly, confusion swirling through her mind. She could barely think, couldn't get past the overwhelming rush of relief that one of her precious children had been saved.

"Back to your parents," Rosamund said without hesitation, "and back home. To the States."

Giselle stared at her blankly, echoing her words. "Back home . . ."

"Listen to me," Rosamund said. "You must leave this island. You can't let anyone know about the child."

"He said he had promised her to you . . ." Giselle began.

"And he had. But I have given her back to you. You're her mother. I'll tell Manfred that she died. If he ever knew . . . if he finds out that you have her, he'll kill me . . . and both of you."

Chilled at her words, and not doubting that Rosamund spoke the truth, Giselle had nodded.

It had all happened so swiftly after that.

Making the endless, perilous, hurried journey down the dark mountain roads, with her newborn child snuggled against her breast . . .

Sneaking into the home she had fled eight months earlier . . .

Confronting the parents who had never stopped hoping for her return . . .

Seeing their tears of joy as they realized she was back, and their shock as they laid eyes on their tiny granddaughter . . .

She had told them the whole story, begging them all the while not to go to the police, not to confront Manfred.

And when she was finished, to her astonishment, her father told her that he would arrange for them to leave immediately—all of them. Not a word about the baby would be said to anyone.

Giselle had been stunned that Harry McKenna had believed what she'd told him.

Her father loved her fiercely, she knew, and would do anything for her. But she hadn't expected him to understand the urgency that was involved, or the danger.

It wasn't until later, much later, when they were safely home in Connecticut once again, that he told her why he had done what he had.

He knew all about Manfred, had ever since they'd arrived. The young man was legendary in Ocho Rios, for his ruthlessness and for his powers.

Harry had heard stories, terrible stories, about the Black Magic rituals over which Manfred presided. He had heard about how the locals feared him, though he was really little more than a boy. Manfred controlled the lives of those who were in his coven, yet he even dominated those who weren't. No one in Ocho Rios dared cross the powerful high priest.

And though Harry and Hope had assumed Giselle had gone back to the States when she'd run away, Harry had always feared, somewhere deep inside, that his daughter had been caught up in the dark side of life on the island. That somehow Manfred had gotten to her.

When she came safely back to him, all Harry could think was that he had to get her away from Manfred and his evil powers.

He had, and for eighteen years, Giselle had felt safe.

Almost.

Giselle wasn't one to worry. She left that to her mother, who, she had always glibly said, worried enough for the entire population of Crawford Corners.

But somewhere, in the back of her mind, when Giselle was caught off guard by the intrusion of dark thoughts, she had sorrowfully remembered the daughter she had lost, the one who had been sacrificed in the name of her father's lust for power.

And she had carried the uneasy knowledge that someday Manfred might somehow find out that Meg was still alive.

If that ever happened . . .

Giselle shuddered to think of his reaction.

Only when she and Meg were safe inside the front door of 41 Meadowview Terrace did Candra give in to the desolate grief that had welled up inside her as they drove silently back from Spring City.

The moment the door clicked shut behind them, she burst into tears over the woman whose loss she felt so acutely that her heart literally ached.

Candra cried not just for Rosamund, for the way she had died, but for the wasted days Candra had spent since she'd left the Drayer house and the woman she'd thought was her grandmother. She cried for the pain she must have caused Rosamund when she'd abandoned her without explanation, and again for the bitterness she had felt over her discovery that Rosamund wasn't her grandmother after all.

Now she knew that no matter what the woman had done, no matter what she'd kept from Candra, she had loved her. Candra had seen it in the old woman's eyes as she lay dying. Rosamund may never have shown it, may not have been an affectionate woman who verbalized her emotions. But she had loved Candra. And she had, for whatever reason, taken in a baby who wasn't her flesh and blood, or her responsibility. And she had made sure Candra had food to eat and a bed to sleep in and clothes to wear . . .

She sniffled miserably, remembering the worn navy blue New York Yankee T-shirt that Rosamund had bought her for a dime, secondhand. The T-shirt Candra had loathed wearing, because it was so shabby compared with what the girls in Crawford Corners wore. The T-shirt she had traded for Mcg's private school uniform, and a week of deception that had nearly ended in the death of her own sister.

And now, as she felt Meg's warm arms wrapping around her, steady and reassuring, she sobbed harder.

"It's all right, Candra," Meg murmured. "It's going to be okay."

Meg's hand stroked Candra's hair and her voice soothed her until Candra finally sniffled and pulled back, regaining some control.

"Are you all right?" Meg asked, concern in her eyes.

"I'm fine." She wasn't, but she couldn't fall apart again. She couldn't let her emotions rule her. She never had. And now she needed her wits about her more than ever.

"Meg"—she said, wiping at her wet cheeks—"we have to figure this out, and there's no time to waste."

"You mean about our brother . . ." Meg's voice still held a note of incredulity at the very notion.

Candra nodded. "Our brother, whoever he is . . . and the person who killed Rosamund. Whoever he is, he's after us, too. She warned us."

"I know, but who can it be? We have to get ahold of my mother. She might know something. I'll check the machine and see if she called while we were gone." Meg went into the other room, leaving Candra to search through her pocket for a tissue.

She found a crumpled one and blew her nose, and wiped her eyes dry. And by the time she was done removing traces of her grief, Meg was back.

"The only call was from my grandmother," she reported. "She wanted to see if Carrie and I were all right. Candra, we have to call the police."

Candra flinched inwardly at the mere word. "Why?"

"What do you mean, 'Why'? We can't just leave your grandmother lying on the ground in the mud! We have to—"

"Meg, no." Candra cut her off, grabbing her arm and looking into her face. "We can't get the police involved."

"But why not? Someone murdered Rosamund, someone who wants to kill us . . . and this brother who—we didn't even know he existed! Now we have no idea who he is, or where he is. How are we supposed to warn him? And how can you even think of not doing anything about it? How can you just leave Rosamund there in the dark, all alone?"

"It's not Rosamund, Meg. She's gone, hopefully to a place where nothing matters anymore. That thing on the ground in the railyard is a shell. And someone will find her, sooner or later. We can't worry about that now. We have to find out who killed her."

"But how?"

"There's only one person I can think of who would know, besides . . . Mother." The word tasted strange on her tongue, less so than an affectionate *Mom* would have been, and yet not comfortable.

Not *right*.

"Who?" Meg asked. "Who's the other person?"

"Rosamund's sister . . . Aunt Tish. She might know something. She lives over on Elmont. We have to go back there."

Though it was relatively early on a Saturday evening—not quite nine—Elmont Avenue was in full swing, teeming with its usual illicit action.

The Alleycat Inn was a run-down tavern on the district's shabbiest block; it was a low, cement-block building with a neon sign that had seen brighter days.

As he walked through the door into the dim, smoky room, he saw that there were only a few customers slouched on stools along the scarred bar. They were pathetic specimens, every last one of them—barflies whose bleary eyes were focused on the grainy screen of the television above the row of bottles. There was no top-shelf liquor here, only the most basic stuff that would offer a reprieve from the disheartening world outside.

No matter. It would suit his purposes.

He was still trembling from the exertion of plunging that dagger, over and over, into Rosamund's resisting flesh. It wasn't that the attack hadn't given him pleasure, he told himself, because it had. Of course it had.

And yet . . .

She had stubbornly refused to give him the last piece of information he needed—the one thing he was desperate to know.

So she had deserved to die.

And yet . . .

Somewhere, deep in his hardened black heart, maybe . . . just maybe, he had felt a flicker of remorse as he killed her.

But he couldn't let that weakness take hold, couldn't let it grow so that he wouldn't be able to carry out the rest of his mission.

He needed a drink, to fortify his resolve, to quiet the trembling.

He walked swiftly across the sticky floor to the bar, and fixed the bartender with a stare. The man, a middle-aged Hispanic who wore a faded Red Dog T-shirt, looked up.

His eyebrows bobbed as he looked his new customer over. He

rested his burning cigarette in an ashtray, then strolled over wearing an amused expression.

"Can I help you?" he asked, removing the rag that had been hooked at the waist of his cheap, stained jeans. He leisurely wiped up a ring of moisture left on the wooden surface.

"A shot of dark rum, straight up."

The bartender just looked at him, and he wondered, with a sudden stab of anxiety, if the man could smell the cloying scent of blood that clung to his clothes. He'd gone back to the room behind the shop to wash up, and he'd carefully blotted the few small dark stains on his black coat. But even now, he was aware of the telltale, vaguely metallic scent that lingered.

The bartender shook his head. "I can't serve you."

"What are you talking about?"

"You're underage. I can tell just by looking at you. You're a kid."

He stiffened, wrath darting through him. "I'm *not* a kid," he said icily.

"Oh, yeah? Prove it. Got some ID that says you're twenty-one?"

Of course he didn't.

His body tense with rage, he turned away from the bar and strode toward the door.

And as he went, he muttered under his breath.

A curse.

A curse on the man who had denied him the drink he needed, on the man who even now was exulting in how he had brandished his own miserable little allotment of power.

And, as he shoved the door open and swooped out into the night, he heard the groan that erupted suddenly behind him.

He didn't need to look back to know that the bartender had doubled over in pain.

Seventeen

Meg stood in the foyer with her coat on, fiddling with her keys while she waited for Candra, who was upstairs changing her clothes. She had told her sister to just borrow anything she wanted from her closet or drawers, and wondered if it was her imagination or if Candra had looked a little uncomfortable at the suggestion.

You have to stop questioning her, even just mentally, Meg warned herself. She had already chosen to believe Candra over everyone else: Shea and Mirabelle and Ben. And now that she had made that choice, she had better stick to it. Wholeheartedly.

A car door slammed out front.

It must be Carrie, Meg thought, turning to look out the window as another door slammed. *She must have someone with her . . . and it had better not be that dirtbag Eddie.*

She peered through the glass, and realized she didn't recognize the small, expensive compact car that sat on the driveway . . . or the two boys who were walking up the front steps.

Frowning, Meg walked to the door and opened it just as the taller boy was reaching for the bell. Startled, he glanced up at her. That was when she realized that she did know him, after all.

It was the boy who had been with the police last night, when they had found her and Candra at the park. He was broad shouldered and good-looking, with dark, wavy hair and a muscular build. He was looking Meg over intently with eyes that were an unusual, clear color—not quite blue and not entirely gray or green, either. The expression in them was bemused, and she realized that he was trying to figure out which sister she was.

"I'm Meg," she said, and offered a tentative smile.

She couldn't tell if he was relieved or disappointed as he smiled back. "Hi. I'm Landon Keller. We kind of met last night, but . . ." He trailed off and shrugged.

"Yeah," she said. "I know."

She looked over his shoulder, at the other boy. He had straight dark hair and tanned skin and intense dark eyes that caught and held hers.

Meg nodded slightly, wondering where she had seen him before.

"This is Jack," Landon said, motioning at him. "Is Candra around?" Landon asked, looking past Meg.

"She's upstairs, getting ready—"

"You're on your way out?" For the first time, Landon seemed to notice that she was wearing her coat and clutching her keys.

"Yeah, we have to go, um . . ." Meg hesitated, not sure what to tell him. Certainly not that they were headed over to Elmont Avenue in Spring City. Everyone knew that nice girls didn't venture into that neighborhood after dark.

Landon's expression clouded over, and Meg sensed what he was thinking. That Candra had a date. This guy was crazy about her sister. It was written all over his face.

"Meg?"

Behind her, she heard Candra's voice, calling as she walked down the stairs.

Meg turned and saw her sister at the exact moment her sister laid eyes on Landon. In the first fraction of a second, she seemed pleased . . . and then, immediately, she appeared indifferent.

"Candra?" Landon asked tentatively, stepping around Meg, into the foyer.

"What are you doing here?"

Meg watched as her sister calmly tossed her long, just-brushed hair over her shoulders. Candra was wearing Meg's black cashmere turtleneck tucked into a pair of snug black jeans. The outfit hugged her slender figure and made her appear to be about six feet tall and all legs.

For a moment, it seemed as though Landon was going to shrink back at Candra's haughty tone.

Don't, Meg wanted to tell him. *Don't let her push you away. She doesn't mean it. Can't you see that she's protecting herself from getting hurt?*

And even as that thought crossed her mind, she wondered how she knew that. Her twin was still a virtual stranger to her, and she had no idea what Candra's relationship with Landon Keller was all about. And yet, intuitively, she knew exactly what was going on here.

"Listen, Candra." Landon took a step closer to her, and his voice was filled with conviction. "I care about you, a lot, and I'm not going to let you shove me away as though you don't care about me, too. Because I know you do."

Way to go, Landon! Meg applauded mentally.

She glanced at Jack, to see if he was watching the little scene unfolding in the hall. He was, and he raised an eyebrow at Meg as if to say, *Do you know what's going on?*

She shrugged.

"You have no right to tell me who I care about," Candra was saying, and Meg turned back to see that her sister had planted her hands firmly on her hips and was standing her ground a foot or so away from Landon. "And you might think you have feelings for me, but trust me, you don't."

"What the hell are you talking about, Candra? How do you know what I feel?"

"I just do."

Meg noted that Candra's voice had lost a little of its arrogant tone. And she had taken a step back, away from Landon. He was blocking Meg's view, so she couldn't see her sister's expression.

"Do you think that I would drive all the way over here from New London if I didn't have feelings for you?" Landon asked.

"You didn't drive. Jack did," Candra observed, glancing for the first time at the other boy, who was standing beside Meg in the doorway. "Right?"

"What does that have to do with anything?" Landon asked incredulously.

"I don't know," Candra said, suddenly sounding deflated and weary.

"Listen to me, Candra." Landon put his hands on her upper arms and bent forward so that his face was on her level, only inches from hers. "I've never felt like this about anyone before. I'm crazy about you. Last night when I thought you were out there in the woods somewhere, in that storm . . . you don't know how worried I was. Don't play games with me now. Tell me what's going on."

"I can't . . ."

"Why can't you?"

"Because it's none of your business."

"I want it to be my business. I want *you* to be my business, Candra."

"Well, I'm not. I think you should leave."

"This is ridiculous," Landon said. "What's with you? Why are you doing this to me?"

Candra shrugged and leaned to the side, looking at Meg. "Will you please tell these two to get out of your house so we can leave, Meg?" Her prickly tone was back, but Meg detected a wistful note there, too.

"We do have to go," Meg said, semi-apologetically.

"Where?" Landon asked again.

Candra bristled. "I told you—"

"It's none of my business. I know." Landon spun and stalked away from her, to the door.

Meg stepped aside to let him pass, and she and Jack exchanged a glance before Jack followed Landon down the steps.

"Nice meeting you," Meg called after them, knowing that the words sounded ludicrous, but feeling as though she had to say something.

Landon didn't reply, but Jack responded, "You, too," before getting into the driver's seat of the car.

Only when they had driven away did Meg turn to her sister, who stood motionless in the foyer behind her.

"Do you want to tell me about him?" she asked Candra.

"No. I don't ever want to talk about him, or see him, again."

Meg knew better than to push. Her sister was obviously not the type to go around spilling details about her private life under normal circumstances. Tonight, with everything that had happened, Meg would have been astonished if Candra actually did elaborate on her relationship with Landon Keller.

There was nothing to do but wonder . . .

And head for Elmont Avenue to confront Candra's Aunt Tish.

"Would you like another glass of champagne?" the pretty first-class flight attendant asked pleasantly.

"I will," Lester said, before Giselle could open her eyes to respond. "But shhh . . . my wife is sleeping."

Giselle kept her eyes closed, listening.

"Do you think she'd like a pillow?" the woman whispered.

"Nah, she's fine. What did you say your name was?"

"I didn't," the flight attendant said, sounding a little less jaunty than before, "but it's Missy."

"Missy? As in Melissa? Nice name," Lester said. "Listen, Missy, will you do me a favor?"

"If I can," she said, sounding leery.

"My wife and I are celebrating our wedding anniversary tomor-row—"

"Oh, congratulations," Missy said, obviously relieved that he wasn't hitting on her, which was probably what she'd been expecting.

It was what Giselle had been expecting, too. Now she wondered what he was up to, since their anniversary wasn't actually until November.

"Thank you," Lester said politely. "Anyway, because of all these flight delays, by the time we land in Connecticut, it will be the middle of the night. I'd been planning to surprise my wife with a home-cooked, candlelight dinner and a bottle of good champagne for dinner tomorrow night, but you can't buy liquor in Connecticut on a Sunday. So I was wondering . . . you wouldn't have an extra bottle of this delicious bubbly back there, would you?"

"Oh, I—I just . . . I'm not sure I can—"

"I understand, of course, Missy, if you can't let me have one. It's just that my wife and I toasted with this particular champagne on our wedding night, and it would mean so much to her if—well, you know."

"Let me just see what I can do," Missy said, and Giselle heard her walking away.

"You," Giselle said, opening her eyes and looking directly at Lester, "are the biggest cheapskate I've ever known in my life."

He looked startled, and dismayed. "What are you talking about?"

"I heard what just went on. You just lied to that poor girl about our anniversary, just so you can get a free bottle of champagne."

"Would you keep your voice down?" he hissed, glancing about at the other first-class passengers, none of whom appeared to be paying attention. "Maybe I lied about our anniversary, but I really was going to surprise you with a candlelight dinner and—"

"Bull," Giselle snapped. "You were not. You're cheap, Lester, and that's all there is to it."

"Oh, get off your high horse, Giselle," he shot right back in a low voice. "A crummy bottle of booze is the very least this stupid airline can give us after stranding us in L.A. for hours on end."

"The storm wasn't their fault, Lester. And I don't see anyone else around here trying to scam free goodies to take home. I've really had it with you."

"What's that supposed to mean?"

"It means I want a divorce."

The words had tumbled out of her mouth before she could stop them. She hadn't meant to tell him this way—impulsively, in the heat of anger.

And yet, now that it was out, she felt relieved . . .

And pleased by the bright red flush that rushed over his face, and by the shock and fury etched in his watery light blue eyes.

"What are you talking about?" he asked in a barely controlled whisper.

"I want a divorce," she repeated almost glibly, and settled back in her seat to glance out the window. They must be somewhere over the

heartland now, she thought, seeing only a vast patch of darkness below, marred only by an occasional cluster of small-town lights.

"Well, *I* don't want a divorce," Lester said, touching her arm.
"Giselle, look at me. Would you look at me, for God's sake?"

"No," she told him. "I'm tired of looking at you. I've been looking
at you for the past fifteen years, and frankly, I wouldn't care if I never
laid eyes on you again."

There was silence while Lester apparently contemplated that insult.

Then he said, sounding surprisingly composed, "You won't divorce
me."

Caught off guard by his tone, Giselle turned to him. "Oh, I won't?
Why not?"

"Trust me. You just won't. I'm not going to go into it here," he said,
glancing again at the other passengers, all of whom remained carefully detached.

But Giselle knew they were probably listening, most of them
caught up in the domestic drama being played out in seats 3A and 3B.

She shrugged and tried not to let Lester know that she was curious
about why he thought she wouldn't divorce him.

Much as Giselle wanted to think he was simply being his usual irritating, argumentative self, she couldn't help wondering at the smug
little grin that sat below his pale red mustache.

It was almost as if . . .

As if Lester were up to something. Something other than an affair.
Hmm.

"Here we are, Mr. Hudson. . . . One glass of champagne." Missy
reappeared in the aisle, wearing a conspiratory smile, and lowered her
voice to a whisper, "And one bottle to go."

All troubling thoughts of Landon Keller vanished from Candra's
mind the moment she and Meg arrived in the familiar third-floor hallway of the shabby apartment building where her aunt lived.

She fought back a lump in her throat as she recalled how many Saturday afternoons she and Rosamund had visited Aunt Tish here. Always, they were greeted by the smell of ammonia—though she
worked full-time as a maid, Aunt Tish kept her own home meticulous,
too, and was always in the middle of scrubbing something, usually
with the television blaring in the background. Her aunt was crazy
about American TV—she'd watch anything that was on, even those
crazy infomercial shows that Rosamund had always scoffed at.

But tonight, there was no smell of ammonia and no sound of the television. Only silence from beyond the door to apartment 3B, with its peeling olive-colored paint.

"Aren't you going to knock?" Meg whispered.

Candra hesitated. "She can't be home."

"How do you know?"

Because nothing smells or sounds right, Candra wanted to tell her. And yet, she knew, somehow, that despite the silence, her aunt was there. She could feel Tish's presence, as tangible as Rosamund's had been earlier in the railyard.

Then, Candra had let her instincts take over, leading her to where her grandmother lay in the bushes.

Now, she did the same, and knocked tentatively on the door.

There was no sound from behind it, and yet Candra knew her aunt was there, poised, listening . . . and frightened. The vibration of fear reached out from behind the door, grabbed Candra, and made her tense all over.

She turned to Meg, wondering if her sister felt it, too.

Meg's eyes were wide, and she caught her lower lip in her top teeth. She nodded slightly, as if to tell Candra that she knew what she was thinking.

"Aunt Tish?" Candra called softly. "It's me. Candra."

No answer.

"Aunt Tish, please. I have to talk to you . . . it's about Grand-mother."

At that, there was the sound of bolts and chains being undone on the other side of the door. Startled, Candra realized that her aunt had been hovering right there all along.

The door opened a mere crack, then wider, and Tish said in a hushed voice, "Okay, come in. But hurry—"

She stopped short as she caught sight of Meg. Her jaw literally dropped and she stared from one sister to the other.

"This is my twin, Meg," Candra told her.

Aunt Tish snapped out of it, nodded, and hurried them both inside. Then she closed the door behind them and triple locked it again.

Candra faced her aunt, and again was seized by a twinge of grief. The image of her sister Rosamund, Tish had finely wrinkled dark skin and short, curly, salt-and-pepper hair. But unlike her sister, who still wore bright island clothing reminiscent of her native Jamaica, Tish's overweight figure was clad in an outfit that was distinctly American: blue jeans, white sneakers, and a red sweatshirt that read WAIN-WRIGHT COLLEGE in navy blue letters.

"Aunt Tish, we have to—where are you going?" Candra interrupted herself, catching sight of the two bulging duffel bags sitting just inside the door.

Her aunt hesitated, then said, "I have to leave." Her gaze was still resting on Meg, as though she couldn't quite believe what she was seeing.

"Leave? Where are you going?"

Tish shrugged and wearing a closed expression turned back to Candra. "What are you doing here? What do you have to tell me about Rosamund?"

"She . . ." Candra paused, stricken with a sudden rush of sorrow, not sure if she could bring herself to say the words aloud. She cleared her throat, and saw that Meg was watching her sympathetically.

"Aunt Tish," she began again, determined not to lose control of her emotions, "my grandmother—Rosamund—is dead."

"*What?*" The woman clasped her hands to her lips and let out a tortured sob. She managed to utter one more word—"How?"—before breaking down into tears. She sank into a chair, her body trembling all over.

Candra felt her own mouth quivering.

"She was murdered," Meg said, after glancing at Candra, who stood unable to speak. "We found her, just before she died, in the railyard near here."

"No . . . no . . ." Tish wailed, rocking back and forth.

For a long time, there was only the sound of her bitter sobbing. Candra laid a hand stiffly on her aunt's shoulder, wanting to comfort her but not knowing how.

It was Meg who, when Tish had calmed herself, went on, "Before she died, Rosamund told us that whoever attacked her was after us. She also said we have a brother somewhere, but she died before she could tell us who he is, or how to find him."

Candra watched her aunt carefully. She had stiffened at Meg's words, and now her dark eyes were darting from Meg to Candra and back again. There was a hint of questioning in them, as though she wondered whether they knew anything more.

"Do you know, Aunt Tish?" Candra asked.

"About your brother? No," she said, standing up, and Candra knew she was lying. "Please, I have to go . . ."

"Where?"

"Away. Just . . . away."

"Why didn't the coven meet in the railyard tonight? Why was my grandmother the only one there?"

"Because of what happened to Dalila," Tish said, looking only momentarily surprised that Candra knew about the coven. "We called off our regular meeting. I told Rosamund, but she said she wanted to go to the spot anyway. It's consecrated, you know. There was something she wanted to do there." She checked her watch and looked at the door. "Candra, please . . ."

"You're involved in this somehow." Candra stepped between her aunt and the two bags she was eyeing.

She realized that while Tish's reaction to the news of her sister's death had been authentically sorrowful, she hadn't seemed shocked. It was almost as though she had . . . expected it?

"You spoke to my grandmother about more than Dalila's death today, didn't you?" Candra accused, pointing a finger in her aunt's face. "You knew she was in danger. She told you. And you're involved, too. You're in danger, too. She warned you. That's why you're leaving."

"No . . ."

"Yes."

"Candra, please," Tish said, her voice a pathetic wail. "I have to go. Before he gets to me, too. He's coming. I know he is."

"Can't you just tell us who?" Meg asked.

But Tish's only response was a quick movement as she sidestepped Candra and swooped down over the two bags beside the door. She grabbed them and scurried out into the hall almost before they realized what was happening.

"Aunt Tish!" Candra hollered, starting to go after her.

"I'm so sorry. Be careful, Candra," her aunt called back, already halfway down to the second floor. "You, too, Meg. Don't let him get you."

And then she was gone, and Meg and Candra were left to stare at each other. Candra knew that the apprehension and terror she saw in her sister's eyes were mirrored in her own.

Somewhere out there was a young man who was their brother . . .

And a ruthless man who wanted him—and them—dead.

"Let's get out of here," Meg said, nudging Candra.

"Wait . . . maybe we should snoop around."

"Why?"

"In case we can find a clue," Candra said, but she suddenly had lost any desire to remain in Tish's apartment. The back of her neck was prickling and an uneasy feeling was slipping over her.

"I want to leave," Meg said, her voice rising a little in urgency. "Please, Candra. I'm afraid."

"Okay." Candra couldn't admit to her sister that she, too, was frightened.

One of us has to be strong, she told herself as she followed Meg out into the hall, pulling the door closed behind her.

And yet, as she and Meg hurried down the stairs and out into the seedy, neon-lit avenue, her legs felt wobbly with anxiety and she had to fight the urge to break into a run—almost as though the devil himself was at their heels.

He halted in front of the shabby apartment building and narrowed his eyes, scanning the sidewalk. There was nothing to see but the usual Saturday night crowd of drunks and drug dealers and streetwalkers and junkies.

And yet . . .

He frowned.

Someone was nearby, he realized.

Was it Candra, or Meg, or . . .

Both?

That would explain the overpowering perception of the presence. And of course, after last night, the two sisters would probably stick close together.

He watched the street for a moment, half-expecting them to appear, and wondering what he would do when they did. He certainly couldn't grab them, both of them, out here in front of hundreds of witnesses.

And there was no need to do that, really. He would get to them when the time came. There was no doubt about that. They couldn't hide—not from him.

So, really, he would simply bide his time and wait, even if he did happen to collide with them here, on the street.

Life is full of little surprises, he thought to himself, chuckling under his breath at the coincidence.

But after a few moments, he realized that the presence had grown weaker, not stronger.

That could only mean that they were going in the opposite direction.

He wondered, as he turned and briskly entered the dingy building, what they had been doing here in the first place. Had they spoken with Tish? Had she given them the information that *he* was seeking?

No matter. She would tell him, too. He would see to that . . . and then he would kill her.

But as he approached the door marked 3B, he knew instinctively that it was already too late.

That didn't stop him from knocking on the door, and then, when there was no response, heaving his muscular shoulder against it. All it took was once, and the door burst inward.

He stepped over the threshold, his dark coat flapping around his ankles, and looked around.

Tish was gone. He didn't know where, but there was a sense of finality about the apartment's emptiness.

But she had left something behind, he realized as he walked through the tiny rooms to her bedroom. His gaze fell on the battered desk beneath the window.

In it, he knew, would be the missing piece to the puzzle he was desperate to solve.

Meg sat up in her darkened bedroom with a gasp and uttered her sister's name.

Beside her, Candra stirred, made an incoherent murmuring, groaning noise.

"Candra," Meg repeated, reaching toward the huddled form beneath the down comforter and shaking her sister's shoulder. "Wake up."

"What? What time is it?" Candra asked groggily.

Meg looked at the glowing digital numbers on the clock on her nightstand. "Almost midnight."

"Midnight?" Candra yawned and rolled over, murmuring, "We went to bed less than an hour ago."

It was true. When they'd returned from Elmont, they had realized they were both utterly exhausted. Though Meg had been afraid to sleep, even after making sure the doors and windows were all locked, she must have drifted off anyway.

Now, though, she was wide awake.

"Wait," she told Candra, "don't go back to sleep. I just had this dream." She shivered and pulled her knees up to her chin, wrapping her arms around them. "About our brother."

She heard a rustling as her sister sat up in bed. "What about him?"

"Rosamund was there," Meg remembered, squeezing her eyes closed, chasing the fragmented images of the dream before they could escape her. Already, the details were starting to grow fuzzy.

"What was she doing?" Candra asked breathlessly.

"She was just sitting there, talking to me. To us, actually . . . you were there, too. She was telling us that we had to be careful, that someone was after us."

Candra made a scoffing sound. "That's just what she said today, Meg. That wasn't a dream."

"No, there was more. I asked her who our brother was, and she—Candra, I swear, she told me his name."

There was silence for a moment. Meg turned, and in the shadowy room, saw the silhouette of her sister. She was stiff, tense, and yet when she spoke, her tone was impassive.

"So? It was just a dream. It doesn't mean anything."

"No, Candra, I can feel it. This is real. Rosamund was sending us a message."

"Then why wouldn't she send it through *me*? I'm the one she raised, the one she was supposedly related to, remember? You meant nothing to her."

Hurt by her sister's scornful words, Meg tried to tell herself that Candra was just defensive, that was all. She was that way by nature, and competitive, too. Meg couldn't hold it against her.

"I don't know why she wouldn't go through you," Meg said gently. "Maybe because you *were* closer to her. Maybe she couldn't get past the grief you're suffering over her death."

"So what's his name?" Candra asked, after a moment.

"I don't have the first. Just the last."

"How come?"

Meg shrugged. "That's all I remember, I guess . . ."

"Well? What is it?"

"It's someone that we know," Meg said, suddenly leery of revealing it to her sister. How was Candra going to react?

"Who?"

Meg took a deep breath. "Our brother's last name," she said slowly, "is Keller."

His hands shook with anticipation as he lifted the paper-clipped document he'd found buried beneath piles of other papers—old leases and bills and letters—in the bottom desk drawer.

This was what he had been looking for. The moment his fingers had touched it, he had known.

He carried it over to the window and held it up to the streetlight that filtered between the starched white curtains. Though the typed page was partly hidden in shadow, he could make out the words.

It was a contract, dated eighteen years ago this week.

Letitia Harrison, it seemed, had played a pivotal role in an illegal adoption.

At the time, she had been employed on the household staff of an American family that was living in Ocho Rios for a year. She had placed a newborn baby boy with them, a mulatto child whose parents were unmarried. The mother was an American and the father was a native Jamaican.

Neither of them was named, but he knew, without a doubt, who they were.

He knew that the child was the missing brother of Meg and Candra.

In addition to being paid handsomely for her services, Tish was promised a position as the baby's nanny, and would return to the United States with them when their time on the island was up.

The adoptive father was a contractor with SNE Development, which was based in Crawford Corners, Connecticut.

And the family's last name was Keller.

Eighteen

"Good morning, The Lawson School," said a male voice with a British accent.

"Yes, hello . . . may I please speak to Landon Keller?" Candra asked, clutching the telephone receiver so hard that her hand hurt.

Meg stood beside her, chewing her lower lip and fiddling with the belt on her bathrobe.

"It's rather early to be calling a student," came the crisp response on the other end of the line.

Candra cleared her throat and glanced at the clock on Meg's nightstand. It was just past six. She and Meg had spent the last several hours trying unsuccessfully to sleep. Finally, they had gotten out of bed and talked, endlessly going over the details of what had happened, trying to unravel the mystery of their birth and Rosamund's death, and coming up with nothing.

Nothing but the realization that Landon Keller was somehow their long-lost brother, and that they had to get ahold of him, to break the startling news . . .

And to warn him that someone wanted him—all three of them—dead.

"I realize that it's early," Candra said into the phone, "and I do apologize, but this is a family emergency." She had tried this family emergency tact to get to Landon once before, and it had worked, although it had been someone else, a female, who had answered the phone that day.

The voice became slightly less frosty. "I see. I'll ring his room."

Candra nodded, so nervous at the prospect of speaking to Landon that she couldn't reply.

"What's happening?" Meg asked after a few moments.

"Nothing."

"What do you mean, nothing?"

"I'm on hold. They're ringing his room," Candra snapped. Then she quickly added, in a softened tone, "Sorry. I didn't mean to bark at you."

Her sister didn't seem fazed. "It's okay. I know how you must feel. If I ever found out that Shea might be my brother, I don't know—"

Candra cut her off with an abrupt "Shhh!" as she heard a click in her ear.

"Hello, ma'am?"

It was the Brit again, sounding a little distressed.

"Yes?" Candra asked, and held her breath, not sure whether she felt relief or disappointment over not hearing Landon's voice.

"I'm afraid Mr. Keller is not available."

"Excuse me?"

"Oh, dear . . ." The man cleared his throat. "Apparently, Mr. Keller is not in his room. In fact, his roommate has informed me that he left last evening and never came back. As you may be aware, Mr. Keller has been restricted to his room ever since he violated curfew on Friday evening."

Candra hadn't been aware of that. Friday was the night she and Landon had been planning to run off together. The night she'd abandoned him at that gas station near the state park. It must have been almost dawn by the time he'd been driven back to school by the police. She should have realized that he would be punished.

"It's all right," Candra cut in, as the man on the phone babbled on about how this type of thing rarely happened at a fine institute of learning like The Lawson School, how they prided themselves in discipline.

"May I deliver a message when I do locate Mr. Keller?"

"No, it's okay," Candra said curtly. "Thanks anyway. Good-bye."

With that, she hung up the phone and met her sister's anxious gaze.

"He's gone?" Meg asked.

Candra nodded. "He never went back last night. He and Jack must have—"

She broke off in midsentence and stood there motionless, stunned.

"What?" Meg asked urgently. "Candra, what's wrong?"

"I just remembered something. Oh, God, I can't believe I managed to overlook it . . ."

"What?"

"Jack," she said, feeling an overwhelming surge of relief. "He's Landon's cousin. They told me that when I met them, and I must have forgotten . . ."

"So what does that— oh!" As though she'd just figured out what Candra was getting at, Meg clapped a hand to her chin. "You mean, Jack's last name is Keller, too?"

Candra nodded.

"So Jack might be our brother, instead of Landon?" Meg asked, in disbelief. "But he doesn't look like us."

"Neither does Landon."

"No . . ." Meg said slowly, pondering that. "But just because we're identical doesn't mean our brother looks like us. Does it?"

Candra shrugged and said, "I don't know."

"They both have dark coloring," Meg observed. "You know? Dark hair and dark eyes. And Jack's skin is pretty dark, too. Darker than Landon's. Although it could just be a tan from the summer. Still . . . I don't know. Do you think it's Jack?"

"I'm not sure." Candra shook her head, trying to calm the flutter of excitement that hovered in the vicinity of her heart. "Not that it matters, anyway. Landon and I aren't . . . involved. Not anymore."

"But you do care about him, Candra. I know you do. And he cares about you. It was obvious."

Irritation mingled with pleasure at her sister's words. Still, Candra scowled and said, "The only thing that's obvious is that one of those two guys might be our brother. Which means that he's in terrible danger. And if we don't find him, and warn him—"

"But how can we possibly find him?"

"I don't know. Both Landon and Jack are from an island. No," she corrected herself, remembering, "they're from a state with island in the name."

"Rhode Island," Meg said. "That's just east of Connecticut, less than two hours from here. But even if they are in Rhode Island, we have no idea where they might be."

"No," Candra mused, "but there is a way to try and locate them . . ."

Meg looked incredulous. "How?"

"I know a spell," Candra said, mentally conjuring a list of the items she would need in order to cast it.

"Welcome to JFK International Airport, ladies and gentlemen. We'll be arriving at the gate shortly. Thank you for flying with us, and have a safe and pleasant stay in the New York area."

The Captain's voice over the loudspeaker and a bumping sound as the plane taxied to a stop intruded upon Giselle's deep, dreamless sleep.

Yawning, she opened her eyes, glanced out the window, and saw the milky gray light of dawn illuminating the airport runway. Beside her, Lester was stirring, and she turned to see him fumbling for his glasses, which he had placed in the seat pocket in front of him.

Considering, and promptly discarding, the notion of helping him, Giselle finger-fluffed her hair, which must be a wreck. She reached beneath her seat for her bag and took out a compact and a tube of lipstick.

"Ladies and gentlemen, please remain seated until we have come to a full complete stop at the gate and sounded the three-bell signal," announced Missy, the flight attendant. She was walking down the aisle toward coach.

Lester, who had found his glasses at last, put them on and checked his watch.

"What time is it?" Giselle asked, yawning.

"Where's *your* watch?" was his reply.

"I took it off before I went to sleep. It's somewhere in the bottom of my bag."

He raised an eyebrow, and she knew he would never be so careless with his own Rolex. He rarely took it off—and especially not when they were sitting in first class. Giselle was fully aware that he wanted everyone to know that he had money—that he had paid full price for his seat.

He had even commented, on the trip out, that these days, too many frequent fliers were using their mileage points to get bumped up from coach.

"It isn't fair"—he'd told Giselle, glancing about the first-class cabin with a wrinkled nose—"that just *anyone* can sit up here these days."

Apparently, Lester didn't consider himself to be "just anyone." At the time, Giselle had chuckled to herself, thinking that after she divorced him, he would be riding in coach for the rest of his life . . . *if* he could even afford to fly.

But now, remembering that cryptic statement he'd made last night—"You *won't* divorce me"—Giselle couldn't help feeling a little unsettled.

"Please, Lester . . . what time is it?" she asked again, smiling sweetly at him though she wanted to gag.

He sighed, though he looked pleased, and said, "It's six-eleven."

He always did that—gave the exact time, instead of a rough estimate, like *It's ten after six.* It was one of the countless things that irked her about him.

But this time, she didn't automatically think that she wouldn't have to deal with his stupid idiosyncracies for much longer. This time, she thought, *What if he really does have a way to make me stay with him? What if I'm trapped in this hellish marriage forever?*

She thanked Lester stiffly and went back to applying her makeup in the compact mirror. But as she glided the copper-colored tube over her full lips, she couldn't help wondering, again, what Lester thought he was up to.

What could he possibly be planning to do to her if she left him?

There was nothing he could do that would make her stay . . .

Giselle tried to ignore a vague sense of unrest as she recalled the secret she had shared with Lester not so long ago. About Meg's birth. And Manfred.

She frowned, remembering that it hadn't been long afterward that Lester had started acting secretive. Holding whispered phone conversations in his study. And taking that supposed business trip to St. Louis.

Giselle glanced at him.

He was removing the sleep from the corners of his eyes, rubbing it onto the back of the seat in front of him.

Nah, Giselle told herself. *The only thing he's up to—if he's up to anything at all—is an affair with some pathetic bimbo.*

Nothing more than that.

Giselle snapped her compact closed decisively and tossed it back into her bag.

Meg's bedroom was as dark as Candra could get it, now that the sun was up. She'd drawn the shades and the floral-patterned drapes, and turned off the lamps.

Now the only light in the room came from Meg's dresser, where a solitary candle flickered. Its wax was a light shade of purple, which, according to Candra, symbolized psychic power. It had taken some searching for Meg to locate the right color. Luckily, her mother was crazy about votive candles—she liked the way they smelled—and Meg had finally located a lilac-scented one sitting inside a glass globe on the sink in the guest bathroom.

Now, Meg stood back trying not to get the creeps as Candra presided over the makeshift altar she'd created on the bureau. She sprinkled some kind of oil, which she'd mixed herself after fifteen minutes of rummaging through the cabinets in the kitchen, over the candle, then chanted some kind of gibberish under her breath as she waved her arms around.

Finally, she closed her eyes, raised her hands high above her head, and said clearly,

> *Spirits of the dawn,*
> *Now fill my mind*
> *With visions of the one*
> *I need to find.*

She bowed her head and stood for a long time, motionless.

Meg watched her from across the room, where she perched on the edge of her bed, waiting for something to happen. It was impossible to believe that this stuff she had found around the house—a candle and some herbs and oil—could possibly help them find their missing brother.

Besides, they were basing this whole thing on a mere dream. The more time that had gone by since Meg had awakened this morning, the more she was beginning to doubt that her vision of Rosamund meant anything. It certainly wasn't proof that their brother's name was Keller, though Candra seemed to believe that it was.

And yet, now, as she watched her sister, who appeared to be slipping into a daze, Meg was filled with a tingling awareness, as though something were about to happen.

But nothing did.

At least, not before the shrill ringing of the telephone on the desk broke the mood.

Candra jumped at the sound, looking around in confusion, as though she were disoriented.

"I'll get it," Meg told her, already halfway to the desk. "It might be Mom. Hello?" she said, snatching up the receiver.

"Meg?" The voice was masculine, and unfamiliar.

"Yes?"

"I'm sorry to call you so early. This is Ben Schacter—we met at the hospital the other day?"

"Right, I remember . . ." Her heart sunk, and she wondered if Mirabelle's condition had worsened, if she had—

"Mirabelle regained consciousness a little while ago," Ben said, and Meg's knees turned to liquid.

"Thank God," she breathed, sinking into her desk chair. "How is she now?"

"She seems okay, but they're keeping a close eye on her. She has broken bones and bruises from the crash, but they don't think there's any internal damage. And Meg, she's begging to see you."

"She is?" Meg glanced at her sister.

Candra still stood by the dresser, as if frozen. She seemed lost in her own little world, staring off into space.

"If you could come down here to the hospital right away, it would be a good idea," Ben said. "She's been through a lot, and they don't want her to get all worked up. And besides, she's exhausted, and I don't know how long she's going to be able to stay awake. She said she wants to tell you something."

"I . . . okay. I'll get there as fast as I can," Meg agreed, putting aside her protests. She wasn't sure she wanted to hear what Mirabelle wanted to say to her—not if it was about Candra. Not if Mirabelle wanted her to believe that her sister was up to no good.

No matter what, Meg knew now that her sister cared about her. Candra had had a rough life, and she wasn't the most easygoing person Meg had ever met. But she certainly wasn't dangerous. And Meg refused to believe otherwise.

"She's in a private room now," Ben was saying. "On the fourth floor. Just tell the nurse who you are when you get here."

"Okay. I'm on my way." Meg hung up the phone and turned back to her sister. "Candra . . . ?" she asked tentatively.

Candra looked startled, and her eyes flew to Meg's face. "What?" she asked in a faraway voice.

"That was Mirabelle's—boyfriend, I guess. Ben. I have to go to the hospital now. She's awake."

"Okay." Candra's expression was slightly glassy, and she spoke in a faraway voice, as though she were in a trance.

Was she? Meg studied her sister carefully, frowning. Candra appeared to be concentrating on something, and her eyes were drifting closed again.

"Is it okay if I leave you like this?" Meg asked hesitantly.

"Please," Candra said. "Leave me alone."

Meg shrugged and headed for the door.

As she walked down the stairs and grabbed her coat and car keys, she realized that she suddenly felt overwhelmed. It was all too much—finding Candra, and Rosamund's death, and knowing she and Candra had a brother out there somewhere, and that all three of them were in danger—and now Mirabelle . . .

One thing at a time, she told herself, taking a deep breath and going out the front door into the sunny Sunday morning. *That's all you can handle. Just take it one thing at a time.*

* * *

The purple wax was dripping steadily onto the crate as the wick burned lower, but he barely noticed.

All was silent in the back room of the occult shop; Elmont Avenue, outside, was at its quietest in the early morning hours of a Sunday.

The young, dark-skinned man stood beside the improvised altar, his eyes closed tightly in concentration.

Somewhere out there was the missing triplet, the child who should never have been allowed to live.

And as long as that boy remained alive, Manfred would never achieve the greatest power of all . . . the power he had mistakenly believed was already his.

But there was no need for panic.

Where are you, young Mr. Keller? he asked mentally, waiting for a vision.

Where are you?

The spell had to work.

It had to.

And yet, he felt nothing—not the usual electricity that darted through him whenever he chanted the spell that would draw psychic awareness.

Today, his mind remained a blank screen.

And the more he struggled to concentrate, the more his frustration grew—making concentration all the more difficult.

It was a vicious circle, and now anger was beginning to eat away at him, destroying what was left of his powers to focus.

Finally, incensed, he slammed his fists down on the crates and screamed, long and loud and primal.

But it had released only a tiny portion of his pent-up fury.

Seething, he bent and abruptly blew out the candle's flame. Then he stalked to the door, threw it open, and headed out to avenge his wrath.

Giselle settled back against the leather seat as the limo pulled out onto the Van Wyck Expressway. It was inexplicably jammed for this hour of a Sunday morning, and she scowled out at the traffic, thinking of how much she hated the city.

It wasn't as though she came here a lot, but Crawford Corners was too close for comfort, in her opinion. Maybe, after the divorce, she and the girls would move someplace where there was more . . . space. Where no one could find them.

Where had that thought come from? she wondered, puzzled. She must have been thinking of Lester—but then, escaping him for the rest of her life was too much to hope for. There was Carrie to consider, after all. Lester was her father; he would have to have visitation rights.

No, maybe it hadn't been Lester she was thinking of, after all.

Maybe it was Manfred.

The mere thought of his name sent a chill through Giselle, despite the warm sun that beamed through the tinted windows.

Why, after all these years, are you suddenly thinking of Manfred again?

She tried to force her thoughts away.

Think of something pleasant . . . like the divorce.

Which reminded her . . .

"Lester?" she said, turning to him. She saw that he had opened the business section of the Sunday *Times* he'd bought in the airport after they landed. He always made a big show of reading the financial pages, throwing out little comments about the stock tables as if to prove he knew that he was a big financier.

"Hmm?" he murmured, his eyes focused on the paper.

But Giselle could tell that he wasn't reading it. His whole body was tense, as though he was just waiting for her to bring up the divorce.

Which she did, promptly.

"I want to talk about our so-called marriage," she told him, glancing at the driver and seeing that he was looking at the road, out of earshot behind the privacy panel of glass. "I'm planning to see a lawyer tomorrow."

"I wouldn't recommend that," he said, turning the page of the paper with an un-Lester-like aplomb that contradicted the tension that still emanated from him.

"Oh, you wouldn't? Why wouldn't you, Lester?"

There was a pause, and she thought he wasn't going to answer her at all.

Finally, he set down the paper and said, in a perfectly unruffled voice, "I told you. You won't divorce me."

"Oh, but I will. I have every intention of doing it."

"After I tell you what I have to tell you, I'm sure you'll change your mind."

"Lester, this is ridiculous." She looked out the window, fighting to keep her emotions under control. The last thing she wanted was to give him the satisfaction of playing his stupid game. He probably wanted her to get all worked up, wanted her to beg him to tell her his little secret.

Giselle refused to play into his hands.

After a few moments, he said, "When we get home, I'll be happy to tell you what I have to tell you, Giselle. All right?"

She shrugged, not turning back to him, not wanting to see the self-satisfied look on his insipid, sunburnt face.

"Oh, I think it's something you'll want to know, Giselle," he said, chuckling softly. "I hadn't planned to tell you . . . not until I had exhausted my other options. But since you've forced my hand by bringing up this preposterous suggestion that we split up . . . well, I'll have to let you in on it."

Fed up, she twisted in her seat and saw that he was picking up the *Times* again. He pretended to ignore her pointed stare, but she was satisfied to see that his hands trembled as he unfolded the newspaper.

Giselle smiled to herself despite her sense of apprehension. Lester might think he was capable of controlling her, but when it came right down to it, the man was a weenie, just as she'd always suspected.

With a sigh, she turned back to the window and stared out at the crawling traffic.

In Meg's darkened bedroom, Candra centered every ounce of her being on a single thought . . .

Where are you, Landon—and Jack?

Her entire body tingled with the energy that coursed through her, the energy she'd conjured with her spell.

It was working . . .

She knew that it was. She had felt a surge of power the moment she'd finished the chant.

All she had to do was focus . . .

Focus . . .

Where are you?

Where are you?

Somewhere outside, a dog was barking . . .

No distractions. She couldn't let anything divert her attention.

She was sinking deeper into the pool of concentration, approaching a remote, tranquil place where nothing could reach her.

Nothing but that which she sought.

Where are you? she beseeched her unknown brother, as her rhythmic breathing carried her further into the trance.

Where are you?

Nineteen

Meg hesitated in the doorway of the hospital room, seeing that Mirabelle wasn't alone.

An attractive, worried-looking middle-aged couple sat beside her bed. Meg knew they had to be Mirabelle's parents. The woman was the complete opposite of Mirabelle—a powder-puff blonde, with thick makeup and teased hair and long, brightly polished nails that she kept running over her daughter's arm. The man was tall and distinguished looking, and Meg saw, in the instant that he turned and noticed her standing in the doorway, that Mirabelle was the image of him.

"You must be Meg—we've been waitin' for you," he said, in an accent that sounded like Kevin Costner's in the movie *The Big Easy*. "I'm Michael Moreau, and this is my wife, Jeanette."

"Hi," Meg said, nodding first at Mirabelle's father, and then at her mother.

Her friend Zoe had often scoffed about her Aunt Jeanette. Tara Cunningham's older sister was a former Miss Connecticut, and Zoe often said that she was as brassy as Tara was elegant. Now Meg noticed the large gold hoop earrings that brushed against Jeanette's brightly rouged cheeks, and saw that her tanned wrists were stacked with flashy gold bracelets.

"Hello, Meg, honey," Jeanette drawled, and Meg remembered that Zoe had said her aunt had an exaggerated Southern accent despite having grown up in Connecticut. "Mirabelle has been waitin' for y'all, haven't you, sweetheart?"

There was a murmur from the bed. Meg's eyes fell on Mirabelle, who lay beneath several blankets, her head propped on a pillow.

"Come in, Meg," Mirabelle said, her voice sounding hoarse.

Meg stepped into the room. Only then did she see Ben, who stood just inside the door, leaning against the wall. He had changed his clothes. Now he wore a pair of pressed khaki pants and a dusty blue sweater, and his dark hair appeared to have been combed carefully. He glanced at Meg, and then his eyes, which were filled with concern, slid back to Mirabelle.

"Why don't we go downstairs to see if we can make a hotel reservation for you, Mr. and Mrs. Moreau?" he suggested.

When Jeanette started to protest, her husband said, "Come on, Jeanette. Let's leave Mirabelle alone to talk to Meg."

As soon as the three of them had left, Meg perched awkwardly in the chair Mr. Moreau had vacated, and looked at her friend.

"Hi," Mirabelle said weakly, offering a faint smile.

"How do you feel?" Meg asked, barraged by a sudden attack of guilt. If it weren't for her, Mirabelle wouldn't be lying here, battered, in the hospital.

"Way too hot," Mirabelle said.

"Excuse me?"

"You asked how I feel, and I feel way too hot," Mirabelle told her. "Would you mind taking a few of these blankets off of me? My mother insisted on burying me in them, even though this room is about ninety degrees."

Feeling comforted by Mirabelle's grin, Meg stood and peeled off several layers of wool, folding the blankets carefully and stacking them at the foot of the bed.

Then, reluctantly, she returned to her seat and met Mirabelle's direct gaze.

"You're in danger, Meg," her friend said bluntly.

"Mirabelle, I know what you think about Candra, but she—"

"It's not Candra," Mirabelle cut her off, and Meg raised her eyebrows. "I thought it was, but . . . I don't know, maybe I was wrong. I'm not feeling animosity from her—at least, not now. It's someone else. Someone far more powerful than your sister."

"I know," Meg said, and it was Mirabelle's turn to look surprised.

"How do you know?"

"Candra's grandmother warned us that someone is after us," she said. "And then she died. He—whoever he is—had attacked her. Look, I know this sounds crazy," she said, seeing Mirabelle's wide-eyed reaction to her words, "but strange things have been happening to me ever since the last time I saw you. I have no memory of what happened to me last week—"

"That's because you were under a spell," Mirabelle said.

Meg's mouth dropped open. "*What?*"

"Dalila Parker cast it on you, and I have no idea why. All I know is that you were in her apartment, unconscious, and Candra was posing as you."

Meg's thoughts were reeling. Shea had told her the same thing. But he had also said Candra had tried to kill her. And Meg couldn't—wouldn't—believe that.

"How do you know about this?" she asked Mirabelle when she could find her voice again.

"I saw you," Mirabelle said simply. "I used astral projection to get into Dalila Parker's apartment, and I saw you there."

"How do you know it was me? How do you know it wasn't Candra?"

"Meg, you have to trust me."

"Candra is my sister, Mirabelle," she said, fighting to keep her voice from rising.

"And I'm your friend. I risked my life for you, Meg."

Those words hung in the air, instantly filling Meg with remorse.

"Look, Meg," Mirabelle said more gently, after a moment, "I'm not trying to make you feel guilty for what happened to me. I only want you to understand that something very serious . . . very deadly . . . is going on. Regardless of what you want to believe about what your sister did or didn't do. You're in danger. Both of you . . . and your brother."

She said those last words tentatively, slowly, as though she wasn't sure how Meg would react.

"I know about him, too," she told Mirabelle. "Candra's grandmother, Rosamund, told us. She said he has some kind of amulet, something that's supposed to protect him. But she didn't say from who."

"I don't know who he is, either, Meg," Mirabelle said, and her words were becoming more urgent, even as exhaustion stole over her face. "But he's pure evil. I'm getting the darkest, most frightening vibes from him."

"When?" Meg asked. "When did you sense all of this?"

"While I was out. It was as though I was trapped in some other world, trying to fight my way back, and I kept getting images. About you, and about Candra, and your brother. And this dark man was always there . . ."

Meg shivered despite the steam heat blasting from the register by the window. "Are you sure you don't know who he is, Mirabelle?"

"I'm sure. But I know who your brother is."

Meg's heart skipped a beat. "Who?" she asked breathlessly.

"I don't know his first name," Mirabelle said, "but he was adopted by a couple whose last name is Keller. Does the name ring a bell?"

That was it, Meg realized. That was the proof she'd been looking for, the proof that her dream really *had* been a vision—a message from Rosamund. Mirabelle's coming up with the same name was too much of a coincidence.

Their missing brother was definitely a Keller—but which one? Landon . . . or Jack?

Giselle unlocked the front door as Lester paid the limo driver, signing off on their joint credit card.

That was the first thing she'd do, Giselle promised herself as she stepped over the threshold—cancel all their credit cards. Lester would be lost without his plastic.

"Hello?" she called as she walked briskly into the foyer, glancing around to make sure everything was just as she had left it. Sometimes, Sophie liked to move things around when she cleaned, even though Giselle was always telling her not to rearrange anything.

Everything was silent. Meg's car wasn't in its usual spot outside, and Giselle wondered where she could be so early on a Sunday morning.

But Carrie must be home. The house didn't feel empty.

Anxious to greet her daughter, Giselle hurried upstairs and opened Carrie's bedroom door. "Carrie? We're home."

But the room was deserted.

That was odd.

Giselle felt a vague uneasiness. Something didn't seem quite right.

She turned and glanced at the closed door to Meg's room. Maybe Carrie was in there, for some reason. She knew her younger daughter had, on occasion, snuck in to borrow her sister's clothes. Giselle suspected Carrie mostly did it to pester Meg, since the two girls had vastly different taste in wardrobes.

Sighing, Giselle started toward Meg's room, planning to burst in and catch Carrie red-handed.

"Giselle?" Downstairs, the front door slammed shut, and Lester's footsteps headed for the stairs. "Are the girls here?"

"No," she said, turning away from Meg's door. If Carrie was in there, she would come running as soon as she heard her father's voice. She adored her daddy. Giselle knew why. Lester doted on his "real" daughter.

"Where are they?" he asked, arriving in the hallway.

"Do I look like Kreskin?" Giselle headed for the master bedroom, kicking off her pumps as she walked. Her feet were killing her, and she couldn't wait to get into the shower. She'd been wearing the same clothes for far too long, and her hair felt disgusting.

"Where are you going?" Lester asked, following her.

"To take a shower."

"I think we should talk *now*, before the girls come home. I don't want them involved in this."

"Involved in what?" Giselle opened the door to their bedroom.

He was right at her heels. "I don't think you'd want Meg to know what I found out," he said pointedly.

Giselle stopped and turned slowly, standing in the middle of the room. "What are you talking about, Lester?" she asked, as a wave of panic rose in her gut.

"I happen to know that Meg's real father—*Manfred*—is a powerful voodoo priest in Jamaica. And that you had—*two* babies. One was sacrificed—right, Giselle? And Manfred never knew that you took the other back to the States with you. She was supposed to stay there, with some old woman, as a reward to her for destroying the other child. But the old woman felt sorry for you. And Manfred was told that she died, too."

Reeling in shock, Giselle fumbled her way to the bed and sank onto the mattress. How could Lester know about Manfred?

"Who told you that?" she asked weakly, hating him, hating the way he stood there, watching her through those watery blue eyes behind his glasses.

"Does it matter?"

"Yes."

"Well, I can't give you that information," he said, taking his glasses off and breathing onto the left lens. He busied himself polishing it on his shirt.

Giselle felt sick inside. She had triggered this herself. After all these years, why had she ever told Lester anything about Meg's birth?

Because he kept badgering you about going to the Caribbean.

Now, remembering the trip Lester had supposedly taken to St. Louis, when he had come back sunburnt, she wondered if he had actually gone to Jamaica. Had he poked around until he discovered the truth about her past?

Had he . . .

Had he spoken to Manfred?

Manfred would be in his late thirties now, a decade younger than Lester, but, Giselle knew, infinitely more powerful. A man like Manfred would *shred* a man like Lester.

The thought was comforting . . . and yet, not.

Giselle didn't want to think about what a man like Manfred would do to her, or to Meg, if he found out she was still alive.

"Lester," she said, panic edging up inside of her, "he doesn't know, does he?"

"Who?" he asked blandly, putting his glasses back on. "Who doesn't know what?"

"You know damn well what I'm talking about! Manfred doesn't know that I brought Meg back with me . . . that she's still alive?"

"No, he doesn't know. Not yet."

She wanted to kill him. She wanted to throw herself on him, and claw at him, and screech at him that he had no right to do this to her . . . or to Meg.

Somehow, she managed to keep her emotions under control. She cleared her throat, asked Lester, "What do you want from me, Lester?"

"It's simple. I want you to stay married to me."

She expelled a heavy sigh, buried her face in her hands for a moment, then looked up at him. "Why? We don't love each other."

"No," he agreed. "We don't. But I'm comfortable, Giselle. And I have no intention of giving up my lifestyle now. This is where I belong—with you. I took care of you and Meg when you had no one else. Now it's your turn to take care of me."

"Lester, I will. I'll make sure you have everything you need if we split up," she promised blindly. "Whatever you want."

"No, you won't," he said. "We signed a prenuptial agreement, courtesy of your dear daddy, remember?"

She hated him for the sarcastic tone he used when he spoke of her father.

And Harry McKenna had never liked Lester, either. He had warned her not to marry him, warned her that he was a gold-digger, warned her not to trust him.

But you were weak, Giselle cursed herself. *And a fool. You couldn't see past Lester's all-out adoration of you, past the constant compliments he gave you.*

And after Manfred, he was so . . . safe.

"Lester," she said, pulling herself together for Meg's sake. "Listen to me. You cannot go to Manfred. If you do, he'll kill me, and he'll kill Meg."

"I'd hate to have that happen, Giselle."

You bastard, she thought, keeping her expression neutral.

"I promise that if we split, you can have as much money as you need. You can have your car . . . and the house," she added desperately.

"What about my daughter?"

Her stomach churned. "You can spend as much time with her as you want," she assured him.

"But I wouldn't be able to live with her, is that it? I would have the house, but I wouldn't have my family here where they belong? What good is that?"

"You just said that you don't love me!" she protested, her voice rising. "And I sure as hell know you don't love Meg."

"I never said that."

"You didn't have to! The only person in this house that you care about is yourself."

"And Carrie," he added. "And I won't let you have my daughter. I won't let you take away my lifestyle. It's that simple. I like our social life, Giselle. Playing golf and having dinner at the 4C . . ."

4C was the local slang for Crawford Corners Country Club, and Giselle knew his membership would be revoked the moment she divorced him. They had strict policies at the club. Giselle's father had been a member, and his father before him. She, and not Lester, had the membership legacy.

"And I like our travels, and our friends."

My friends, she corrected mentally. She knew they only tolerated him. Without her, he'd be cast out of their elite circle, and he knew it.

"I like my job," he added.

And she knew what he was thinking. That without her, he wouldn't have a job. When Giselle had insisted on marrying Lester, Harry McKenna had fought to get one of his friends to offer Lester a position as a financial consultant. Giselle knew they just kept him on out of respect for Harry and Giselle. Lester knew it, too. If she ever dumped him, he'd be fired in two seconds flat.

"I can make sure you keep your job," she lied, desperate to appease him.

"No, you can't," he said. "The only way I get to keep everything I want is if I keep *you*, Giselle. I'm no fool. I won't pretend that I control my lifestyle. But I can control *you* . . . thanks to what I've discovered."

She couldn't argue with him. He had her right where he wanted her, and they both knew it.

She watched desolately as he disappeared into the alcove off their bedroom, the small space he insisted on calling his dressing room. A few minutes later, he emerged wearing lime and tangerine plaid pants and a matching golf shirt.

"Don't look so unhappy, Giselle," he said, glancing over at the bed. "Just think, it wouldn't be easy to be single again at your age. I don't know very many men who would want a woman who's approaching middle age when they could find someone young—someone who isn't saddled with two kids and a rather . . . demanding ex-husband."

His words stung, and they were meant to. *Middle age.* She cringed at the knowledge that there was truth in his words. She was getting older. Years of worshiping the sun seemed to have caught up with her all of a sudden. Her skin grew more wrinkled by the day. And her once firm figure seemed a little soft lately.

Panic-stricken, she saw Lester sizing her up. He nodded, and she knew he had concluded that he was right. She wouldn't leave him.

"I'm going over to the club to play a few holes," he told her, heading for the door. "I'll be back later. Think about what I've said. Although I'm sure your decision has already been made."

She was silent as he left.

Then she gave a little moan, thinking that her whole world had come crashing in on her. Tears started trickling down her cheeks, and she didn't try to stop them.

She was about to fling herself into her pillow and sob her heart out when something stopped her.

A thumping sound.

And it had come from Meg's bedroom.

He had decided to pay a *real* visit to Meadowview Terrace, rather than project himself there. He needed the full force of his power with him, and there were times, when he used astral projection, that he wondered if his strength wasn't slightly diminished that way.

He would need every ounce of power he possessed to accomplish the tasks that lay ahead of him.

Getting from Spring City to Crawford Corners meant taking a bus. As he disembarked at the busy intersection of Broad Street and Highland Boulevard, the Episcopalian Church services were just letting out.

The streets were crowded with residents who were dressed in their expensive Sunday best. He was fully aware of their suspicious glances as they passed him on the sidewalk.

He knew these well-to-do suburbanites were wondering what an outsider—a young, black teenager—was doing here among them. And he knew what they were thinking—that he was up to no good.

Well, they were right, he thought to himself, amused. But imagine if they knew what he was really involved in.

At the edge of town, he turned toward Long Neck Road, the broad expanse that led out to winding, tree-lined Soundview Drive. Giselle's home was in that exclusive neighborhood of quiet mansions and sweeping lawns overlooking the water.

As he walked, he felt a twinge of trepidation stealing over him. He recalled how he had attempted to locate the missing boy through a spell—and failed.

No, he warned himself. *You must never doubt your powers.*

He set his mouth grimly and turned onto Soundview Drive just as a familiar black Honda drove by, splashing him with water from a deep puddle in the road.

Megan McKenna, he thought, watching as the car disappeared around the bend, heading in the direction of Meadowview Terrace.

He wiped the muddy droplets from his long black coat and narrowed his eyes.

Candra removed a pen and a scrap of paper from the desk drawer, then started writing without bothering to close it. She couldn't waste any time. She had snapped out of her trance only moments before, and she had to jot down everything she remembered of her vision before the details started fading.

It had come to her slowly, yet so vividly that she knew it had to be real.

Landon and Jack were together, in some kind of cabin or lodge. It was located in a place called Hillside Haven or Hillside Heaven. There was a road nearby, a highway that bore the number 44. And the cabin sat on a rise above a creek or stream.

Candra swiftly got everything on paper, then started toward Meg's bookshelf, to see if she had an atlas.

Something stopped her in her tracks.

Footsteps just outside the door.

She frowned, thinking that Meg must be home—she had been so far gone that she hadn't even heard her come in downstairs.

And then there was a knock, and the bedroom door was opening, and a voice was calling, "Meg? Carrie?"

A voice Candra had never heard before . . .

Or at least, not since the very first moments after her birth.

The sound slammed into her, stole her breath away, sent a rush of emotion coursing through her.

She stood there, rooted, as the door opened all the way and she found herself face to face with Giselle McKenna Hudson.

Her mother.

"You *are* home," Giselle said, moving toward her. "I didn't see your car, so I thought you were out."

Candra allowed herself to be pulled into her mother's arms, to be squeezed tightly and kissed on the head. She was enveloped in warmth, in the scent of expensive perfume, in the musical voice that was saying something about how long it had taken to get home, and how exhausted she was, and . . .

"Meg," her mother said, pulling back abruptly and looking at her. "Did you . . . did you hear us talking just now? Lester and me? In our bedroom?"

Candra could only shake her head, too overwhelmed to even attempt to find her voice. Her lips were quivering and she felt as though if she moved any other part of her body, she would absolutely fall apart. She would start sobbing and fling herself into this beautiful blond woman's arms, and she would call her *Mom* and tell her how she had been longing for this moment all her life.

But she didn't move; she didn't do any of those things.

She only stared at Giselle.

Her mother.

The photographs Candra had seen had captured Giselle's flaxen-haired beauty and youth, and the impish sparkle in her light green eyes. But in person, she looked slightly different. A fine network of wrinkles wove around her eyes, and instead of reflecting frothy light-heartedness, they showed . . .

Exhaustion?

Concern?

"Meg," Giselle repeated, "I can tell by looking at you that something's wrong. You heard us, didn't you?"

Again Candra shook her head, unable to wrench her gaze away from her mother's face. She had waited so long, so impossibly long, to see her. There was so much to take in—the deep tan that made her cheeks glow and the long, sun-streaked tresses that looked soft and naturally wavy. Candra wanted to reach out and touch that hair, wanted to catch and clasp the manicured hand that fluttered nervously to smooth it.

"Meg," her mother started again, and then stopped short.

Candra had heard it, too. A car door slamming someplace nearby.

And now the front door was opening, and footsteps were pounding up the stairs.

Giselle looked toward the door expectantly. "Carrie must be—"

The rest of her words were lost to a high-pitched gasp the instant Meg appeared in the hallway.

* * *

"Mirabelle?"

She looked up sleepily and saw Ben standing at the foot of her bed.

"Hi," she murmured.

"Hi." He came closer, slid into the chair Meg had vacated, and took her hand gently. "Did you tell Meg?"

She yawned and nodded. "I did. She already knew."

"About having a brother?"

"Mmm hmm. And that someone is after her."

"Does she know who it is?"

"No. But, Ben, I'm worried." She felt him squeeze her fingers and realized that his grasp made her feel safe. What had she done without him in her life?

"You need to get some rest," he said softly, and reached up to push a strand of hair back from her face.

"I'm not tired," she lied, and fought back another yawn. "I have to make sure that Meg—"

"You've done everything you can do for Meg, Mirabelle," Ben said. "Now you have to concentrate on getting better. For me."

She raised an eyebrow. "For you?"

"Yup." He smiled at her, a smile that told her exactly how he felt. And she realized that she had always known, anyway. From the moment their eyes had first met several weeks ago in Philosophy class.

The odd thing was, it no longer bothered her.

Ben wasn't Alex. He wasn't going to hurt her the way Alex had. Ben was someone she could count on.

"Where are my parents?" she asked, suddenly remembering.

"In the lobby, arguing."

"About what?"

"Your mother wants to stay at her sister's. Your father wants to get a hotel."

"That's because Aunt Tara drives him crazy. She freaks out if there's a crumb in her kitchen." She paused to yawn. "And she doesn't let anyone in the house with their shoes on. He says he always feels like he's going to be scolded when he's there."

Ben smiled. "That's what he told me. He's a nice guy. And your mom's all right, too."

"Yeah," Mirabelle agreed, and felt her eyelids trying to flutter closed.

"They were so worried about you," Ben told her. "They were upset they couldn't get here right away yesterday. But I told them that I was taking care of you, even though the nurse wouldn't let me into the ICU unit."

"Why wouldn't she?" Mirabelle mumbled, as sleep struggled to claim her.

"Because we're not related."

"Mmm."

"She wanted to know who I was. I told her I was your boyfriend."

"Mmm."

"Am I?" she heard Ben ask.

She smiled. "Mmm hmm," she said, and then drifted away toward pleasant dreams.

Twenty

Meg looked from her mother to Candra, even as Giselle's astonished gaze darted rapidly between Candra and herself.

For a moment, no one spoke.

Then her mother clapped a hand to her mouth and weakly said, "Oh my God," as Meg burst out, "Mom, this is Candra!"

Giselle just shook her head in disbelief.

"My twin sister, Mom," Meg went on gently, laying a hand on her mother's arm. She could feel Giselle trembling violently beneath her touch, and she propelled her a few feet to the rose-colored chair beside the bookcase.

Her mother sank into the cushions, still looking dazed and staring at Candra.

Meg glanced at her sister and saw that she hadn't moved. She was riveted on Giselle, and Meg realized, with a start, that Candra's eyes were shiny. Her sister blinked, and teardrops escaped her lashes, plopping onto her high cheekbones and glistening there. Candra didn't seem to notice. Joy radiated from her face—pure joy, as she looked at their mother—and Meg had to swallow hard over a lump in her own throat.

"Mom," she said thickly, her voice choked with emotion, "Candra has been waiting a long, long time to meet you."

"My God," Giselle breathed at last. "My other baby. I never knew you were still alive."

She stood and moved toward Candra, gathering her into her arms with a sob. The moment she felt her mother's touch, Candra seemed to crumple, collapsing against Giselle and weeping herself.

Meg smiled as she watched them, her mother and her sister, squeezing each other and crying and laughing in sheer joy and relief.

Finally, Giselle held Candra back slightly and said, "Let me see you. You're beautiful. You look exactly like Meg."

Candra smiled and nodded. "I know . . ."

"I can't believe this," Giselle said, and then repeated it. "How did this happen? Where did you come from? Where have you been all these years?"

"With Rosamund Bowen, in Ocho Rios," Candra said, her expression growing somber. "She raised me."

Giselle nodded. "He—your father—he had promised that she would get one of you. But I thought—Rosamund said she was giving you to me, and that she was going to tell him you had died."

A chill shot through Meg. "She was going to tell our father that Candra had *died?* But why?"

"Candra," Giselle repeated in a far-off voice, ignoring Meg's question. "So that's your name. I like it."

"Rosamund must have given it to me, if you didn't," Candra said, almost seeming shy. "She always said it meant 'white fire.'"

"White fire . . ." Giselle echoed.

"Like the moon."

Her mother nodded. "It suits you."

"Mom," Meg cut in, "Why would Rosamund have told our father that Candra was dead? And you said *you* thought she was dead."

Giselle's jaw stiffened grimly. "Your father," she said hesitantly, "wasn't . . . he wasn't . . ."

She trailed off, and Meg waited, breathlessly, for her to go on. All her life, she had wondered about her father. Now, at last, she was about to hear the truth. And she had a feeling, from the look on her mother's face, that the truth was far from pleasant.

"Manfred was his name," Giselle told them after a long pause.

Candra gave a little gasp, and Meg saw recognition in her sister's eyes.

"He was Jamaican, the high priest of a Black Magic coven. He was probably around my age, but he was respected and feared by everyone he encountered. He was very powerful."

Feared, Meg thought, and the back of her neck prickled.

"I never knew that Manfred had made a pact with . . . *his gods* . . . to sacrifice his firstborn child in exchange for more power," Giselle went on in a faraway voice.

Her chilling words caught Meg off guard. Shocked, she glanced at Candra. Her sister met her gaze, mirroring Meg's horror.

"The birth was very difficult," Giselle was saying. "Rosamund and her sister were there with me, but I have very little memory of the experience. When I came to, I held one of you. I have no idea which one. Then you were taken away from me. I later discovered that you had supposedly been . . . killed. By Rosamund. On Manfred's behalf."

"Oh, my God," Meg whispered, stunned.

"But apparently, she lied to me *and* to him. I thought she had carried out his orders and killed one of you. I thought that the baby she gave me was the one she was supposed to keep for herself. Now I realize what she did. She kept one of you and gave the other to me."

"You mean," Candra said, seeming to find her voice at last, "that my father was *Manfred*? Oh, God."

"You know who he is," Giselle said.

"Everyone knows who he is. But no one has ever really seen him. He lives in the mountains above town, and people tell stories about him. They say—that he's evil . . ." Candra's voice trailed off.

"He is." Giselle nodded, and her voice shook. "If he knew that Meg was still alive—that I had her—"

"Mom," Meg interrupted, "he *does* know. He's after us. It has to be him," she told Candra, her voice rising as the horrible reality sunk in.

The dark person Rosamund and Mirabelle had warned them about, the one who was trying to kill her and Candra . . .

He was their own father.

Hot tears spilled out of Meg's eyes and a wave of nausea rose in her throat.

"What do you mean?" Giselle asked, her eyes wide and her tone high pitched. "What do you mean he's after you?"

"He killed Rosamund," Candra said, and Giselle flinched. "And before she died, she told us that someone was out to get us. And . . ."

"And our brother," Meg finished when Candra hesitated, watching Giselle intently.

Her mother frowned. "Who?" she asked, staring hard at Meg, as though she sensed what was coming next . . . as though she feared it.

"There were three of us, Mom," Meg said quietly. "Not twins. Triplets."

The look of shock on her mother's face was even more intense than when Meg had first come into the room. "*What* did you say, Meg?"

"You had triplets. We have a brother. And he was born first."

"I never knew . . ." She shook her head, and clutched the arm of the chair as if to steady herself. Then she took a deep breath and asked faintly, "Does Manfred know?"

"We think he just found out."

Giselle closed her eyes, as if to shield herself from pain. "Where is he? Your . . . brother, I mean."

"He was adopted—we think, by an American family. And we think we know who he is," Meg said slowly. "The name is Keller."

"Keller," Giselle repeated, opening her eyes abruptly.

"Is it familiar to you?"

"I think there was a family named Keller in Jamaica back when we were there. Yes, there was. A couple, and they were a lot younger than my parents. The man was with SNE, too, working on the resort project with my father. But after we got back to the States, I never heard anything more about them. I don't know if they lived here in Crawford Corners, but I doubt it."

"You told me that both Landon and Jack are from Rhode Island," Meg reminded her sister.

"Landon and Jack?" Giselle asked.

"Friends of Candra's—both of them are named Keller. They're cousins. We think one of them is our brother."

Giselle's hand flew up to her face, and she ran her fingers through her hair, looking distraught. "This is . . . I can't . . ."

"Mom," Meg said, quickly putting a hand under her elbow. "You need to lie down."

"And we need to get to Landon and Jack," Candra said. "I know where they are."

"You do?" Startled, Meg looked at her sister, who nodded.

"Did you ever hear of a place called Hillside Haven? Or Hillside Heaven?"

"No."

"How about a road called Forty-four?"

"Route Forty-four? It runs across the top of Connecticut, from Rhode Island all the way to New York, I think. They could be in any of the three states."

"They're in a cabin off that road," Candra told her. "And it's in Connecticut."

"Are you sure?"

Her sister raised a brow as if to say, *Of course I'm sure.*

"Let's go," Meg said, looking down at her mother. "Mom, we have to go there."

Giselle nodded, still looking numb.

"But where are we going?" Candra asked. "You said the road cuts across the whole state."

"Well, it would make sense that this cabin's toward the eastern side, closer to the Rhode Island border, since Jack and Landon are from there, right?"

"I have no idea," Candra said.

"Well, whose cabin is it?"

"It belongs to Jack's parents, I think."

"We have to find this Hillside place." Meg started for the door.

"Lester has all kinds of atlases and tour books. You help Mom to bed while I look it up."

Candra nodded and took their mother's arm as Meg, her heart pounding, hurried down the hall to Lester's study.

The black Honda again, he thought, slipping into a clump of trees at the edge of the road as the car went barreling down Meadowview Terrace toward Soundview.

He glimpsed two heads inside. Meg . . . and Candra? Where were they going?

Torn, he looked from the car back to the stately brick home marked number 41.

Giselle is there, he thought, sensing her presence, and his mind was made up.

It was time he confronted her.

Swiftly, moving with deadly purpose, he covered the remaining quarter of a mile to the Hudson home. He moved stealthily across the expansive lawn, slipping to the bushes that bordered the front of the house. And he saw, as he crept toward the front door, that it was standing partly open, almost as though it were an invitation for him to enter.

Meg and Candra must not have closed it all the way in their haste to get to wherever they were going. He frowned, and again looked down the street in the direction where the car had disappeared.

Then he glanced back at the door, and once again made up his mind.

This time, it would be Giselle.

He was inside the house moments later, standing in the foyer and listening.

There was only silence, and he decided she was home alone. He didn't feel another presence. Of course, if he was wrong . . . if that fool Lester was here, too—or Giselle's younger daughter, the blonde who looked just like her . . .

Well, he would just have to take care of them, too.

As he moved up the stairs, he looked around, remembering how it had been dark when he was here on those other occasions. He had crept in to snoop around, to see if he could discover Lester's secret. Once, he had bumped into Meg's sister, the little blonde, and she had been terrified.

He'd entertained the notion of killing her, but he'd seen a spark of defiance in her frightened light green eyes, and it had filled him with admiration. She was no pushover, Giselle's younger daughter. She had a steely core of inner strength, and a dark side that Giselle and Meg lacked.

So he hadn't bothered to harm her. Instead, he'd simply vanished, projecting himself back along the astral plane to his body, no doubt leaving the young blonde rubbing her eyes in astonishment.

At the top of the stairs, he turned toward the master bedroom, and his heart beat faster as he approached the door. Behind it, he knew, was the woman who had fallen under his spell once before.

The woman who had borne his children . . . and then betrayed him.

"What if this Hilltop Haven isn't it?" Meg asked, looking over her shoulder as she merged onto Interstate 95 headed north.

"It is," Candra said, studying the map in the seat beside her. From what she could see, they had to follow 95 to Route 91, which led from New Haven up to Hartford. From there, they would pick up 84, and then 44. It seemed complicated.

"Are you *sure*?" Meg asked for what seemed like the thousandth time.

Candra sighed and felt in her pocket for the scrap of paper where she'd scribbled the notes about her vision. It wasn't there. She must have left it back in Meg's room . . . though she was pretty positive she'd brought it with her.

"Candra?"

"Yes, I'm sure, Meg," she said, feeling slightly exasperated.

"But at first you said it was called Hillside something," Meg reminded her. "You said Hillside Heaven, didn't you?"

"I saw a sign," Candra said. "I couldn't read it exactly, and I thought it said Hillside, and not Hilltop."

"Where?" Meg's head swung around, searching the side of the road. "What sign?"

"In my vision," Candra said impatiently. "When I cast the spell."

"Oh."

Candra searched her other pocket and came up empty. She must have left the paper behind.

"I can't believe how lucky we are that Lester is so anal when it comes to his travel books," Meg was saying. "He must have more geographic information than some libraries do."

Candra nodded. They had found a listing for Hilltop Haven in a book called *New England Resorts: Something for Everyone*. It was a rural summer community in eastern Connecticut off Route 44, and according to the book's description, a "babbling brook, perfect for trout fishing" ran right through it.

"Lester thinks he's such a world traveler," Meg said derisively, changing lanes to pass a slow-moving pickup truck. "He's always planning these trips for him and my mom—I mean, *Mom*"—she amended, glancing at Candra, then she went on—"to take with her money. He always wants to go off to these spas and ski chalets, you know?"

Candra nodded, suspecting that Meg was keeping up a steady stream of chatter so they wouldn't be able to discuss what was really on both their minds.

The fact that they had an evil murderer for a father.

That right this very minute, he might be closing in on their unsuspecting brother. His firstborn.

"Listen," Candra interrupted, looking at the map again, "how long does it take to get to New Haven?"

"Less than an hour if I speed," Meg said.

"Then speed."

"Giselle . . . wake up, Giselle."

The voice traveled to her as if across a great distance, shattering the tranquil twilight world where she had retreated as soon as Candra had left her in her bed.

"Giselle . . ."

I'm not waking up, she thought, confused. *I'm sleeping. This is a nightmare.*

Only in a nightmare would she hear that voice.

Unless . . .

Her eyes snapped open and she gasped.

"Hello, Giselle."

Manfred.

He stood over her, smiling down at her, his white teeth gleaming in that dark, dark face.

But it couldn't be, she realized a split second later. It couldn't be Manfred, because he looked exactly the same as he had eighteen years ago. The man standing above her wasn't yet twenty.

But . . .

"Confused, my dear?" he asked, and his voice was Manfred's voice. And his eyes—those hard, bottomless, probing black eyes—they, too, belonged to Manfred.

But this couldn't be the man she had known almost twenty years ago. Manfred would be around her age now. This was someone who looked and sounded just like him. Someone who, like Manfred, was pure evil.

It radiated from the man standing over her bed, like a heavy shroud that threatened to descend and smother her.

There was only one person, Giselle thought, searching her mind frantically and hating the knowledge she retrieved, only one person who would look and sound like Manfred, who would have inherited his dark powers.

Manfred's son.

Could this person—this boy who was watching her with such venom in his gaze—actually be her child, too?

Please, no, she begged silently, and yet she knew it had to be the truth. He looked nothing like her, and his skin was dark—far darker than Meg's, and darker than Candra's, too. But if he had grown up in the islands . . .

"Who are you?" she whispered, and waited in dread for his answer.

Meg looked over at Candra, wondering if she was asleep. She hadn't spoken in several minutes.

But she was awake, Meg saw, and staring bleakly through the windshield at the road ahead.

"What are you thinking about?" Meg asked.

"Him."

"Our father?"

"In a way, but mostly about . . ."

"Our brother."

Candra nodded.

"Do you think it's Landon or Jack?" Meg asked her sister, focusing her eyes on the road again as she passed a large Stop & Shop truck.

"I don't know," Candra replied. "I spent some time talking to Jack the night we met, and I remember him telling me about his background, and Landon's, too. I wish I'd paid more attention. At the time, I was only interested in keeping an eye on Landon. We were at a party out at some park—"

"Moseby!" Meg interrupted, as something clicked in her mind. "On a Friday night, right?"

When Candra nodded, Meg went on, "A lot of my friends were there, too. People saw you with someone, and assumed it was me. They told Shea that I was cheating on him."

"I'm sorry," Candra said quietly, and it was so out of character that

Meg looked at her in surprise. "I'm afraid I've caused you a lot of trouble, Meg."

"What do you mean?" Something told Meg that her sister was talking about more than just that night at Moseby.

Candra took a deep breath. "There's something I have to confess."

"There is?" Meg held her breath, not daring to remove her eyes from the road as they rounded a curve going nearly eighty miles an hour, but longing to look at her sister. Then she realized that it was probably easier for Candra not to meet her gaze as she spilled whatever secret she was about to reveal.

"You know how you can't remember anything that happened to you all week?" Candra asked, and Meg nodded. "Well, you don't have amnesia. I mean, you *do* . . . but it's because of a spell. Dalila cast it on you—because I asked her to." Those last words tumbled out in a rush, as though Candra had forced herself to expel them.

"What kind of spell?" Meg asked slowly, struggling to focus on the road.

"Nothing dangerous," Candra told her quickly. "Just . . . I wanted to get you out of the way for a little while. I wanted to see what it was like to be you, instead of me. I wanted . . . to meet Mom."

Meg thought back to the scene in her bedroom, remembered how her sister had clung to their mother, how her eyes had been filled with tears of joy. She wondered what it would have been like if *she* had been the one left behind in Jamaica, left to a lonely life of poverty, raised by an older woman who didn't know how to show affection . . . a woman who had kept the truth from her.

And she understood.

If she had been in Candra's shoes, she might have done the same thing.

"It's okay," she said after a long time, and she heard Candra let out a deep sigh, as though she'd been holding her breath.

"I didn't mean to hurt you, Meg," her sister said.

Meg looked at her, and saw that Candra was crying. Her dark eyes were begging Meg's forgiveness.

"Hey, it's okay," Meg reminded her, wanting nothing more than to pull over to the side of the road and hug her sister, to reassure her and comfort her. But there wasn't a minute to spare. She had to keep driving.

"You didn't hurt me," she told Candra as she glanced back at the road. "Not really."

"But I almost did. I wanted to."

Meg's hands stiffened on the steering wheel. "What do you mean?"

"I told Dalila . . ." Candra paused, then took a deep breath. "I told Dalila to kill you."

"Who am I?" he echoed, and chuckled softly, watching the woman on the bed carefully. "But I thought you knew."

"I don't." Her voice came out in a near-whimper, and the pathetic sound filled him with pleasure.

"Think carefully, Giselle. Who am I?"

"I . . . don't . . . know." She was crying now, her large green eyes riveted on his face.

"Of course you do. I'm Manfred."

She seemed to stiffen at the sound of his name. Then she shook her head.

"No," she whispered. "You can't be him."

"Oh? Why can't I be?" He was enjoying this, far more than he had ever anticipated.

"Because you . . . you can't even be twenty years old. Manfred was my age."

He shrugged. "Age is a number."

"What do you mean?"

"First, Giselle, are you convinced that I am who I say I am?"

"No." Her chin lifted stubbornly. "Of course I'm not. You're too young to be Manfred."

"I'll prove to you that I am."

"How?"

"Like this." Slowly, he bent over her, lowering his face until his lips brushed against hers. She tasted as sweet as he remembered, and he deepened the kiss, probing into her mouth with his insistent tongue and tangling his fingers in her silky blond hair. She moaned and sighed, and opened herself up to him—helpless, he knew, to resist him.

Even now.

Even after all these years, after what he had done to her.

Heady with his own power, he broke the kiss and pulled away.

Her eyelashes fluttered and she stared up at him in disbelief.

"It is you," she said in a hushed voice. A wanton expression had replaced the dread that had been in her eyes only moments before. Now she looked at him in awe . . . and blatant yearning.

He smiled. "I told you."

"But how can you look the way you do?"

"I'm powerful, Giselle, more powerful than any man you have ever known or will ever know. Even now, I have you slipping under my control."

She shook her head, as if to deny it. But he was well aware that she was falling under in his spell, just as she had been eighteen years ago. He had always been able to charm women this way, had always had the ability to captivate them before they knew what hit them.

With Giselle, it had been even easier than with the rest. She was so weak, so frivolous, so ready to be overpowered.

"My powers led me to a secret. A way to maintain my physical youth, even as my mind obtains the wisdom and potency that comes with age. My body will remain nineteen forever. I will live for eternity."

"How?" she breathed, wide-eyed, and he knew he had her.

"A spell," he said, thinking back to the glorious day when he had stumbled upon the magical incantation and realized that it meant immortality.

"A spell?" Giselle echoed. "Cast it on me."

He laughed aloud at her petulant tone, then firmly said, "No."

"Please, Manfred . . ." Her voice was filled with urgency, and her eyes were wild with need.

He wanted to laugh again, this time at how very simple it was. He should have realized . . . He should never have doubted that he could win her.

He had always known that Giselle's greatest weakness was her vanity. She was a creature of pride, a woman who had always based her entire sense of self-worth on her appearance. To her—and to most people—beauty meant youth.

He looked more closely at her face, noting the wrinkles that lined her lovely seafoam-colored eyes. "You're aging, my dear," he said, and she winced.

"Please, Manfred," she begged again, this time more fervently. "Please share your potion and your spell with me."

He watched her closely.

She was running her fingers over her face, tracing the web of fine lines that betrayed her age. "Please, Manfred . . . can't you erase these wrinkles?"

"Of course I can. I can restore the face you had eighteen years ago."

Her eyes widened. "Oh, Manfred, please . . . I'll do anything."

His gaze narrowed and he shrewdly repeated, "Anything?"

"Anything."

"All right," he agreed, nodding. "I want to know where Meg and Candra have gone . . . and where I can find our son."

* * *

Candra wanted, more than anything, to be able to take back the words she had uttered—the words that had clearly stung her sister harder than if Candra had slapped her.

She wanted to be able to tell Meg that it wasn't true, that she was just joking, that of course she hadn't tried to kill her.

But it was time that the truth came out. She would never be able to live with it bottled up inside of her.

For a long time, there was silence in the car, the only sound coming from the air rushing through the vent on the dashboard. Then Meg inhaled, exhaled, and, still looking straight ahead through the windshield, uttered a single word.

"Why?"

And so Candra tried to tell her. How she had been caught up in greed, and in her own fury over how Giselle had abandoned her, and how she'd chosen Meg over Candra. Now that she knew it hadn't happened that way, she felt sick over how much energy had been wasted, channeled into a negative cause.

She sounded pathetic to her own ears, but Meg listened intently. At least, she seemed to be listening. She nodded thoughtfully when Candra was through.

And she said nothing.

Not for a long time.

Candra sat there, alternately watching the highway and her sister, fighting back the tears that were so ready to spill over again. In her whole life, she hadn't cried as much as she had in the last twenty-four hours. She had always thought tears were a sign of weakness. Rosamund had told her that.

But now Candra knew that emotions weren't always easily controlled. That sometimes, you had to let go. Sometimes, you had to give in.

Finally, Meg spoke.

"I understand," she said simply, "and I forgive you."

"You do?" Candra stared at her sister in disbelief.

"I have to," Meg said, nodding. "You're my sister. And I know you did what you did because you had to. I know—don't ask me how, I just do—that you'll never do anything to hurt me again. I trust you."

Meg had said it once before, just yesterday, but it seemed like years ago. Then, Candra had been racked with guilt when her sister said those words. Now, she was elated. Meg trusted her. Meg had forgiven her!

"All my life," Meg was saying, "I felt as though something was missing. I felt as though some part of me was incomplete. When I found you, I knew that we belonged together, Candra. We were together before we were born, and we'll be together from now on."

Candra wiped at her eyes again. This was one of those times when you had to give in to emotion. "Thank you, Meg," she said, and her heart overflowed with love of her sister.

"Now we have to find him," Meg said, looking at the road again.

"Our brother." Candra wondered again if it was Landon or Jack.

"He's a part of us, just like we're a part of each other. He belongs with us too, Candra."

She nodded, not wanting to voice the words Meg had left unsaid.

If only we can get to him in time.

Twenty-one

Hilltop Haven.

"Is that the sign you saw in your vision?" Meg asked Candra as she turned the Honda onto the narrow road leading upward, around a bend.

"Yes," Candra said, sitting forward in her seat and drumming her fingertips on the dashboard.

Ever since they'd left the Interstate behind a short time ago, Candra had been fidgety.

Meanwhile, Meg had fought the urge to step even harder on the gas, knowing it would be dangerous to go much above sixty on the rural two-lane highway 44. It was dotted with farmhouses and produce stands and antique stores, and it seemed to have taken forever to reach the resort community, which was tucked into a wooded hillside.

Now, as they followed the road upward, deer darted into the underbrush and birds chirped from the boughs of ancient trees that towered above. They passed cottages and cabins where families barbecued and children splashed in kiddie pools.

"Maybe we should stop and ask someone if they've heard of the Kellers," Meg suggested after a few minutes of driving.

"No, keep going. It's up there," Candra said, her eyes on the grassy, tree-dotted slope ahead. "We can't be more than a few minutes away."

Meg's heart was pounding so loudly that she was sure Candra could hear it. "What are we going to do when we get there?" she asked, chewing on her lower lip and feeling uncertain.

But Candra would know, of course. Candra always seemed to know.

Not this time, Meg realized in dismay.

"I have no idea," Candra said, shrugging.

"I mean, do we just burst in and tell Landon and Jack that we think one of them is our brother?"

"I don't know," Candra said again. "What do you—there it is!" she interrupted herself, pointing at a cabin nestled on the hillside ahead.

Meg's stomach flip-flopped.

"Are you sure that's it?"

"I'm positive. I saw it in my vision. That's the place. There's the stream," she said, and Meg saw a groove carved out of the hillside, lined with tall grasses and dense undergrowth that marked the water's path.

The cabin itself was isolated from the rest of the resort, perched in its own little world, looking like part of the land that surrounded it. It had been built of dark rough-hewn logs, with a massive stone chimney going up one side. It was two stories tall, with lots of windows and red-painted shutters, the kind that actually closed.

"How close should we get?" Meg whispered, as if the boys could somehow overhear them. Which was, of course, impossible, since they were in the car with the windows rolled up and there didn't seem to be a soul hanging around outside the cabin, anyway.

"I don't know. I guess you should pull up right outside the door." Candra's voice was a whisper, too, and Meg felt slightly less foolish.

Moments later, as she put the car into Park and turned the key in the ignition, the cabin door was suddenly thrown open.

Candra let out a little gasp, and Meg looked up to see Landon Keller standing in the threshold. He wore navy sweatpants and a matching sweatshirt, and his feet were bare. His hair was disheveled, as though he'd been sleeping.

He looked startled, and his hand shielded his eyes from the sun as he peered through the windshield at them.

"Candra?"

Meg easily read his lips, and even from several yards away, she could see the elation in his eyes at the sight of her sister. With all her heart, she hoped that Landon wasn't their brother.

"Let's go," she told Candra, and saw that her sister was staring at him, as if frozen in her seat.

"I can't . . . you do it," Candra said in a small, frightened voice that didn't sound at all like her.

"Candra, you have to face him," Meg said gently. "Come on. It might not be him. It might be Jack."

"That's not what I'm afraid of," Candra protested, and Meg knew she was lying.

Candra was terrified that Landon Keller was their brother because she was in love with him. Meg could see it on her face.

And she suddenly thought wistfully of Shea. She had been head over heels with him . . .

I still am, she realized.

He'd been right about Candra. She *had* been trying to harm Meg.

He had been trying to save her, trying to do what he thought was right. He couldn't know what Meg knew about her sister.

Would he ever be able to understand?

You have to give him a chance, Meg told herself, putting her hand on the car door handle. *The first thing you have to do when this is over is explain everything to Shea. Maybe it's not too late to salvage what you had together.*

"Meg?" Candra said.

"Yeah?"

"Come on." As though she'd suddenly been infused with strength, Candra opened her car door and stepped out to face Landon.

"How did you find me?" he asked, taking the few steps down to the dirt driveway and coming face to face with her.

Meg got out and joined them, but hung back a little. This was Candra's territory.

"It's not important how we found you," Candra said.

There was a sound beyond them, and Meg looked up to see that Jack had come out of the cabin. He was rubbing his eyes as though he'd just woken up, and he, too, wore sweatpants. But his chest was bare.

Meg was about to call to Jack, to tell him they all needed to talk, when suddenly two things caught her eye.

One was a five-pointed pendant on a chain around Jack's neck, glinting in the sun.

Rosamund's words echoed through Meg's mind.

". . . *he has an amulet . . . made of steel . . . a pentagram . . .*"

And the other thing . . .

The other thing she noticed was the tall dark shadow that suddenly loomed in the doorway behind Jack.

The boy had no idea he was there, Manfred realized, and a delicious shiver slithered down his spine.

But Meg knew. He saw the way her eyes widened in disbelief. And now Candra had seen him, too. And the other kid—Landon.

All three of them were staring, motionless, as though they were paralyzed with fear.

Only the boy was oblivious.

Jack.

His son.

"What are you guys doing here?" Jack called to the girls, taking a step out onto the cabin's small porch.

None of them dared reply.

"What's going on?" Jack asked.

Manfred couldn't see his face, of course. But he could imagine the bafflement that would be in Jack's eyes. He would be wondering what his friends were looking at . . .

And now he would be realizing that whatever it was, was behind him.

And now he would look over his shoulder.

The moment his son turned and locked eyes with him, Manfred felt a surge, as though he'd been zapped with an electrical current.

This was the moment he had been waiting for. He had been so filled with anticipation as he tried to project himself across the astral plane to the cabin, in fact, that it had taken him longer than usual to leave his physical self behind.

That unprecedented difficulty had ignited a tiny flicker of doubt— doubt in his powers. Now that he knew he hadn't held up his end of the bargain with the gods, he couldn't help but wonder if he was as strong and capable as he'd always assumed.

Now, as Jack gasped in surprise, there was no more room for doubt. The moment of reckoning had arrived. Manfred summoned all of his power, reached out and closed his massive black hands around the boy's shoulders.

For a second, the two stared—*glared*—at each other.

And Manfred saw that the boy resembled his sisters more than was immediately obvious. Though his features were larger, more masculine, his dark eyes had the same exotic slant as Meg and Candra's . . . and the same depth, as though they were full of mystery and secrets and an inner fortitude unusual for someone so young.

"Who are you?" Jack asked finally, squirming beneath the iron grip that held him.

But his tone wasn't plaintive, as Manfred would have expected. He sounded curious . . . yet not afraid.

Why wasn't he afraid?

Thrown, Manfred loosened his hands for the merest moment.

That was all it took.

Jack wriggled out of his grasp and darted down the steps onto the ground, instantly positioning himself between the other three and the cabin. As though he could protect his sisters and Landon, Manfred thought, bemused—yet still unsettled by the boy's startlingly unruf-fled, assertive reaction.

When he turned to face Manfred again, Jack's expression was one of defiance.

"Come back here and face your fate," Manfred said, struggling against a tiny shred of misgiving that had somehow flitted through his mind.

"And what would that be?" Jack asked, a gleam in his dark eyes, as though he was daring Manfred to say it.

"Death," he spat out promptly, ominously. "You were my firstborn, a son. Death is your destiny . . . has always been your destiny, before you were ever conceived."

"So you're my father," Jack said, nodding. "Lately, I've had visions of you—of a man with evil eyes, stalking me. I suspected who you might be, but I never wanted to believe it."

Visions? Manfred thought. *So he has inherited my powers. Not surprising. But . . . to what extent?*

"Until recently, I never knew *you* existed," Manfred told Jack, trying to quell the questions that thrust at his consciousness. "But I'm going to make up for those lost years. I made a pact to sacrifice my firstborn child to the gods, in exchange for supreme power. Now it's time to honor that deal."

He took a step toward the boy, who stood his ground.

Manfred felt an absurd, unwanted prickle of admiration.

He's my son, he told himself, with a curious sense of pride. *Of course he's no coward.*

And though he knew what he had to do, someplace deep inside of him, in a place he hadn't even known existed, he wavered.

Only for an instant, but it was enough to fill him with apprehension.

You cannot bend now, he told himself. *You must remain strong enough to do what is expected of you.*

"It's time for you to pay for my great gift," he thundered at the boy who stood before him. "To pay with your life. And you, too, must pay," he said, looking past Jack to the two girls who stood watching him in dread.

Jack's gaze narrowed. "What are you talking about? Why would you want to hurt them? They're nothing to you."

"Nothing to me?" Manfred's lips spread into a smile. "They haven't told you yet?"

"Told me what?" For the first time, Jack looked uncertain.

Pleased, Manfred took strength from that uncertainty, regained a sense of his own dominance.

"They haven't told you who they are," he crooned to Jack. "That they're your sisters."

Pure astonishment spread over Jack's face.

The boy turned to look at Meg and Candra, and Manfred seized his chance.

As he charged forward, he reached inside his long coat for the dagger that he knew was there.

This isn't how it's supposed to happen, he thought, even as he brandished the weapon for the attack. *The sacrifice was supposed to be part of a ritual . . . not an impulsive act of . . .*

Self-defense?

The notion confused him. Defense against what? He himself was the almighty. No mere mortal could depose him of his power.

In the instant before he leapt at Jack, Manfred saw something that changed everything.

An amulet . . .

The amulet.

Sunlight bounced off its polished steel surface, searing into Manfred like a ray of fire.

Stunned, he stopped in his tracks and stared.

"Where did you get that?" he rasped, looking from the pentagram to his son's icy eyes.

"I've had it all my life," Jack said, and as he spoke, he reached for Meg's hand with his left, and Candra's with his right.

Manfred felt his insides quivering. An unfamiliar sensation was stealing over his body.

He didn't have to look closely at the amulet to know that it was etched with symbols—Black Magic symbols that, combined, represented supreme protection and strength. Even from a few feet away, its energy radiated at him.

On a normal human, a person without the mystical powers that can only be passed down through the generations, the amulet would be a mere ornament. But its significance was profoundly enhanced when the charm was worn by one who possessed inner forces that greatly surpassed a mere mortal's.

And there was only one way for the legendary amulet to come into a person's possession: it had to be bestowed by the gods at birth. Manfred had heard tales of this happening—it was part of island lore. But never, in all his life, had he encountered someone who actually possessed the mystical charm.

"That should have been mine!" he boomed, reaching out to wrench the amulet off his son's neck.

Instantly, his arm was charged with excruciating pain. He whimpered and stepped back.

He dropped the dagger, clutched his arm, and looked up at the triplets.

Their hands were linked to form a stalwart chain of defiance. Three identical sets of ebony eyes bore into him with an intensity that unnerved him. He was forced to look away, to avoid the hatred that hurtled at him like a thousand daggers—and the intimidating might they had inherited from Manfred himself.

He again became aware of the foreign feeling that made his heart pound rapidly and his legs feel like liquid.

Fear.

It came upon him swiftly—the realization that he, Manfred, was afraid . . .

Afraid of mere children.

But they were *his* children.

And together, they represented a force that could never be crushed.

With that shattering knowledge came the ultimate enemy to a person who has astrally projected himself across a great distance.

Panic.

It descended upon him in a sudden, lethal torrent, and Manfred began to thrash about wildly, helplessly, desperate to save himself.

He howled, a primal sound that beckoned the forces of evil that had always given him sustenance.

For the first time in his life, there was no reply.

Frantic, Manfred clawed for the silver cord that connected his astral self to his physical self, which lay inert, miles away.

And then the horror of his plight struck him in a devastating final blow.

It was already too late.

The cord had been severed.

Back at 41 Meadowview Terrace, Giselle slowly opened her eyes and looked around, dazed.

She saw the familiar floral decorator wallpaper and drapes and knew that she was in her bedroom . . . lying on her bed.

Sun streamed in the window, and the clock on the nightstand announced that it was just past noon.

Noon?

She stretched, yawned, and got up, wondering what she was doing asleep so late in the day.

Halfway to the door she froze, struck by the sudden, terrible memory of what had happened.

Manfred.

He had been here.

It all came back to her in a rush, and she remembered that he had demanded that she tell him where Meg and Candra were . . . where he could find their brother.

He had promised to cast a spell on her, a spell that would guarantee her eternal youth.

All she had to do was tell him where the children were.

Giselle gasped and clapped a hand to her lips.

"Oh, no," she whispered, shaking her head. "Oh, please, no . . ."

In a panic, she rushed out into the hall and down the stairs, running blindly, wanting only to escape the chilling reality of what she had done.

How could you have sacrificed your own children? Oh, God, you're no better than he is . . .

And then, at the bottom of the stairs, on the floor of the foyer, she saw him.

Manfred.

He lay still, on his back, his black coat spread around him on the polished hardwood floor.

Summoning every ounce of courage she possessed, Giselle took a hesitant step toward him.

And then another.

And then, cautiously, she bent over him.

His face looked stiff, as though it had been carved of wax. His eyes were open and unblinking. She looked into those cold black depths, searching for a glimmer of the evil that had always been rooted there.

But she saw only emptiness, and realized that this wasn't Manfred. Not anymore.

It was only a shell.

He was gone.

Relief coursed over her in a great wave, only to be followed by despair.

Her children . . .

Where were her children?

What have you done?

Giselle straightened and spun around in a near panic.

And as she did, she caught sight of a movement across the room.

She gasped, then saw that it was her own reflection in the enormous mirror that hung opposite the front door.

Slowly, her breath suspended in dread, Giselle moved toward it.

She squeezed her eyes closed as she arrived in front of it, terrified of what she would see.

Then she forced herself to open them, prepared to confront her own face—and her own unspeakable sin.

The first thing Giselle saw was the anxiety that pooled in her light green eyes.

And then she saw the wrinkles—the network of fine lines that traveled over her face.

I'm middle aged, she realized, and the knowledge brought the most overwhelming flood of joy she had ever experienced.

With it came the deep-seated certainty that her children were safe. Somehow, she knew they were all right: Meg, and Candra, and the son she had yet to meet. She hadn't betrayed them to Manfred.

And now, as she turned back to his body, she remembered what had happened.

She had wavered on the verge of accepting his dazzling offer to restore her youth and beauty, tantalized at the prospect of the most miraculous gift she could imagine . . .

Or was it?

Slowly, the memory of another gift . . . a far greater miracle . . . had stolen into her heart and her mind.

She had been carried back to that long-ago day in Jamaica, to the moment when she had cradled her newborn child in her arms.

Now she had no idea which one it had been: Meg, or Candra, or perhaps even her son.

But Giselle remembered the words she had whispered to her baby. "I'm your mommy, and I'll always be there for you. Always."

It had been a promise . . .

A promise she would never break.

"No," she had told Manfred, lifting her chin in defiance, fortified by a sudden sense of love and responsibility, understanding for the first time what it meant to be a parent. "I won't betray my children."

Shock and rage had filled his black eyes. "You'll be sorry," he had spat out at her.

And then he had raised his arms and begun to chant. As he uttered a chain of commands, Giselle had been engulfed by a shadowy tide that bore her away into silent, smothering darkness.

The spell he had cast must have been broken when he died, she realized now.

But what had happened to him?

Again she stepped over to his body. This time, she saw something clutched in his fingers. Bending, she retrieved it and saw that it was a scrap of paper. On it was jotted the information about where Meg and Candra had gone. They must have dropped it on their way out the door.

And Manfred obviously had found it.

Giselle felt a twinge of fear and uncertainty . . . just as the phone rang, piercing the stillness.

Hurrying into the next room, she snatched up the receiver. "Hello?" she asked, her heart pounding in sudden apprehension.

"Mom?"

"Oh, Meg . . ." Giselle's voice was so choked with emotion that she could barely speak. "Are you all right?"

"I'm fine," her daughter said breathlessly. "We all are. And Mom, we're on our way home . . . all three of us. Everything's okay now."

Yes, Giselle thought as she hung up the phone and wiped away the tears of joy that trickled down her cheeks. *Everything really is okay . . . at last.*